Reel

Psychiatry

Movie Portrayals of
Psychiatric Conditions

David J. Robinson, M.D.

Fellow, Royal College of Physicians and Surgeons of Canada
Fellow, American Psychiatric Association

Rapid Psychler Press 🚲

Suite 374
3560 Pine Grove Ave.
Port Huron, Michigan
USA 48060

Suite 203
1673 Richmond St.
London, Ontario
Canada N6G 2N3

Toll Free Phone 888-PSY-CHLE (888-779-2453)
Toll Free Fax 888-PSY-CHLR (888-779-2457)
Outside the U.S. & Canada — Phone 519-667-2335
Outside the U.S. & Canada — Fax 519-675-0610
website www.psychler.com
email rapid@psychler.com

ISBN 1-894328-07-8
Printed in the United States of America
© 2003, Rapid Psychler Press
First Edition, First Printing

Dedication

**For my Aunt Audree and Uncle Jack,
the closest thing we have to celebrities
in our family.**

Acknowledgments

I am indebted to the following individuals for their unfailing support and enthusiasm in assisting me with this text.
- **Monty & Lilly Robinson**
- **Brian Chapman**
- **Dr. Donna Robinson & Dr. Robert Bauer**
- **Brad Groshok & Susan McFarland**
- **Tom Kay**

I am fortunate to have a group of friends and colleagues who read the early drafts of this book and made numerous suggestions regarding both style and content. Their input was invaluable and I am indebted to them for their kind assistance. A special thank you to:

- **Tom Norry, BSc.N.**
- **Noel Laporte, M.D.**
- **Marnie Desjardins, R.N.**
- **Vinay Lodha, M.D.**
- **Emily Fuhrman**
- **Sue Fletcher-Keron**
- **Martha Wilke, BSc.OT**
- **Kumar Naidu, M.D.**
- **Sandra Northcott, M.D.**
- **Maria Santos**
- **Catherine Mallory, B.A., M.A., R.N.**
- **Brenda Fuhrman, BSc.N., LL.B.**

Many of the nurses, medical students, psychiatry residents, occupational therapists, social workers, secretaries, and consultant psychiatrists at the London Health Sciences Center, South Street Campus in London, Canada gave me movie suggestions over the three years it took to write this book. My thanks to you all, and please keep the movie recommendations coming!

I am also indebted to **Martha** and **Tony Feenstra**, owners of Cinema City in London, Canada. They have a huge selection of movies and were extremely generous with the number of titles I could borrow at once and the length of time I could keep them. Martha and Tony are quite familiar with the demands of technical writing and have helped many instructors from the University of Western Ontario.

Table of Contents

Section II — Personality Disorders and Mental Retardation

Section III — Substance-Related Disorders and General Medical Conditions

Author's Foreword

Researching and writing *Reel Psychiatry* allowed me to combine two of my passions — teaching psychiatry and watching films. Movie audiences are privy to a character's inner thoughts, feelings, and motivations, which outside of a theater is the domain of psychiatry. I chose to become a psychiatrist not because of any particular depiction, but due to an inherent curiosity about people that was furthered by watching movies.

Though *Reel Psychiatry* took over three years to write, I have been preparing for it since I started watching films. The first movie I saw alone was *Soylent Green*. Since then, movies have become one of my favorite pastimes. I am an avid fan of entertainment trivia, exchange movie lines with my friends, and often find myself in situations similar to those depicted on the screen.

It was an easy and natural transition for me to incorporate plots and personalities from movies into psychiatric teaching. There is a rich and continuously expanding body of cinematic work that encompasses every aspect of human experience to draw from for psychiatric education. For the past several years I have been working on resources to teach descriptive psychopathology — the basic signs and symptoms that make up psychiatric illnesses. As part of this endeavor, I have been keeping track of movie depictions so that I could recommend them to medical students and psychiatric residents. What I found lacking in the medical literature was a comprehensive collection of movie references. I began working on *Reel Psychiatry* to fill this void.

Many bushels of popcorn were consumed in the process of putting this book together. My cholesterol level has probably tripled. I have kept hundreds of little pieces of paper with movie recommendations on them and still haven't seen them all. I hope the video rental owners were able to retire on the proceeds of my research for this book. For each movie listed in this book, I probably watched four to find the best depiction.

I had initially planned on calling this book *DiagnOscar* (Diagnosis amalgamated with Oscar®), but the *Academy of Motion Picture Arts and Sciences* objected to my use of Oscar® in this manner. I had also hoped to include a variety of stills, but found that the cost is prohibitive and the logistics formidable. If I am able to produce a second edition of *Reel Psychiatry*, I hope to be able to include some black and white photographs.

Even as this book goes to press, there are movies that are just due to be released that may well be more accurate depictions than the ones listed here. I am very keen on receiving movie recommendations from readers, so please email me care of the publisher (**rapid@psychler.com**) if you have suggestions that will make *Reel Psychiatry* a better resource.

I received a lot of helpful advice from the people who proof read the early drafts of this book. Their suggestions led to many improvements and I am profoundly grateful for their assistance. Any errors that remain are my responsibility alone.

Reel Psychiatry was intended for both the general public and professional audiences. I tried to explain technical terms so that they are understandable to people unfamiliar with psychiatry. As a clinician and educator, I also feel that this compilation will be a useful teaching resource.

Now that this book is finished, two years late and twice its original size, I plan to enjoy some free time — by going to go watch a movie!

Thank you for supporting my work.

Dave Robinson

March, 2003
London, Ontario, Canada

Chapter 1

Movies
and
Psychiatry

1

Psychiatry is a reclusive medical specialty. Much of the clinical work in the mental health field goes on in private sessions that take place behind closed doors. Information about psychiatric patients is protected to a greater degree than in most of the other branches of medicine. For example, it is vital for psychiatrists to obtain someone's consent to release information, even to family members. On surgery wards or emergency departments, for example, information is shared more liberally.

It was the practice in the past to isolate patients with mental illnesses from the rest of society. Government run hospitals were built outside of residential areas to house those with chronic conditions. Mental illness continues to have a stigma that often perpetuates the secrecy, and at times the shame, associated with family members who are affected by a psychiatric condition.

Unless someone has a mental illness, or has a close relative who does, the main exposure to psychiatry occurs in the media. Psychiatrists get media exposure when they testify in high-profile cases. Some celebrities reveal personal information about their experiences with mental illness. And then there are movies, which are widely accessible and one of the world's premier forms of entertainment.

There are many ways that movies and psychiatry intertwine. Gabbard and Gabbard (1999) wrote an excellent book called *Psychiatry and the Cinema, 2nd Edition*. Their work encompasses many areas, but principally discusses two main themes: the psychiatrist in the movies, and the psychiatrist at the movies. Included in *Psychiatry and the Cinema* is a filmography of the depiction of psychiatry in the American cinema followed by a cataloguing of these films by their year of release.

Many publications feature movie reviews written by psychiatrists that discuss the film from a psychotherapeutic or character development perspective. These interesting reviews often contain information that is not discussed by entertainment reporters.

2

Movies are a compelling form of entertainment. They go beyond escapism and contribute significantly to society's standards or expectations for character roles. Gabbard and Gabbard (1999) encapsulated this nicely in the introduction to their book, *"Movies have become the great storehouse for the images that populate the unconscious, the chosen territory of psychoanalytic psychiatry."* In the absence of contact with an actual psychiatrist, we are apt to believe that what we see on the screen is what happens in real life.

Movies are an extremely good resource for medical education and can be used in a multitude of ways specifically for teaching psychiatry:
* Understanding the psychological aspects of film characters
* Introducing the viewer to the main features of an illness
* Discussing the suspected causes of psychiatric conditions
* Discussing the treatment of psychiatric conditions
* Depictions of patients in movies
* Depictions of psychiatrists in movies
* Writing case reports using a finite amount of material
* Addressing the stigma of mental illness

Reel Psychiatry was written primarily to assist with one item from the above list — the diagnosis of psychiatric conditions. Making accurate diagnoses in psychiatry is both an art and a science. Psychiatrists use one of two main diagnostic systems:
* *Diagnostic and Statistical Manual of Mental Disorders, Fourth Edition, Text Revision* (**DSM-IV-TR**) published by the **American Psychiatric Association** (**APA**), 2000
* *The International Classification of Diseases, Classification of Mental and Behavioural Disorders, 10th Edition* (**ICD-10**) published by the **World Health Organization** (**WHO**), 1994

The DSM is used primarily in North America. The ICD is used primarily in Europe, though both systems enjoy wide international use. These classification systems have considerable overlap and the portrayals presented in this book would be diagnosable with the criteria set out in either publication.

3

Questions that commonly arise about using films for psychiatric education are as follows:

Why Are Movies Useful Aids for Learning Psychiatry?

Movies, much like therapy sessions, yield a good deal of personal information. In this regard films are an invaluable resource because they remove concerns about the confidentiality of material used for teaching purposes. Movies allow the audience to be given the same amount of information as the instructor and not be limited by other forms of presenting case material, such as reading notes from a patient's chart.

How Many Psychiatric Conditions Are Portrayed in Movies?

With few exceptions, reasonably accurate portrayals of most psychiatric conditions can be found in popular films. This is a fortunate coincidence for psychiatric education because filmmakers are under no obligation to bring to life a set of diagnostic criteria, and entertainment will almost always prevail over accuracy.

How Accurate Are the Portrayals of Psychiatric Illnesses in Movies?

There are some films that have been made for the express purpose of educating the public. The chapter on *Eating Disorders* contains several such films, although most of them were specifically made for television. The chapter on *Substance-Related Disorders* has a number of highly accurate portrayals as well. Biographic films aren't necessarily that accurate because they focus more on the events in someone's life instead of specific symptoms.

Overall, portrayals of the great majority of psychiatric conditions can be found in popular films. The degree of accuracy of course varies, but many are in the good to excellent range.

4

Chapter 2

The Diagnostic
Process
in
Psychiatry

Why Is It Important to Make a Diagnosis?

Rather than simply being a "label," establishing a diagnosis is a crucial step in determining if further evaluation is required and what forms of treatment should be introduced. Each psychiatric condition has a range of possible treatments. Psychiatrists are legally required to include a diagnosis on medical records.

How Is a Diagnosis Made?

The assessment process relies primarily on the interviewing and observational skills of practitioners. There is no blood test, X-ray, or single symptom that identifies a psychiatric condition.

There are four components to making an accurate diagnosis:
*   The interview of the patient
*   The mental status exam
*   Collateral sources of information
*   Laboratory testing

There is a specialized aspect of the interview called the **mental status exam** (**MSE**), in which psychiatrists ask about the symptoms of certain conditions that may or may not have been discussed up to that point in the interview. Specific tests of attention span, memory, calculation, insight, judgment, etc. are often also included. The MSE is the psychiatric equivalent of the physical exam performed by other doctors.

Collateral sources of information are very important for psychiatrists. This is usually provided by friends, family members, medical records, primary care providers, etc.

Psychiatric diagnoses are made in face-to-face interviews. Physical examinations, lab investigations, and other special tests are often arranged in order to exclude the possibility that medical conditions, medications, or recreational drugs are causing the psychiatric symptoms. Interestingly, most mental illnesses can be perfectly imitated by physical illness or substance abuse.

6

What Standard Is Used in Making a Diagnosis?

Signs and symptoms in psychiatry ultimately are subjective, which is probably the single most perplexing aspect for those learning about mental illness. Concepts, definitions, and diagnostic practices vary between practitioners, which is one of the challenges facing the specialty. In 1952, the **American Psychiatric Association (APA)** published the **Diagnostic and Statistical Manual of Mental Disorders (DSM)** in recognition of the need for standardization. The DSM-II, published in 1968, contained paragraphs describing psychiatric conditions. It was not until the DSM-III was published in 1980 that individual criteria for all psychiatric disorders were clearly identified. The **World Health Organization (WHO)** publishes a similar set of diagnostic criteria called the **International Classification of Diseases**, currently in its tenth edition (**ICD-10**). Greater integration between the DSM and the ICD classification systems is planned for the future.

In order to get as complete an understanding as possible of a person's unique situation, the DSM-IV-TR uses five **axes** to make a complete diagnostic summary:
- **Axis I**: Major Psychiatric Syndromes or Clinical Disorders
- **Axis II**: Personality Disorders and Mental Retardation
- **Axis III**: General Medical Conditions
- **Axis IV**: Psychosocial and Environmental Problems
- **Axis V**: **Global Assessment of Functioning (GAF Scale)** which ranges from 1 to 100 and gives a score to the person's level of functioning (ability to manage in society)

This multiaxial approach to diagnosing mental illness provides clinicians with a method for organizing, recording, and transmitting information. By considering each person's unique set of circumstances, treatment plans can be individualized. It is for this reason that patients with the same diagnosis often receive different types of treatment.

7

Axis I Disorders

The disorders listed on Axis I are the major clinical disorders seen in psychiatry. In order to make the categories listed below more familiar, examples of some of the better-known illnesses are listed in brackets.

- **Psychotic Disorders** (e.g. schizophrenia, delusional disorder)
- **Mood Disorders** (e.g. depression, bipolar disorder)
- **Anxiety Disorders** (e.g. panic disorder, phobias)
- **Somatoform Disorders** (e.g. hypochondriasis, body dysmorphic disorder)
- **Factitious Disorders** (e.g. "Munchausen" syndrome)
- **Dissociative Disorders** (e.g. dissociative identity disorder — formerly called multiple personality disorder)
- **Sexual and Gender Identity Disorders** (e.g. fetishism)
- **Eating Disorders** (e.g. anorexia nervosa, bulimia nervosa)
- **Sleep Disorders** (e.g. narcolepsy, sleep apnea)
- **Impulse-Control Disorders** (e.g. kleptomania)

Axis II Disorders

Axis II is concerned with aspects of a person's character which are established by adulthood and that have an enduring quality. While many Axis I conditions do indeed last a lifetime, some can affect people in an episodic manner. The principal considerations on Axis II are those of adaptability of personality and intellect. Specifically, **personality disorders** (defined as an extreme set of characteristics going beyond the range found in most people) and **mental retardation** (subnormal mental functioning present by the age of 18 years) are the main features recorded on Axis II.

While personalities can be "beyond the range found in most people" in an multitude of ways, the DSM-IV-TR has distilled this down into 10 conditions:

- Paranoid Personality Disorder (a persistent and unwarranted mistrust of others)
- Schizoid Personality Disorder (absent social relations and restricted emotional expression)

- Schizotypal Personality Disorder (eccentricities of behavior with frequent perceptual distortions)
- Antisocial Personality Disorder (flagrant disregard for the rights and safety of others)
- Borderline Personality Disorder (tumultuous relationships; unstable self image; trouble regulating emotions)
- Histrionic Personality Disorder (excessive emotional expression and dramatic efforts aimed at becoming the center of attention)
- Narcissistic Personality Disorder (a sense of entitlement and a strong need for admiration)
- Avoidant Personality Disorder (feelings of inadequacy and hypersensitivity to the comments of others)
- Dependent Personality Disorder (excessive need to be taken care of; significant or complete submission to others)
- Obsessive-Compulsive Personality Disorder (overly concerned with rules, order, and perfection)

Axis III Disorders
Axis III lists general medical problems. Psychiatrists are always on the alert for physical problems that can either start or perpetuate a mental illness.

Axis IV and V
Axis IV lists psychosocial and environmental problems. Axis V uses a scale to rate the person's global assessment of functioning.

Other categories of psychiatric illness in the DSM-IV-TR are:
- **Disorders Usually First Diagnosed in Infancy, Childhood, or Adolescence**
- **Delirium, Dementia, and Other Cognitive Disorders** (while not considered to be mental illnesses, these conditions do cause a number of psychiatric symptoms)
- **Substance-Related Disorders** (as with general medical illnesses, screening for substance-related disorders is imperative because they can perfectly mimic psychiatric conditions)

Understanding Mental Illness

Perceiving
(sight, smell, hearing, touch, and taste)

Thinking
(Cognition)

The Environment

(external reality, other people, society, etc.)

Feeling
(Emotion)

Behaving
(Action)

The schematic shown on the previous page is useful in conceptualizing mental illness. Any condition that affects one area will have an effect on all the others. For example, consider depression, which is primarily a disorder of mood, and causes people to feel sad, blue, or empty. The effects that a depressed mood has on someone can be mapped out as follows:

Depressed Mood
• diminished interest in activities that are usually pleasurable

Cognition	**Behavior**	**Perception**
• reduced ability to concentrate or to pay attention • guilt and worthlessness • may have thoughts of suicide	• decreased energy • appetite changes • sleep changes • agitation, or visible slowing of movement	• sensations lose their intensity • in severe forms of depression hallucinations can occur

The majority of the criteria used to diagnose mental illness in the DSM-IV-TR can be categorized as being changes in perception, cognition, emotion, or behavior. Though it is a simplification, many types of treatment can be viewed as assisting primarily with one of these four areas, which in turn will have a beneficial effect on the other aspects of mental functioning:

Function	Possible Types of Treatment
Perception	Medication
Cognition	Cognitive Therapy; Rational-Emotive Therapy
Emotion	Psychoanalysis; Psychodynamic Psychotherapy
Behavior	Behavior Therapy; Behavior Modification

Field of Dreams

This film demonstrates the need for mental health professionals to understand a person's situation as fully as possible, and in particular, to consider cultural factors in making diagnoses. One day Ray Kinsella (Kevin Costner) hears a voice (called an **auditory hallucination**) when he is out in his Iowa cornfield. This voice whispers to him, *"If you build it, he will come."* The message makes no sense to Ray initially, but when he has the visual hallucination of a baseball field he at least understands what he has to build. His friends and family do not share these perceptual experiences (at least early on in the film), making these true hallucinations. Ray experiences other hallucinatory messages that inspire him to set out on a cross-country mission to seek out the reclusive writer Terrence Mann (James Earl Jones). Ray believes he must take Mann to a baseball game where another message will guide him on his quest (this idea can be considered a **delusion**). With the considerable acreage that needs to be set aside for the ball field, Ray puts his family in serious financial difficulty and comes within one day of losing his farm. He also experiences **dissociative spells** where he goes back in time and speaks with people who have long since passed on.

To an overzealous and narrow-minded diagnostician, Ray would be seen as having a serious mental illness. He meets some of the principal diagnostic criteria for schizophrenia. One might also speculate that Ray's condition was drug induced, as he admits to marijuana use (though it was years before the story begins). Ultimately, Ray doesn't suffer from a mental illness. Anyone familiar with American culture and having some insight into human nature would understand this is a movie about forgiveness and redemption. Ray struggles to come to terms with his place in life, and in particular with the regrets he has about his father whom he had alienated until just before his father's death. Because baseball figured so prominently in Ray's relationship with his father it is the most fitting motif for him to make amends, understand his father, and be able to more fully appreciate his own life.

Chapter 3

Organization of
Reel Psychiatry
and
Movie Rating
System

Organization of
Reel Psychiatry

Section I

Section I contains descriptions and movie portrayals of core psychiatric disorders. When these disorders occur naturally they are called **primary psychiatric disorders**.

An expanded presentation of psychotic, mood, and anxiety disorders is included in this text. The degree to which these illnesses affect the people who suffer from them (**morbidity**) and their presence in the general population (**prevalence**) warrant the additional explanation. This does not imply that other conditions are any less serious, just that in many cases the symptoms are more easily understood.

The expanded presentation consists of movie portrayals of individual symptoms as well as of the disorder itself. For example, schizophrenia is diagnosed on the basis of five diagnostic criteria (see page 23). Movie examples of each of the criteria are presented in order to facilitate a more comprehensive understanding of this disorder. Portrayals of individual symptoms precede the presentation of the disorder and were not rated by the statuette system described below. The conditions listed in section I correspond to those listed on Axis I in the multiaxial approach to diagnosis used in the DSM-IV-TR. The diagnostic process in psychiatry is explained in Chapter 2.

Section II

Section II contains disorders that correspond to those listed on Axis II. One aspect of Axis II conditions is that they are permanent (such as mental retardation) or change very slowly (personality disorders). The listing of disorders on Axis II does not imply that they are any less serious that Axis I conditions. The rationale in the DSM-IV-TR for developing Axis II was to ensure that these disorders are not overlooked when attention is directed to the usually more florid Axis I conditions.

Section III

Section III contains descriptions of conditions that affect the brain in such a way that psychiatric symptoms or illnesses develop. The two main groups of disorders are:

- **Substance-related disorders**, such as use of illicit substances or the abuse of prescription medication
- **General medical conditions (GMC)** which cause a disease process that affects brain function (such as strokes or head injuries)

GMCs are listed separately on Axis III in the DSM-IV-TR multiaxial assessment. Substance-related disorders are listed on Axis I.

Towards the end of the book there is a chapter that lists resources that provide education and support for many of the conditions listed in *Reel Psychiatry*. A chapter listing the references used in this book is also included.

Terminology

The term "patient" has two meanings: bearing or enduring discomfort without complaining or losing self control, and a person who has a medical condition and has agreed to accept treatment. Throughout this book the word "patient" and "person" are used interchangeably.

The terms "consumer" or "consumer-survivor" reflect an unfortunate trend that is pejorative towards mental health care, labeling it as if it were a trade or business instead of a profession. These terms are also ambiguous, as it is not clear what is being "consumed" or "survived." The terms used in *Reel Psychiatry* are established psychiatric nomenclature, and diagnoses are from the current diagnostic manual published by the APA.

Boldface Print

Throughout this book, various terms appear in **boldface print** to allow for ease of identification. Many of these terms are defined in this text the first time they are used. Some are only mentioned because a detailed description is beyond the scope of this book. A more detailed explanation of any term in boldface print can be found in standard psychiatric reference texts.

Movie Rating System

 A portrayal of limited accuracy. One or two features of the condition may be well demonstrated and discussed in the presentation that follows but the overall example is relatively weak.

 An overall good portrayal with many features being consistent with the actual condition.

 An excellent portrayal. The depiction is particularly accurate and conveys a strong sense of what the condition is actually like.

Chapter 4

Author
Disclaimers

Disclaimer #1

In *Reel Psychiatry*, I have offered opinions on how accurately the character's role depicts an actual psychiatric illness. In the films that are portrayals of true stories, I am clearly NOT offering an opinion on the real person's condition. I have not done any supplemental reading, reviewed no case reports, and have interviewed none of the people whose lives are depicted in the movies listed in this book. Because of the artistic license taken by filmmakers, I ask you to please keep in mind that someone may be affected by a very different illness than the one shown in a film, or indeed, may suffer from no illness at all.

Disclaimer #2

For ease of identification, the name of the actor is listed in parentheses after the name of the movie character. Again, I am offering an opinion on how close the portrayal is to a "real" patient. I am not giving an opinion on the quality of the performance. Many excellent films have fascinating characters that unfortunately are not suitable for the purposes of this book. In some cases it is the minor characters who provide accurate (but also often brief) portrayals. For some psychiatric conditions I have had to review less popular films although I have tried to discuss movies that are easily accessible for rental. I am also most assuredly not making comments about the actors' personal lives.

Disclaimer #3

Knowledge of the material in this book will not provide the reader with a sufficient enough basis for making psychiatric diagnoses. Mental health professionals spend years training to be able to distinguish the signs and symptoms of psychiatric illnesses and to be able to coalesce these findings into an accurate diagnosis. *Reel Psychiatry* offers no shortcut to this process. Anyone professing expertise based solely from the material in this book is doing themselves, as well as the person being offered the opinion, a great disservice. I consider it akin to reading a book about swimming and then trying to swim across a lake (and drowning).

18

Disclaimer #4

This book concerns itself primarily with diagnosis. I have largely avoided discussing the suspected origins of mental illness and how these conditions are treated. Where I have included such information, it should be considered to be of a general nature and not necessarily pertinent to the character being discussed. In some cases information about etiology was included to enhance the presentation of the material from the movie.

Disclaimer #5

I completed a reasonable but not exhaustive survey of films in order to produce *Reel Psychiatry*. I am certain that I have missed excellent portrayals from a wide variety of films. I encourage readers to contact me to share their knowledge of films that I have not listed here (I can be reached at **rapid@psychler.com**).

Disclaimer #6

I am not a world-renowned diagnostician. Certainly, a fertile discussion could ensue from any of the movies presented in this book and would generate a lengthy list of possible diagnoses. For the purposes of clarity and brevity, I have chosen to focus on what appears to me to be the principal diagnosis and then note features that are less commonly seen or are inconsistent. I have not listed each possible condition that may apply to a certain portrayal.

Disclaimer #7

Moviemakers have been given the task of providing depictions of each psychiatric condition. In some cases it was not possible to find portrayals of a certain illness. In other cases characters are amalgamations of many symptoms that do not lend themselves to a coherent diagnosis.

Where necessary, specific aspects of a portrayal or certain scenes consistent with a diagnosis are presented, though the character's overall portrayal may not be that accurate a depiction.

Disclaimer #8

It has not been possible to include depictions of all the conditions or diagnostic categories listed in the DSM-IV-TR. The most significant deletions are:

- Disorders First Diagnosed in Infancy, Childhood, or Adolescence
- Delirium, Dementia, and Other Cognitive Disorders
- Adjustment Disorders

Disclaimer #9

I am not a film critic or gossip columnist, though it was tempting at times to add some social commentary. I haven't selected the movies presented in *Reel Psychiatry* because they won awards, didn't win awards, featured a certain actor or were particularly notable for some reason. I have listed films that I believe have educational merit for readers interested in psychiatry. In the very few instances where I thought that viewers might be offended at the film's content, I have made comments to this effect.

Disclaimer #10

I have no financial connection to any studio, actor, video rental outlet, or other commercial source from which tapes or DVDs might be obtained. I recognize that the listing of a movie in this text may well lead to a number of people renting the title. I am pleased with the prospect of the creative people who produced these movies benefiting from their hard work. In the *Eating Disorders* chapter I suggested a source for readers who wish to purchase movies. Again, I have no financial connection to this enterprise and in fact did not use this service to acquire the films listed in that chapter.

Disclaimer #11

All of the movies listed in this book are property of their respective studios, agencies, distribution companies, etc. Instructors who wish to use film clips in teaching situations are required to contact the proper representatives to obtain their permission.

Chapter 5

Psychotic Disorders

Schizophrenia

Understanding the Condition

Schizophrenia is probably the most misunderstood of all psychiatric illnesses. This condition is not that of a "split personality." Literally defined, the term means a schism or splitting of the mind. This schism often manifests itself as a mismatch between a person's thoughts and emotions, or emotions and behavior. Prior to the use of the term schizophrenia, this condition was called **dementia praecox**, because many people afflicted with this illness develop it at an early age (praecox) and exhibit a decline in their mental or cognitive abilities (dementia).

While schizophrenia is not the most common psychiatric illness (about 1% of the population will develop it), it is widely considered to be the most serious. It can have devastating effects on individuals, families, and society, though such effects often remain unappreciated by those unfamiliar with the illness.

Schizophrenia is present in all cultures and affects males and females in equal numbers. Interestingly, some areas in the world have a higher-than-average prevalence of this illness (e.g. regions in Scandinavia), while other regions have significantly lower rates (e.g. Ghana).

The cause of this illness is unknown. As with most psychiatric conditions, both genetics (nature) and environment (nurture) are thought to play a role. Intense research efforts have been directed at the biological aspects of schizophrenia (such as trying to find which genes may be associated with the illness). Accompanying this effort has been the development of new medications to reduce the more debilitating aspects of this disease. Schizophrenia is a syndrome that can be understood as being a group of illnesses that share a common set of signs and symptoms. Affected individuals often have symptoms that change over time, and have a highly variable long-term outlook (**prognosis**).

Making the Diagnosis

Schizophrenia is a condition that principally causes individuals to experience a highly altered sense of reality (both of themselves and their environment), which is called **psychosis**. The core symptoms of schizophrenia are as follows:

i.   *Hallucinations* — a perception experienced when no stimulus is present (e.g. hearing a dialogue between two voices when no one is there); hallucinations can occur in all senses, though in psychiatric illnesses the most common types are heard (auditory) or seen (visual); a misperception of an existing stimulus is called an **illusion** (e.g. mistaking a hat and coat on a rack for a person)

ii. *Delusions* — fixed, false beliefs that are maintained despite obvious proof to the contrary; delusions are ideas that are not shared by the majority of people, are not due to cultural factors, mental retardation, substance use, or medical illnesses

iii. *Speech abnormalities* (indicating disturbances in thought production) — common ones are: a lack of discernable connection between ideas, making up nonsensical words that the person believes will be automatically understood, and missing the abstract qualities of words, ideas, etc.

iv. *Behavioral abnormalities* — can range from stupor to bizarre mannerisms to frantic, purposeless activity

v.   *Negative symptoms* — a decline in key areas of functioning: motivation, attention span, enjoyment of activities, emotional expression, socialization, ideas, verbalizations, etc.

The first four symptoms are often called **positive symptoms**, though not because this implies that something good is occurring. These symptoms are "added" to the clinical picture of those with schizophrenia (i.e. unaffected people don't have these symptoms). **Negative symptoms** refer to diminished or absent adaptive qualities or features (that are present in unaffected people). There are five different subtypes of schizophrenia — the two most widely known are **paranoid** (preoccupation with thoughts of persecution) and **catatonic** (prominent changes in behavior). The others are called disorganized, undifferentiated, and residual.

Cinematic examples of the five main symptoms of schizophrenia (from the previous page) are portrayed in the following movies:

The Snake Pit
(Illustrating Hallucinations)
In the opening scene of this movie Virginia (Olivia de Havilland) experiences auditory hallucinations of her (male) psychiatrist asking her questions. She answers them aloud, as if he was standing behind her. Later in the film, while in a bathtub, she has the hallucination of falling backwards into the ocean.

Jacob's Ladder
(Illustrating Hallucinations)
This film is ostensibly about a Vietnam veteran's descent into psychosis some period of time after returning home. Among other things, Jacob (Tim Robbins) sees ghouls in passing vehicles and experiences intrusive images of carnage. At the end of the movie, we see that these are drug-induced hallucinations that he experiences as he lays dying in Vietnam from a bayonet wound. This movie provides a good example of how vivid, compelling, and complex hallucinations can be. "Hearing voices" is widely recognized as a symptom of schizophrenia, although this occurs in a variety of disorders.

A good example of the general awareness of this symptom can be seen in *Field of Dreams* when Ray (Kevin Costner) asks farmers in a store about "hearing voices" when they are out in their fields. Everybody within earshot stares at Ray after he says this. The hallucination most consistent with schizophrenia is that of a voice keeping a running commentary about a person's behavior or thoughts. Two or more voices conversing with each other is also a common finding. While these "voices" can be muffled, they are usually heard as clearly as one would hear someone speak in a conversation. It is common for people with schizophrenia to experience auditory hallucinations that are often critical, obscene, accusatory, threatening, insulting, or derogatory in nature.

Conspiracy Theory
(Illustrating Delusions)

Mel Gibson plays Jerry Fletcher, a New York City cabbie espousing a plethora of paranoid ideas to his fares. His theories are multifactorial: Nobel Prize winners forced at gunpoint to donate sperm, fluoride water treatment making the population slaves to the State, etc. Without a clear reason, Jerry takes a man's picture and refuses to allow him into his taxi. He pores through newspapers and cross-references articles that he believes are government conspiracies. After distilling a mass of information he prints a newsletter, which he mails from separate mailboxes to avoid detection. Many of Jerry's behaviors are consistent with delusions of persecution: he scans his apartment building before entering, places a toothpick in his door to see if it has been opened, and locks his refrigerator and its contents in solid metal containers. Jerry regularly visits the Department of Justice to report conspiracies (called **querulent paranoia**). This portrayal is accurate because the delusions become the focus of Jerry's life, and he is able to provide a "rationale" for his lack of evidence — that a good conspiracy is unprovable. Unlike most people with delusions, Fletcher maintains his sense of humor.

Don Juan Demarco
(Illustrating Delusions)

Don Juan Demarco (Johnny Depp) comes to psychiatric attention after climbing a billboard and demanding to engage in a sword fight with a Spanish nobleman. He believes that he is Don Juan, the world's greatest lover, and the son of a famous swordsman. Later, he tells his psychiatrist a lavish tale of his upbringing in Mexico, replete with intimate encounters. He firmly believes in his identity, and does not alter his views even when presented with proof to the contrary. As is typical of delusional thinking, this character minimizes, denies, or rationalizes inconsistencies between reality and his view of the world. His false ideas become the focus of almost all of his activities, which is a key feature of delusional thinking.

Speech Abnormalities

Speech and language are often used interchangeably, but do not precisely refer to the same thing. Speech is any verbal expression, which can consist of utterances, words, phrases, or sentences. Language is the communication of comprehensible ideas. Language can be conveyed by means other than speech – posture, gestures, expressions, actions, and signing (sign language) all transmit clear messages without verbal expression. The primary disturbance in schizophrenia involves thought production. Since thought cannot be examined directly, it is assessed by its two principal means of expression: speech and behavior. The following paragraph was written by someone with schizophrenia and demonstrates a disjointed thinking process: *My head is reacting as if I was becoming a kid. My muscles would come back: #2 would come out every five days, #1 would always not come out yellow. If you x-ray me, my eyes would go around in the seals. Have a dentist come — my teeth are reacting by the second.*

The speech abnormalities seen in schizophrenia are variable, but can be severe. A useful metaphor is that of a "train of thought" traveling with a certain direction and speed. Logical thought progresses along a track where ideas are linked to each other. One of the terms used to describe a thought disorder is **derailment**, meaning that the train of thought has slipped off the tracks (demonstrated above) and there is no logical connection between the ideas. Thought disturbances in schizophrenia can be so severe that the person becomes incoherent.

Shine

(Illustrating Speech Abnormalities)

David (Geoffrey Rush) provides a good demonstration of derailment, and at times, incoherence. The opening scene contains a monologue with the central theme of a cat, but is otherwise extremely difficult to follow. When David trudges to the bar at the beginning of the film, the employees are hard pressed to understand what he is trying to say.

Behavioral Abnormalities

As with speech (language), behavior is a manifestation of the altered thought processes that occur in schizophrenia. However, the behavioral changes in most cases are not under conscious control. Patients feel compelled to do certain things, such as to: keep moving (called **agitation** or **catatonic excitement**), stop moving (**catatonic stupor**), or carry out certain acts (such as those that might be related to **auditory hallucinations**). The DSM-IV-TR specifies that two changes characteristic of schizophrenia are **grossly disorganized** and **catatonic behavior**. Grossly disorganized behavior in general refers to impairment in any form of goal-directed activity. This can be manifested in a variety of ways: a pervasive child-like silliness, periods of agitation for no clear reason, poor hygiene, and inappropriate sexual behaviors. Behaviors that maintain independence and self-preservation are generally affected.

The Snake Pit

(Illustrating Behavioral Changes)

The scenes of interest take place on Ward 33/33A. They are illustrative of patients exhibiting grossly disorganized behavior, with their thoughts so jumbled that they cannot make themselves understood (**incoherence**). Many people equate catatonia with being in a stupor, but the term is used to describe a diverse array of behavioral abnormalities:

- Copying the body movements of others (**echopraxia**) or repeating the words of others in a parrot-like fashion (**echolalia**)
- **Stupor**: complete disconnection or lack of awareness of the environment
- **Posturing/Rigidity**: assuming a rigid posture and resisting any effort to be moved

- **Excitement**: frantic, excessive, purposeless activity
- **Waxy flexibility** (**catalepsy**): allowing someone to reposition limbs and holding that position (shown below)

1   2   3

- **Negativism**: automatic opposition to all requests (regardless of how reasonable the request) or attempts to be moved (irrespective of the degree to which this would benefit the person)

Awakenings
(Illustrating Catatonia)

Awakenings is a movie based on a book by the same name written by the neurologist, Dr. Oliver Sacks. In the movie, Malcolm Sayer (Robin Williams) is a researcher who agrees to work in a chronic care hospital. The ward where Sayer works is occupied by patients that have either psychiatric or neurologic difficulties. Patients with mental health problems are shown throughout the film, but with less emphasis than the residents who have neurologic difficulties. Dr. Sayer rediscovers that five inpatients suffer from a post-encephalitic syndrome. The first patient shown with this condition is Lucy Fishman (Alice Drummond), who is mute and unresponsive to her surroundings. The **odd postures** she adopts are a good example of some of the movement abnormalities seen in catatonia. Later, she exhibits **negativism** when Dr. Sayer tries to help her toward a water fountain. Very good depictions of catatonic behavior can be seen in the old film clip shown by Dr. Peter Ingham (Max von Sydow). Patients seen in the hallways of the chronic ward can be seen engaging in repetitive activities such as rocking or grimacing that also constitute some of the behavior changes seen in schizophrenia.

Negative Symptoms

Negative symptoms, also called **deficit symptoms**, are features or capabilities that are normally present, but are reduced because of the disease process in schizophrenia. Five main areas of functioning are affected:
* Blunted or absent emotional responses (**affect**)
* Reduced production of speech or ideas (**alogia**)
* **Apathy**
* **Anhedonia** (lack of enjoyment of usual activities)
* Decreased ability to pay **attention**

One Flew Over the Cuckoo's Nest
(Illustrating Negative Symptoms)
In this film, one of the supporting characters displays several negative symptoms. Mr. Scanlon (Delos V. Smith, Jr.) is portrayed as an unkempt, disinterested man who can barely indicate that he doesn't want to participate in a group discussion. He watches television instead of socializing and even then doesn't pay attention to what is being shown. He displays limited emotional reactions, remaining indifferent even after being soaked with a water hose. Later, we learn that he is a voluntary patient, but he lacks the motivation or interest to start a life outside of the facility.

I Never Promised You A Rose Garden

This movie is based on a book by the same title. Deborah (Kathleen Quinlan) is a young woman taken to a psychiatric facility by her parents. Shortly after her arrival, we see some of her difficulties. Deborah experiences auditory hallucinations that sound like whispered words spoken backwards. Then, in front of an elevator, she has a more complex hallucination of an aboriginal man who sternly warns her to say nothing of the "secret world." These two examples demonstrate part of the range of hallucinatory experiences: the first is mainly distracting, while the second is called a **command hallucination** (patients who have them frequently feel compelled to carry out what they are being told to do). The hallucinatory voices also warn her that she'll be caught in a trap, and later in the film condemn her as a traitor for talking about her imaginary world.

Deborah often slips back into her secret world, a symptom called **autistic thinking** (**autism** itself is a psychiatric condition that involves a lack of responsiveness to the external world with a focus on internal events, like a persistent daydream). In her sessions with her psychiatrists, Deborah demonstrates some of the language abnormalities seen in schizophrenia. She has developed a unique vocabulary from her autistic world (phonetically called *"Yeeri"*). This phenomenon is called a **neologism** (literally a "new word"). As an example, she uses the word "nawsa" for no, and "nagwa" for poison. In one intriguing scene, a psychiatrist tries to relate the sounds of these neologisms to Spanish or Native American languages. A neologism may combine elements of actual words, but the meaning for the patient is idiosyncratic — there is no logical assembly of the sounds. For example, consider the word "snackmosphere" (a condensation of 'snack' and 'atmosphere') used to describe the explosive layer of air at the top of a potato chip bag. This term, while not an actual word, still has an understandable meaning. Real neologisms do not. For example,

30

"rocer" is neologism and might be used to refer to the lipstick left on a coffee mug. No logical thought process was used in developing this word. The depiction in this movie is somewhat incorrect in that patients are typically unaware that others don't understand them. Deborah is aware that her "Yeeri" words won't be understood by others. For example, a patient with schizophrenia might say something like, *"I was in serious need of some coffee. I found a jar of instant, but the only mug I found had a rocer on it, so I had to use a styrofoam cup instead."* The person would continue on with her story and be oblivious to others' lack of comprehension of the **neologism**. Another speech abnormality seen in schizophrenia is demonstrated by one of the other inpatients on Ward D, *"Aren't you very young to be in a place like this? This is an evil place. Are you a virgin?"* The descriptive term for this example is **loose associations**. Here, the speaker's ideas do not follow in a logical sequence often referred to as a **non sequitur**. The degree of connection between ideas is called the "tightness" of thought. Deborah also has the conviction (a delusion) that she has the power, possibly through vibration, to poison others.

In one scene, we see an example of some of the abnormalities of movement present in schizophrenia. Deborah holds her left hand to her lips, while her right hand is outstretched as if she is touching a wall. Some schizophrenic patients adopt unusual postures and hold them for periods of time ranging from minutes to hours. These postures can be rigid, or at times, patient's limbs can be repositioned (**waxy flexibility/catalepsy**).

Early in the film we see Deborah cutting her forearm with a tin can. Prior to this event, she was being punished in Yeeri, but in reality, she is so disconnected (**dissociated**) that she feels no pain, a demonstration of how powerful a grip psychosis can exert. Her condition is revealed to be schizophrenia, and the portrayal justifies this diagnosis. However, there are a number of less consistent features, such as Deborah eventually finding a way to leave Yeeri behind and then making an abrupt flight into health.

31

Possessed

First, a note on filmography. Joan Crawford starred in two movies with this title, one in 1931 and the other in 1947. This section deals with the later release. Louise Howell (Joan Crawford) is a private nurse for Mrs. Graham, the invalid wife of a wealthy man. Louise falls in love with David (Van Heflin), a business associate of her employer. David rebuffs her affections, and except for an outburst where she warns that she'll resort to anything to keep him, Louise manages to stay composed after he departs. Mrs. Graham exhibits a **delusion of infidelity** when, without any evidence, she accuses Louise of having an affair with her husband, which the audience knows is not true. Shortly afterwards, Mrs. Graham's beliefs are confirmed as being delusional by her husband, who says that his wife believes he has liaisons with many women. Shortly afterwards Mrs. Graham mysteriously commits suicide.

While the audience does not find out until much later in the film, Mrs. Graham's accusation and death form the genesis of Louise's eventual psychotic decompensation.

There are many good examples of psychopathology in this film. In the opening sequence, Louise is seen wandering in a disorganized state misidentifying every man she sees as David. She lapses into a **catatonic stupor** and is taken to hospital. Once there, she is quickly identified as a psychiatric patient and given a further assessment. The conversation that ensues between the two examining physicians is accurate both in terms of their observations and use of psychiatric terminology. After receiving an injection in the emergency department, Louise has the **auditory hallucination** of a piano playing a piece by Schumann.

Most people are familiar with **catatonia** being a state in which a person is mute and immobile, and these are the most prominent features that Louise displays. She exhibits two other features of catatonia: **echolalia** and **waxy flexibility**. Echolalia is the simple repetition of words said by others without understanding the meaning (she repeats the word David when it is spoken by the doctor). Waxy flexibility (**catalepsy**) is demonstrated when the doctor moves her arm into a particular position and she keeps it there. Prior to receiving treatment for her catatonic state, Louise is unable to express her thoughts (**thought blocking**).

Much later in the film, Louise exhibits a profound sense of guilt regarding Mrs. Graham's death and has convinced herself that she was there on the evening in question. Her role in the suicide is refuted when she confesses her guilt to Mr. Graham, who tells her that he was actually with his wife on the evening that she died. Louise's ideas are not of delusional intensity because she can still be persuaded that she was not responsible. Ideas of less than delusional intensity are called **overvalued ideas**.

Louise also exhibits **erotomania**, the delusion that David is in love with her long after they part. After he makes it clear to her that he's not interested, she still clings to the idea that he'll want her someday. She marries Mr. Graham in order to have continued contact with David, and so that her wealth might attract him. His lack of interest does nothing to dissuade her. Ultimately, she kills him before he can marry Mr. Graham's daughter. This depiction of erotomania would be more accurate if Louise and David had not had a relationship, though we are not told of the details of their time together. A more typical portrayal would involve a brief meeting with something innocuous occurring, such as a handshake or a conversation that Louise would misinterpret as an indication of David's feelings for her. Also, the objects of erotomanic delusions tend to be unavailable to patients, either by way of social status, marriage, etc. Louise's life as a lonely woman of lower social standing than David's is a typical feature of erotomania.

Given Louise's auditory hallucinations, delusions (of erotomania, and at other times of a paranoia), thought blocking, and catatonia, this is a good overall depiction of schizophrenia (particularly **catatonic schizophrenia** when she is in hospital).

Shine

Shine is a true story that follows the life of child piano prodigy David Helfgott. In the first scene, we see an example of his largely incomprehensible speech pattern, which seems to center around the theme of cats. The linkage or tightness between his ideas is lost, or at least is extremely difficult to follow, which is an excellent example of **loosening of associations**. A little further into the movie, David's attempts to communicate with the staff of a bar are largely lost on them.

The film depicts David as a socially awkward boy who is driven by his father to excel at the piano. As with many creative people, the child becomes an instrument used to pursue a parent's unfulfilled dreams. Well before the onset of his illness David is depicted as having principally intellectual pursuits — the piano and chess. He is discouraged from developing friendships, though it is unclear to what extent he actually desired them. He is unable to express emotion except when he is seated at the piano.

While schizophrenia is increasingly being found to have a genetic cause, one of the key psychosocial aspects is well illustrated in this film. A **double bind** is a "damned if you do, damned if you don't" situation. A double bind in and of itself does not cause schizophrenia but may induce vulnerable individuals to withdraw into psychosis to avoid unsolvable conflicts. In this film, David is pushed ruthlessly to not only master difficult musical pieces but to win competitions. Despite this, his father resists getting him a teacher and ultimately agrees only when someone offers to provide lessons free of charge. David's father later prohibits him from accepting a scholarship in the U.S. David's father suffers from **paranoid personality disorder**, a condition discussed on page 216. Finally, David's talent earns him another scholarship in England, and if he is to develop as a musician, it is clear that he must leave his native Australia. Again, his father vehemently opposes his leaving, saying that it will destroy the family. When David insists on leaving, his father tells him he cannot return, that he will have no family, and that he will be punished for the rest of his life. David is thus placed on a locomotive-driven track towards a breakdown as he leaves for England and prepares to perform a particularly difficult piano composition. David's descent into psychosis, which takes months to develop, is depicted during his performance as an abrupt dissociation from reality. After becoming ill, he has clearly changed and doesn't have the capacity to study music in the way that he did previously.

What follows is a depiction of **negative symptoms**. David is markedly inattentive to his surroundings — leaving water running, musical scores scattered around, and other objects strewn about. He is ambivalent about important matters, living largely in an autistic world of cigarettes, obscure language, and finally, a return to the piano. In one scene, a woman takes him from an institution and offers to drive him to her home, but asks him not to smoke in her car. He obliges, but instead of putting out his cigarette, he walks alongside her vehicle and keeps smoking. This is an example of **concrete thinking**, where people lose their ability to understand an event in its fuller context and cannot grasp abstract meanings. David has difficulty coping on his own, and relies on the kindness and tolerance of others to ensure his safety. All of the above features are consistent with schizophrenia, and in particular, its development over time. The peak onset in males is from age 15 to 25 years, often occurring in the first year or two after leaving home.

As an adult (the scenes played by Geoffrey Rush), David demonstrates a persistently jovial mood, seeking hugs from everyone, and is rather disinhibited regarding where his hands travel around women that he fancies. His speech pattern is unusual and at times lacking clear connections between ideas. On other occasions it contains puns and references which are off topic but can be understood as being related to some central theme. These features make the condition portrayed in *Shine* more consistent with **schizoaffective disorder**, which is discussed on page 48.

Benny and Joon

Benny (Aidan Quinn) is the older, overly protective brother of Joon (short for Juniper, portrayed by Mary Stuart Masterson). Benny lives with Joon, which seems to be a posthumous promise he made to their parents, who perished in a car accident. Joon interrupts Benny at his job because of an emergency — she is out of peanut butter. While her character at first seems to be somewhat eccentric (wearing a helmet in the car, holstering a ping-pong paddle), we soon learn that she requires the supervision of a housekeeper because she is prone to setting fires. More convincing features of schizophrenia (**undifferentiated type**) soon follow. We are told that Joon experiences **auditory hallucinations**, does well with a stable routine, and takes medication on a daily basis. Her use of language is one of her most interesting attributes. She uses the last housekeeper's surname (*"Smail"*) to refer to anyone who might fill the position, which is how Sam (Johnny Depp) enters her life. In one scene, Sam watches Joon doing something in the kitchen. Joon refers to his persistent observation as a *"Boo Radley moment"* (from the character in *To Kill a Mockingbird*). At many points in the film, her speech contains idiosyncratic references.

Later in the film Joon's stress level increases dramatically when her new relationship with Sam angers Benny, who wants to send her to a group home. She leaves the house with Sam and decompensates into psychosis while on a bus. At this time, we see her responding to hallucinatory voices and becoming very agitated. She requires immediate hospitalization, but makes an excellent recovery. The accumulation of stressful events leading to a period of decompensation is common in schizophrenia. Family members are educated to minimize **expressed emotion (EE)** around patients. This film is also a good portrayal of the effects serious mental illness has on family members. Benny's commitment to Joon interferes with the running of his business, and makes him reluctant to begin a romantic relationship of his own.

David and Lisa

This movie is based on the book by the same name by Theodore Isaac Rubin. David, a troubled teenager, is taken to a "school" by his mother. The administrator of the school is a psychiatrist and the other students seem a little eccentric, although they do not exhibit clear signs or symptoms of mental illness.

David (Keir Dullea) exhibits many features of paranoid schizophrenia. Throughout most of the movie, his character is arrogant, hostile, suspicious, detached, and superior. David insults the psychiatrist's wristwatches and says he doesn't wear one himself because no timepiece would be worthy. In another scene, David offers a psychiatric opinion based on the reading that he's done, fully expecting to be treated as a learned colleague.

In two scenes, David demonstrates unusual emotional responses. In the first part of the movie, we see him bidding farewell to his mother in a robotic fashion — he exhibits no tenderness, no inflection in his voice, and in fact doesn't even look at her. Later, after "dismissing" the administrator from their first meeting, he breaks down into tears.

Lisa (Janet Margolin) has a more severe type of schizophrenia, called **disorganized**. When we first see her, she is attempting to play hopscotch, a game which seems younger than is age appropriate. Lisa is quite childlike and remains under the constant scrutiny of an attendant. Her speech is unusual in that she speaks in rhymes. Her initial chant is a nonsensical verse using the words 'cow,' 'sow,' and 'how.' Using words because they have similar sounds, regardless of their meaning, is called **clanging** or **clang associations**, and is seen in schizophrenia and as well as several other disorders. In general, Lisa's behavior can be described as disinhibited and regressed. Her affect is often inappropriately jovial, though she does display anger. In contrast to David's studious nature and academic ability, her illness likely prevents her from progressing scholastically.

Pi

Pi is an independent release starring Sean Gullette as Max Cohen. Shot in black and white, the film pulls the reader along a "descent into madness" with its grainy, disorienting views and menacing soundtrack. Max is a mathematical genius. He states his assumptions about life as follows, *"Mathematics is the language of nature, everything around us can be represented and understood through numbers. If you graph the numbers of any system, patterns emerge."* Max seeks to elucidate the pattern of the most perplexing of all entities — the stock market. Though he is an accomplished mathematician at the beginning of the film, Max lives a secluded, marginal existence. As he pursues the 216-digit number that he thinks is the answer to his quest, he begins to unravel. Early on he demonstrates a number of **paranoid traits**: having several locks on his door, checking the hallway carefully, and shunning a friendly sounding woman who calls him for a lunch meeting.

A complicating factor in making an accurate diagnosis is that Max suffers from severe migraine headaches, which can cause **visual hallucinations**. Max's first perceptual disturbance is of his front door being breached, which is more consistent with schizophrenia than the typical visual disturbances caused by migraine headaches. Max goes on to develop difficulties that are in excess of those caused by headaches. Max's first visual hallucination (unrelated to headaches) involves a man singing *I Only Have Eyes For You* (an appropriate choice for a paranoid person). Max sees a double of himself with blood dripping from the double's arm. Later, he experiences seductive auditory hallucinations emanating from his computer. As the movie progresses, it becomes more difficult to distinguish reality from Max's perceptual distortions, making this aspect a superb portrayal of schizophrenia. Max also demonstrates a **somatic delusion** — believing that his headaches originate from a spot on the right side of his head, which he attacks with a pair of scissors and an injection device. At the end of the film, he drills a hole into this part of his brain to end his torment.

Sophie's Choice

At the beginning of this movie, we see a dinner invitation being extended to Stingo (Peter MacNichol) in the form of an eloquent letter written by Nathan (Kevin Kline). Stingo is a neophyte writer who has come to New York to pursue his vocation. Shortly after the invitation is delivered, Nathan has a heated argument with his lover Sophie (Meryl Streep), accusing her of lying and then telling her how little she means to him. Such contrasts make up Nathan's life. Nathan is passionate and animated, but there is an undercurrent of unfounded suspiciousness and unpredictability. For much of the movie, Nathan exudes a stilted, condescending manner towards Stingo, a demeanor associated with paranoid schizophrenia. Another aspect of this portrayal consistent with this illness is persistent **grandiosity**. While not a researcher, Nathan says that he is, and tells his landlady that he developed the cure for polio (a **grandiose delusion**). Nathan tells Stingo that he is constantly bringing him the *"best of Brooklyn"* in the form of food, entertainment, and of course, friendship. When caught in the throes of delusional jealousy, Nathan becomes physically abusive and launches into a number of inflammatory tirades aimed at Stingo's southern heritage. In one scene, he misinterprets a surprise party as catching Stingo and Sophie in a romantic tryst. He vents his suspicions, accusing Sophie of having affairs with a number of men. Nathan steps softly on stairs and enters rooms silently so that he might catch Sophie in an act of betrayal. He follows her during the day, and upon seeing her with her employer, believes they are having an affair even after a convincing explanation for their time together is given to him.

Nathan's brother indicates that a diagnosis of **paranoid schizophrenia** was made when Nathan was age 10, which would be unusual. Typically, the paranoid subtype of schizophrenia occurs later than others, often becoming evident in one's late 20's or 30's. It is associated with a better overall prognosis. Because of the later age of onset, patients are able to finish school, find work, and start a family, all of which improves the outcome of this illness. Someone with paranoid schizophrenia could very well have a research position or other demanding occupation. Although we don't see it in the film, his brother indicates that Nathan abuses cocaine and benzedrine (an amphetamine). The use of these substances would certainly affect schizophrenia, and provides a plausible explanation for his unpredictability. Interestingly, use of amphetamines can cause a clinical picture indistinguishable from paranoid schizophrenia.

The haunting double suicide (or murder/suicide) also deserves mention. At least half of those with schizophrenia attempt suicide, with up to 15% being successful. While there is some debate in the psychiatric literature about the rates of violent crime among mentally ill patients, there is no doubt that untreated psychosis is strongly associated with violent behavior. Patients with persecutory delusions (paranoia) are at particularly high risk for violence when they believe they are being threatened, or see a situation as inevitably turning out to their disadvantage.

Clean, Shaven

Peter Winter (Peter Greene) is a young man who leaves a mental institution in search of his daughter, who was given up for adoption years earlier. Peter suffers from psychotic symptoms for most of the film, and at times has vivid hallucinatory experiences that leave the viewer wondering what has actually transpired.

Peter believes that he had surgery while in the psychiatric hospital and has a transmitter embedded in his finger and a receiver somewhere in the back of his head. These **somatic delusions** help explain Peter's self-mutilation — cutting his scalp and excising a fingernail. He is so disconnected from reality at these times that he doesn't even feel any pain. He also removes most of his body hair, but no explanation is given.

Peter cannot tolerate seeing his reflection, so he smashes all the windows in his car and covers up every mirror around him. Peter experiences a variety of hallucinations during the movie. At first, they are difficult to discern and have a bizarre mechanical quality. Later, they take the form of an angry black man who shouts messages that seem to push Peter to do things (**command hallucinations**). The hallucinations seem to travel down power lines and are often fragmented, like the voices heard on a radio as the tuning knob is being quickly turned between stations. Peter expresses the **persecutory delusion** that *"people are being killed out there"* when he speaks to his mother and daughter.

In the library and office scenes where he hopes to track down his daughter, Peter has considerable difficulty expressing himself (**alogia** — a **negative symptom of schizophrenia**).

Peter's behavior is erratic. Aside from self-mutilation he does a number of odd things, including banging his head against the shelves in the library and collecting unusual pictures for the inside of his car. He seems to be socially isolated. After leaving the hospital he has no friends to visit and lives in his car after a brief stay with his mother. Peter's emotional responses are quite flat, particularly compared to the main characters in *Shine* and *The Fisher King*. The portrayal in *Clean, Shaven* is a more accurate example of schizophrenia than in the films listed above.

Peter is also a suspect in the bludgeoning death of a young girl who was in the vicinity of a hotel he stayed in on the way to his mother's house. The evidence against him is weak, but Peter is pursued and ultimately killed by a detective shortly after being reunited with his daughter.

This movie provides the best overall example of schizophrenia listed in this chapter. Unfortunately, *Clean, Shaven* did not become a popular film even though it received significant critical acclaim. The subject matter is upsetting and the outcome tragic, which may have discouraged some viewers, especially in light of the more optimistic outcomes of many of the films listed in this chapter (with the exception of *Sophie's Choice* and *Possessed*).

Birdy

Birdy is the nickname of the character played by Matthew Modine (we are never told his real name). We first see him perched high in a tree watching a group of neighborhood boys playing baseball. He is fascinated with birds, though how this interest developed is not explained in the movie. Birdy is an unusual teenager. He is able to interest Al (Nicholas Cage) in training homing pigeons, which necessitates a mission to capture some from an industrial building. Birdy has no fear of heights, and when he slips from the roof he seems to look forward to the chance to fly (even though he is injured in the fall).

When Al is able to choose their activities, such as fixing up an old car, Birdy is agreeable but largely disinterested. Birdy's lack of interest in non-avian pursuits is particularly evident in his interactions with women. He is socially inept, indifferent, and disconnected. Birdy pays little attention to Al's amorous activities, even when they occur in plain view, and remains oblivious when an attractive young woman is available to him. As the story progresses, Birdy becomes more withdrawn, wanting to escape into the world of birds and caring less about the outside world. On the night of his prom, he passes up an opportunity for a sexual liaison with his date, and instead sleeps naked in his pet bird's cage. Birdy and Al get drafted into the Vietnam War. After an operation for a serious injury that he sustained in battle, Al is summoned to visit Birdy in a military hospital because Birdy's psychiatrist is unable to connect with him. At this point, Birdy is mute and largely unresponsive to his environment. He constantly stares at a window and allows only one female nurse to feed him. He adopts odd postures that are reminiscent of birds on a perch. Birdy's military experiences are dealt with briefly — he survives a helicopter crash and comes very close to being consumed in a napalm attack.

Schizophrenia is considered to have three phases: prodromal, active, and residual, which are demonstrated to varying degrees is this movie.

42

The **prodromal phase**, which can last for years, is characterized by gradual social withdrawal, deterioration in hygiene and grooming, and the inability to work or study effectively. Behavior can become unusual or eccentric (such as food hoarding). The person may develop beliefs that are inconsistent with previously expressed views and offer vague or superficial explanations for the switch. Other **negative symptoms** can be seen during this period, such as emotional flattening, lack of energy and interest, and a lack of meaningful content in speech.

The **acute phase**, sometimes called a "psychotic break," is dominated by **positive symptoms**. Here, the person becomes acutely ill and is usually taken to a hospital on an urgent basis. This phase generally lasts between one and six months, though it can be dramatically shortened by the use of antipsychotic medication.

The **residual phase** involves a diminution of positive symptoms and a return of negative symptoms. This can last from months to years and may be interrupted by exacerbations of acute symptoms. In order to diagnose schizophrenia, the duration of the illness must be at least six months, and include an active phase of one month's duration (or less if successfully treated).

Prior to seeing combat, it isn't clear if Birdy was in a prodromal phase or just exposed to situations that he couldn't handle. Birdy clearly has difficulties in developing relationships, but this is not necessarily indicative of a prodromal phase. He could be considered to have an **avoidant** or **schizoid personality disorder** prior to seeing combat.

Birdy is shown abruptly decompensating into what is likely the active phase of schizophrenia shortly after a helicopter crash. An accurate assessment is complicated by the additional diagnosis of **posttraumatic stress disorder**, which could certainly account for his difficulties. Birdy's behavior while in the military hospital is suggestive of **catatonic schizophrenia**.

Unstrung Heroes

Uncle Arthur (Maury Chaykin) is a good example of someone who has the **residual subtype of schizophrenia**, exhibiting primarily **negative symptoms**. We meet Arthur when he comes for a family visit after his sister-in-law Selma (Andie McDowell) returns from the hospital. He immediately unravels a twig from a handkerchief and offers it as a present, thinking that leaves connected to a branch represent a rare find. Arthur's pockets are full of garbage. He regularly patrols waste areas and hoards items, dividing them into piles based on the location where he found them.

Arthur's brother Danny (Michael Richards) warns others at the gathering that the latkes may have been *"fried in hemlock"* causing Arthur to immediately throw one away. Danny's antics annoy Selma, who says that she is *"irritated."* Arthur gives a good demonstration of **concrete thinking** when he offers Selma a jar containing a homemade salve as a cure for her *"itching."* Danny's persecutory thoughts are discussed on page 52.

Arthur also misinterprets the label on a record — an oldie that plays at 78 rpm. This particular album has a tag on it that says '79' and Arthur simply assumes that because of this, it would play a little faster than a standard record. He doesn't recognize that this a price tag and that the album cost 79 cents.

In another scene, Arthur waits at a sewer junction to collect balls that have washed into the drains. Somewhat like seashells, he believes that balls contain the sounds of the children who played with them. Arthur then listens, along with his nephew, to a newly found ball. Hearing nothing, he goes on to assume that only dogs are able to hear those sounds.

Arthur's passivity, lack of emotional expression, concrete thinking, odd beliefs, prominent negative symptoms, and unusual perceptual experiences are consistent with the **residual phase of schizophrenia**, as well as the residual subtype of this illness.

The Caveman's Valentine

Romulus Ledbetter (Samuel L. Jackson) is a Julliard-trained pianist who lives in a cave in a New York park. He suffers from a severe form of **paranoid schizophrenia**, which causes him to hear music in his head and see visions of "moth–seraphs" shown in striking surreal imagery (**auditory** and **visual hallucinations**, respectively). Ledbetter believes that a sinister force that he calls *"Cornelius Gould Stuyvesant"* (a **persecutory delusion** combining the names of three significant figures from New York history) lives atop the Chrysler Building and controls people's minds with "y-rays" and "z-rays." The principal inconsistency in this movie is that most people with schizophrenia are not as capable as Ledbetter is at minimizing the symptoms of schizophrenia, even when there is a compelling reason to do so.

A Beautiful Mind

John Nash (Russell Crowe) is a mathematical genius whom we meet shortly after he starts at Princeton on a prestigious scholarship. The viewer isn't made aware that Nash is ill until well into the film, though it becomes clear that something was amiss even in his first few days of graduate school. In contrast to the very elaborate hallucinations depicted in *The Caveman's Valentine*, Nash's **visual hallucinations** are of a devoted roommate and his niece, and a shadowy but very believable figure from the Department of Defense. In a flash of insight, Nash recognizes that the hallucinatory characters never age, and this realization helps him accept his illness. Although his hallucinations never leave him, his **persecutory delusions** improve when he chooses to ignore the hallucinatory figures. Nash suffers from **paranoid schizophrenia** but has a less severe form than Romulus Ledbetter. It is a very rare person with schizophrenia who can selectively ignore visual and auditory hallucinations, let alone work at the high level that Nash does. This is a movie about an exceptional person, and as such is not a typical representation of schizophrenia.

45

Schizophreniform Disorder

Understanding the Condition

Schizophreniform disorder is related to schizophrenia, but is considered to be less severe. The major distinction in schizophreniform disorder is that the symptoms are present for at least one month but resolve in less than six months. The principal aim of including this as a separate disorder is to guard against the premature diagnosis of schizophrenia. Many people diagnosed with this condition go on to develop schizophrenia. Less often, a diagnosis of a mood disorder is eventually made, and in some cases there is a complete recovery. This condition is about half as common as schizophrenia.

Making the Diagnosis

Schizophreniform disorder has the same five main diagnostic criteria as schizophrenia. Apart from the time course, the other major distinction is that there may be less of a disturbance in a person's ability to function in social and occupational roles.

 ## The Bell Jar

This film is based on the book by Sylvia Plath, and incorporates many biographical elements from her life. Ester (Marilyn Hassett) is a straight-A college junior who wins a poetry award, and later, a chance to write for a women's magazine in New York for a summer. Ester experiences a very gradual onset of her illness, a good example of a **prodromal period**. Prior to leaving for New York, two scenes could be considered as being consistent with a psychotic prodrome: her oddly emotionless probing into her father's death, and her marked ambivalence about many things, including her boyfriend's offer of marriage. However, Ester has good reason to want to rile her mother and to be wary of the proposal. In New York, her decline accelerates. A complicating factor in this movie is that a sexual assault takes place, which could certainly account for the emotional difficulties Ester endures. However, for the sake of discussing schizophreniform disorder, it is more instructive to consider the assault as accelerating Ester's difficulties, not causing them. Prior to the assault, we see the quality of her work decline — she becomes distracted and condescending towards others. Ester's room is in complete disarray and she lays motionless in her bed. At dinner, she comes across as emotionally flat and withdrawn.

While in the **acute phase** of her illness (in her mother's house), we see Ester in a regressed state, showing **negative symptoms**, particularly social withdrawal and poor hygiene. Her symptoms worsen, necessitating hospitalization. During her inpatient stay, she makes two comments that illustrate another feature of psychosis — lacking an appreciation for the passage of time. Ester makes a comment about salt being put in her veins as she is taken for electroconvulsive therapy. The original statement about salt was made weeks earlier by a man in a café who was talking about the electric chair. Secondly, Ester reacts badly to her mother bringing roses because the editor in New York (who disparaged Ester's work) had one on her desk. The time course and severity of symptoms favor schizophreniform disorder over schizophrenia. A rough calculation is that Ester was hospitalized two weeks after her return from New York and started to make a recovery about two months later. The total time course appears to be less than six months. Ester also appears to make a full recovery, which happens less frequently with schizophrenia, but is more typical of other psychotic disorders.

Brief Psychotic Disorder

This condition is diagnosed when symptoms are present anywhere between one day and one month. The criteria are the same as the first four outlined for schizophrenia (all the positive symptoms). Patients with a variety of psychiatric conditions (such as severe personality disorders) can develop short-term psychotic symptoms. Brief periods of psychosis can be caused by traumatic or stressful situations, medical conditions, and drug/alcohol use.

Schizoaffective Disorder

Schizoaffective disorder is a hybrid term, amalgamating the "schizo" from schizophrenia, and affective disorders (now called mood disorders). Mood disorders are discussed in a separate chapter but are reviewed here to help explain schizoaffective disorder. **Affect** (emphasis on the first syllable) is the term used to describe someone's visible emotional state, or a reaction to a certain stimulus. It is an objective description. **Mood** refers to a more enduring emotional tone, and is subjective (which is why psychiatrists ask "How are you feeling?"). Disorders of emotional state are those of mood, not affect, though the term "affective disorder" is still used frequently. Schizoaffective disorder is diagnosed when the signs and symptoms of schizophrenia occur with serious changes in mood (both manic highs and depressive lows). This condition blurs the boundaries between psychotic and mood disorders.

The Fisher King

Parry (Robin Williams) lives in a fantasy world of medieval castles, a red knight, and a divine quest. We first see him rescuing Jack (Jeff Bridges) from a serious assault. Parry is a street person dressed in a long coat, wool sweater, and a hat. He carries a quill of soft-tipped arrows and a shield fashioned from a garbage can lid. His actions are goal-directed (saving Jack), though he accomplishes this by first kissing one of the assailants and then launching into a chorus of *I Like New York in June*. Parry alternates between exhibiting psychotic symptoms (specifically **auditory** and **visual hallucinations**, and **grandiose delusions**) and witty repartée (which is characteristic of mania), while at times seeming quite "normal." His behavior is at times regressed and disorganized (characteristic of the negative symptoms of schizophrenia), while he displays a persistently jovial, magnetic quality that is more consistent with mania. Parry also lapses into a **catatonic stupor** after re-experiencing a traumatic event.

48

Shared Psychotic Disorder

Shared psychotic disorder is also known as **folie à deux**, or double insanity. It has also been called **folie imposée** (imposed insanity) and **folie simultanée** (simultaneous insanity). In this condition, one person (the primary case) suffers from a psychotic disorder, and imparts delusional beliefs to another. In most situations, the inducer is related to the inducee, and has a dominant role (parent, older sibling, etc.). Social isolation is also a factor that facilitates the transmission and acceptance of delusional beliefs. This disorder can extend beyond two people, and is called **folie à trois** when it involves three people, **folie à quatre** for four, etc.

 ## Heavenly Creatures

This is a true story involving two young women enrolled in a strict New Zealand school. Pauline (Melanie Lynskey) is a sullen, shy teenager who quickly befriends the new student. Juliet (Kate Winslet) is fanciful, haughty, and artistically gifted. Juliet speaks of a *"fourth world"* — her version of heaven — replete with music and art. This vision is shared between the two women as a medieval fantasy, initially a romance but with a flavor of brutality. Pauline and Juliet escape into this kingdom via a gateway in the clouds which they believe to be open only two days per year. They consider themselves creative geniuses unappreciated by others. Immersing themselves in this fantasy world they assume the lead roles and construct an elaborate tale that they hope to publish. Each woman **dissociates** into this world at times of emotional upset, having the kingdom's murderous heir do away with those who upset them. Eventually, they scheme to do away with Pauline's mother, who opposes their leaving New Zealand. This film is a good example of how a **folie à deux** starts and progresses, but falls short because the mother is killed for reasons unrelated to the girls' delusion. If the mother had been incorporated into the fantasy world as someone who threatened their relationship (e.g. as an evil witch) the portrayal would be more precise.

Delusional Disorder

Understanding the Condition

Psychotic disorders are broadly defined as those that affect a person's perception of self and/or the environment so that reality is distorted. Transient symptoms of psychosis such as brief hallucinatory experiences occur in a variety of conditions. However, their presence does not automatically mean that a serious mental illness is present.

Delusional disorder (DD) is considerably rarer than schizophrenia — thought to be about 30 times less common, and affects more women than men. This condition is quite different from schizophrenia. DD principally involves the presence of **delusions** (fixed, false beliefs not altered in the presence of compelling proof to the contrary). Hallucinations, speech abnormalities, or grossly disorganized behaviors are not typically part of this condition.

DD can be a challenge to diagnose because apart from a patient's preoccupation with his or her beliefs, the ability to function in society is often preserved. This phenomenon is called **encapsulation**, where apart from the delusion, the patient is not obviously odd or unusual.

Delusional thinking can become quite complex (**systematized**) in that selective abstraction of external events serves to reinforce the false beliefs. Any occurrence can be rationalized as being related to the delusions. It is not possible to cure this disorder with logical discussion or by presenting incontrovertible evidence. Delusions often begin with a "kernel" of truth, and then develop into beliefs that dominate a person's life. For example, someone with delusions of jealousy might have a flirtatious spouse (if the spouse had actually been unfaithful, this would not be a delusion). People with DD are typically very aware of their environment, they just misperceive the significance of the events happening around them to be evidence supporting their delusional beliefs.

Making the Diagnosis

The diagnosis of DD is based principally on the presence of one of the symptoms of schizophrenia (delusions) and the absence of others (hallucinations, speech abnormalities, etc.). However, the quality of the delusions in DD and schizophrenia also differ. In schizophrenia, delusions may be **bizarre**, in that they are nonsensical or impossible (e.g. my liver was destroyed by a Martian proton cannon fired at close range). DD involves delusions that are **non-bizarre**, and while often improbable, are at least possible (e.g. my phone is being tapped).

Though a relatively rare disorder, the most common symptoms of DD are readily recognizable:
- **Persecutory** (previously called paranoid delusions) — unwarranted suspicions of others, or a belief that one is being treated malevolently
- **Jealousy** (also called delusions of infidelity) — unfounded belief that one's sexual partner is being unfaithful
- **Erotomania** — (also called **Clérambault's complex**) the conviction that another person (often famous, wealthy, or powerful) is in love with the patient
- **Grandiosity** — an unfounded belief that one has special powers or connections, wealth, knowledge, identity, etc.
- **Somatic** — false beliefs about having a physical defect or medical condition (patients with hypochondriasis and body dysmorphic disorder are usually less firm in their convictions, and can entertain the possibility that they do not have a serious illness or defect in appearance)

The above list can be contrasted with **bizarre delusions** (which may be seen in schizophrenia), such as:
- Change into an animal (dog – cynanthropy)
- Not having a body (**Cotard's syndrome**)
- One's mind being controlled by an outside agency
- Shrunken body parts (micromania)
- One's gender has changed (metamorphosis sexualis paranoia)
- Cosmic identification (uranomania)

51

Unstrung Heroes
(Illustrating Persecutory Delusions)

Michael Richards portrays Danny Lidz, uncle to the main character in this movie. He literally explodes onto the scene at the family gathering where we first meet him. Danny's brother opens a window for him to crawl through, because he (presumably) wanted to avoid detection. Danny immediately pulls the blinds down and closes the door that connects to the patio. He insists that two men followed him, but through a series of sly maneuvers he was able to elude them. He then espouses his belief that everyone in the room is being monitored and talks into one woman's necklace because he thinks she has a microphone hidden there. He accuses his sister-in-law Selma (Andie McDowell) of smoking marijuana, which is untrue. Danny goes on to dominate the gathering with his persecutory beliefs, such as Eisenhower being a Nazi. Meanwhile, he tells Selma that she looks like death and that she should get some air (she is in fact dying of cancer at this time). Later in the film, Danny accuses a grade seven student of being a fascist and believes that life is made up of anti-Semitic conspiracies. He also believes there are only eight trustworthy people in the world.

At times, Danny is fun to be around, especially when he doesn't feel threatened. Some people with delusional disorders can de-emphasize their thoughts, particularly when there is a clear advantage to doing so (such as avoiding hospitalization) or when circumstances require that they focus their energy elsewhere.

His persecutory thoughts are more severe than what one would see in a **paranoid personality disorder**. We do not see anything that would indicate he was hallucinating, and his speech and behavior would not qualify as being disorganized. He is certainly delusional, but his fixed, false beliefs are of the non-bizarre type (in that some people are followed, and there have been anti-Semitic conspiracies). These features combine to give an accurate portrayal of delusional disorder, persecutory type.

Body Snatchers — The Invasion Continues
(Illustrating Persecutory Delusions)

This movie, the second remake of *Invasion of the Body Snatchers*, deals with the delusion that someone has been replaced by an impostor (also called **Capgras' syndrome**). While this is true in the context of the movie, it does provide an example of paranoid thinking (see also *Conspiracy Theory*). In one scene, the base commander's daughter believes her mother has been replaced because she now plays bridge, a change from her previous interests. Patients experiencing Capgras syndrome similarly collect evidence to prove others are not who they claim to be.

The Snake Pit
(Illustrating Grandiose Delusions)

An illustration of a grandiose delusion is presented on Ward 1 by the woman with the lace gloves. She mentions that her husband is very wealthy and owns the Hope Diamond. When Virginia (Olivia de Havilland) teases her by saying that she owns the "Hopeless Emerald," the woman misses the pun and belittles the (fictitious) gem as having a flaw, making it unsuitable for her beautiful hands. This woman misunderstands Virginia's use of the word "general." Toying with her further, Virginia changes the statement about the "general you" to "General Pershing," whom the delusional woman immediately names as a member of a "minor branch" of her family.

David & Lisa
(Illustrating Somatic Delusions)

David becomes enraged when another student touches him (while helping David with his luggage). He screams and immediately uses a handkerchief to undo the insult. David then tells the other student that touching someone can kill, and berates him as if he should have known this. Other examples are **Ekbom's syndrome** (being infested with parasites), and **formication** (insects crawling under one's skin).

Unfaithfully Yours
(Illustrating Delusions of Jealousy or Infidelity)

Claude (Dudley Moore) is a famous orchestral conductor who has recently married the vivacious and much younger Daniella (Nastassja Kinski), an Italian actress. Prior to leaving on a tour, Claude asks his butler to keep an 'eye' on Daniella, but instead a private eye is hired. Claude, wary of their age difference, cannot help but watch the video surveillance tape taken by the detective, which shows a man visiting their apartment late at night. Claude learns that this was Max (Armand Assante) a close friend. Everywhere Claude turns, more circumstantial evidence accumulates to support his fear that Max and Daniella are lovers (Max is having an affair, but not with Daniella). When Claude confronts Max a heated argument ensues but because of their mutual vagueness, Claude's indignation reaches a fever pitch (with predictably humorous results because this is a comedy). In severe cases of delusional infidelity, the affected person might report that his or her partner has dozens of encounters in a day. It can become so extreme that any brief absence from the person's direct view will result in a torrent of accusations.

I Know You Really Love Me
(Erotomania)

Doreen Orion, M.D., wrote this book in 1997 both to describe erotomania (also called delusional loving, **phantom lover syndrome**, and **Clérambault's complex)**, and to relate her own experience with a female patient who has this condition. This book provides many true and sensational stories about erotomania. Examples include the shooting death of actress Rebecca Shaeffer in 1989 and the woman who has stalked David Letterman for many years. Dr. Orion makes the important point that only about 10% of stalkers truly have erotomania. The majority of male stalkers do not have the delusional belief that the victim loves them, but instead hope to make a favorable impression in order to start a relationship.

Movie	Feature/Diagnosis
A Beautiful Mind	Delusions (persecutory) Hallucinations (auditory and visual) Schizophrenia (paranoid type)
Awakenings	Behavioral changes in psychosis
Benny & Joon	Expressed emotion; Hallucinations (auditory); Schizophrenia
Birdy	Personality disorder (avoidant and schizoid); Posttraumatic stress disorder; Schizophrenia (prodromal, active, and residual phases)
Clean, Shaven	Alogia; Delusions (persecutory/somatic)
Conspiracy Theory	Delusions (persecutory)
David & Lisa	Clanging/clang associations; Ekbom's syndrome; Formication; Schizophrenia (disorganized)
Don Juan Demarco	Delusions (grandiose)
Heavenly Creatures	Folie à deux
I Never Promised You a Rose Garden	Autistic thinking; Hallucinations (command); Dissociation; Loose/ loosening of associations; Neologisms; Waxy flexibility (catalepsy)
Invasion of the Body Snatchers	Capgras' syndrome; Delusions (persecutory)
Jacob's Ladder	Hallucinations (visual)

One Flew Over the Cuckoo's Nest	Negative symptoms
Pi	Delusions (somatic); Hallucinations (visual)
Possessed	Catatonia; Delusions (jealousy/infidelity); Echolalia; Erotomania; Overvalued ideas; Thought blocking; Waxy flexibility (catalepsy)
Shine	Abnormalities of speech; Concrete thinking; Double bind; Loosening of associations; Negative symptoms
Sophie's Choice	Delusions (grandiose); Schizophrenia (paranoid)
Snake Pit	Delusions (grandiose); Behavioral changes in psychosis; Hallucinations (auditory and visual)
The Bell Jar	Negative symptoms; Schizophrenia (prodromal and acute phases)
The Caveman's Valentine	Delusions (persecutory) Hallucinations (auditory and visual) Schizophrenia (paranoid type)
The Fisher King	Catatonic stupor; Delusions (grandiose); Hallucinations (auditory and visual)
Unfaithfully Yours	Delusions of infidelity/jealousy
Unstrung Heroes	Concrete thinking; Delusions (persecutory); Paranoid personality disorder; Schizophrenia (residual)

Chapter 6

Mood Disorders

Depression

Understanding the Condition

It is relatively easy to connect with feelings of despondency, melancholy, and hopelessness. Most people have experienced depressive symptoms at least transiently. Possibly the best way of understanding this condition is to imagine losing a loved one. Most people would have difficulty sleeping, a diminished appetite, trouble concentrating, decreased energy, etc. Depression has been described since antiquity. An account of depression appears in the Bible, as well as in Hippocrates' writings from the 4th century BC. An ancient explanation for illnesses consisted of excesses of four body humors:

- Yellow bile: "choleric" — causes irritability and anxiety
- Black bile: "melancholic" — causes depression
- Mucus: "phlegmatic" — causes apathy
- Blood: "sanguine" — causes optimism and hypomania

People with depression often have physical complaints, making an accurate diagnosis a challenge. For example, elderly patients may complain of constipation when it is in fact their mood that is the principal problem. Cultural factors also modify which symptoms are emphasized. Depression appears to be more common in women by a factor of almost two. The lifetime risk for depression ranges from 10% to 20% for women, and 5% to 10% for men. There is clear evidence that genetic factors predispose some people to experience depression. However, almost anyone can become depressed when severe stressors are present, particularly losses. Depression is sometimes called a **unipolar mood disorder**, indicating that someone's emotional state would vary between "normal" (**euthymic**) and depressed.

Many famous people have endured depressive episodes, including Ernest Hemingway, Abraham Lincoln, and Winston Churchill. In recent years, many effective therapies for depression have been developed, giving this illness an overall optimistic outcome.

Making the Diagnosis

It is important to be able to distinguish self-limiting periods of "feeling blue" from mood changes that require treatment. The core symptoms of a **major depressive episode** are as follows:

i.   *Depressed mood* — this includes feeling down, despondent, dejected, dysphoric, down in the dumps, downcast, etc.

ii. *Diminished interest in pleasurable activities* — this is called **anhedonia**, and along with depressed mood is a cardinal symptom of a serious disturbance in mood (**clinical depression**)

iii. *Change in weight* — this can be either a gain or a loss, and is significant if there is a change of 5% of total body weight within a one-month period

iv. *Sleep changes* — can occur in the following ways: **initial insomnia** is difficulty getting to sleep; **middle insomnia** is trouble staying asleep; and **terminal insomnia**, also called **early morning awakening**, occurs when people wake up before they plan to (usually at around 4:00 a.m.) and cannot return to sleep; some depressed people sleep much longer than they usually do, which is called **hypersomnia**

v.   *Behavioral changes* — people who are depressed can become either quite agitated (**psychomotor agitation**) or slowed down in their movements (**psychomotor retardation**)

vi. *Decreased energy* — even minor tasks can seem overwhelming, or even monumental, to a depressed person

vii. *Worthlessness or guilt* — patients may become preoccupied with minor failings or blame themselves irrationally, feeling far more responsible for something than is reasonable

viii. *Problems with intellectual tasks* — memory, concentration, and decision-making ability can be affected by depression; some people become so depressed that they appear to have a form of dementia (**depression-related cognitive dysfunction**)

ix. *Recurrent thoughts of death or suicide* — many depressed patients consider suicide: as a way to stop their suffering; a means of reducing the burden they perceive themselves to be to others; or as a form of punishment that they deserve

59

Cinematic examples of the main criteria for depression (listed above) are demonstrated in the following movies:

Hope Floats

(Illustrating Depressed Mood, Diminished Interest in Activities, Decreased Appetite, Sleep Changes, and Decreased Energy)

Birdee Pruitt (Sandra Bullock) is the unfortunate victim of both an unfaithful husband and being invited to a talk show under false pretenses. After her marriage evaporates on live television, Birdee returns to her home town to live with her mother. Birdee's mood starts to slip in the first few weeks after her separation. She exhibits the following symptoms of depression:

- Depressed mood — both Birdee's mother and a family friend comment that she looks depressed
- Diminished interest in activities — Birdee won't do things with her mother and takes less of an interest in her daughter's activities (such as asking about how she's doing in school)
- Decreased appetite — in one scene, both Birdee and her daughter show no interest in a savory home-cooked meal
- Sleep changes — Birdee tosses and turns at night, and has difficulty falling asleep; she also begins to sleep for extended periods of time and has trouble getting up in the morning
- Decreased energy — Birdee stops making breakfast for her daughter and stays in her bathrobe for much of the day

The Wrong Man

(Illustrating Depressed Mood, Decreased Appetite, Sleep Changes, Behavior Changes, Worthlessness/ Guilt, Decreased Concentration)

Rose Balestrero (Vera Miles) is the wife of a man who is wrongly accused of armed robbery. Her impacted wisdom teeth require treatment, and to pay the dentist, her husband attempts to borrow against her insurance policy. When he is at the insurance office, the clerk believes that he is the guilty party and calls the police.

60

As their financial situation worsens and her husband's case looks progressively bleaker, Rose develops marked symptoms of depression:

- Depressed mood — she becomes markedly detached from, and disinterested in her surroundings; at a time when her husband and children need her support, Rose is too down to help them
- Sleep and appetite changes — when Rose becomes seriously depressed, she isn't able to sleep at all; her husband expresses his concern about her lack of appetite
- Behavior changes — Rose slows down markedly as she becomes more depressed; she and her husband are doing the legwork to document their alibi, but instead of showing enthusiasm for this task Rose sits almost in an immobile fashion (**psychomotor retardation**); in one segment she is desperately clutching at her coat sleeve (**psychomotor agitation**; hand wringing is another common example)
- Worthlessness/guilt — Rose decompensates to the point where she has a profound sense of guilt over her husband's arrest; she believes that she is a poor mother, and that her mismanagement of the household funds led to the entire chain of events; ultimately Rose believes that her husband was arrested because of her failings; when Rose is well, there is every reason to believe that she is a kind, caring, and capable wife and mother, so these feelings of guilt and worthlessness are clearly related to her depression
- Diminished concentration — Rose can't follow the discussion in her lawyer's office that involves a promising lead and renewed hope that her husband will be cleared

'Night Mother

(Illustrating Recurrent Thoughts of Death or Suicide)

This film is based on a play involving two characters, Jessie Cates (Sissy Spacek) and her mother Thelma (Anne Bancroft). Jessie's marriage fell apart and she moved back home to live with her mother. Jessie suffers from epilepsy and due to a variety of factors she has been unable to enjoy anything that life offers. She's tried to find fulfillment, but instead has become both her mother's keeper and housekeeper. This movie is about the last evening of Jessie's life. She has organized all of her belongings into labeled bags, and even takes the time to synchronize clocks and cancel newspaper delivery. Jessie has a distinct aura of sadness about her, avoiding her brother and his family when they come to visit. She tidies up the house and organizes things for her mother, even buying and wrapping presents for events that will take place long after her death. Some people who are planning suicide energetically put their affairs in order and even have a paradoxical lifting in mood, possibly because they foresee that their suffering will come to an end. After misleading Thelma about her reasons for wanting her father's pistol, Jessie calmly tells her mother that she will commit suicide that night. Thelma initially dismisses the comment, but soon comes to realize that Jessie is serious. Anyone faced with this situation would likely become involved in the ensuing exchange. Thelma runs through a gamut of reactions to Jessie's plans: sympathy, anger, denial, bargaining, distraction, guilt, disclosing secrets, etc.

Many people surviving those who commit suicide never come to terms with that person's reasons for doing so. Jessie gives a calm, thoughtful, and insightful explanation for why she wants to end her life at that time. In essence, the movie is a thorough, interactive suicide note. Jessie answers all of Thelma's questions, and gives her rationale for why she chooses to end her life. Whether Jessie's reasons and decision seem valid or not is a personal matter. Albert Camus said two things about suicide that are poignant: *"Death for us all, but his own death to each"* and, *"Suicide is prepared within the silence of the heart, as is a great work of art."*

Almost everyone who attempts suicide has a history of mental illness. Psychiatric patients' risk for suicide can be up to ten times greater than the general population. As a group, mood disorders are the diagnoses most commonly associated with suicide.

Patch Adams

In the opening monologue, Hunter "Patch" Adams (Robin Williams) describes his feelings of disconnectedness and inner torment by using the metaphor of walking in circles for days in a driving snowstorm. He felt as if his legs were heavy and that his shouts were disappearing in the wind. As this is being narrated, Adams, unshaven and listless, stares vacantly out of a bus window and appears disinterested and sad.

Adams realizes that the storm is in his mind, and uses an eloquent quote from Dante to describe his **depressed mood**, "*In the middle of the journey of my life, I found myself in a dark wood, for I had lost the right path.*" Adams is tempted to take an overdose (**thoughts of suicide**), but instead admits himself into a psychiatric facility to seek help.

Once at the hospital his face is blank and expressionless. He walks slowly (**psychomotor retardation**), looks bewildered, and is easily overwhelmed by the events occurring around him. Later, when he tells his personal history to his psychiatrist, Adams reveals that when he was nine years old he lost his father (which is the life event most frequently associated with later episodes of depression). He illustrates **feelings of guilt** when describing how he blamed himself for his father "losing his soul" when in fact it was the Korean War that caused his father to feel soulless.

Adams goes on to indicate that this episode of depression is long standing. He moved seven times in the last year, had a series of jobs, and felt as if he didn't fit in anywhere.

Unfortunately (for the sake of this depiction), Adams doesn't stay depressed for very long. Even in his initial interview, his mood starts to improve. He's aware that his psychiatrist isn't listening very carefully and decides to mock him (successfully) by including some scatological humor delivered in a deadpan voice.

Girl, Interrupted

This movie is based on the book by the same name written by Susanna Kaysen. The title of this movie is an abbreviation of a Jan Vermeer painting called, *Girl Interrupted at her Music*. In a deleted scene available on the DVD, Susanna (Winona Ryder) experiences an epiphany while viewing this painting in a Boston museum.

Susanna is admitted to a psychiatric facility after taking an overdose of ASA and vodka (a serious **suicide attempt**). At the time of her admission, she is emotionally flat and frail, and displays a number of symptoms of depression. In the interview with the psychiatrist in her home, she is distractible and has difficulty describing her feelings (**alexithymia**). She admits to feeling sad (**depressed mood**) and needing a rest (**decreased energy**). Later, she acknowledges her improvement by saying that her sleep and appetite have improved, indicating that they may have been a problem for her though this wasn't emphasized in the film. The portrayal of depression is complicated by two factors in this movie. The first is that Susanna experiences repeated and intense **visual hallucinations** (psychotic symptoms). Psychotic symptoms accompanying depression and mania are not rare. Diagnostic specifiers exist to distinguish whether the themes of the hallucinations or delusions are in keeping with the mood disturbance. For example, **mood-congruent psychotic features** for depression would involve morbid themes such as death, destruction, loss, guilt, punishment, inadequacy, etc. **Mood-incongruent psychotic features** for depression would involve wealth, power, grandiosity, super-human abilities, etc. At the beginning of the film, we see Susanna being resuscitated in a hospital after her overdose. She warns the staff to be careful with her right hand because it has no bones. This is a **mood-congruent delusion**. At times in this movie it is difficult to distinguish between Susanna's hallucinations and flashbacks that help fill in some of the background information.

64

The second complication is that Susanna is tentatively given the diagnosis of **borderline personality disorder** (see page 232). When Susanna hears this term for the first time, she demands to know what she is on the "borderline" between, since her diagnosis hasn't been discussed with her. Later, Susanna has the chance to read the diagnostic criteria for this condition, and agrees that the brief description applies to her. Note that the criteria in the current version of the DSM are different than the ones she recites in this scene, which were:

1. Instability of self-image, mood, and relationships
2. Uncertainty about goals
3. Impulsivity in activities that are self-damaging
4. Social contrariness
5. Generally pessimistic attitude

The diagnosis of borderline personality disorder can be refuted on the following grounds:

- Susanna's mood remains uniformly down for most of the film, and changes neither quickly (instability) nor dramatically (range) as is more typical for borderline personalities
- Susanna develops close friendships with many of the other patients and gets along well with many of the staff
- Susanna decided to pursue her goal of being a writer well before her suicide attempt; this desire never wavers, and she keeps a journal during her stay
- Impulsivity in activities that are self-damaging quickly becomes a question about promiscuity; Susanna had a brief affair with a married man, and an intimate relationship with a high-school student whom she refers to as her boyfriend; she denies that she is promiscuous
- Susanna enjoys the friendships that she has with other patients, various activities, and never loses sight of her goal to be a writer; if her attitude can be deemed as being pessimistic, this could very reasonably be attributed to a bout of depression

Susanna is angry at times with the hospital staff, other patients, and her parents, but in general she appears to be agreeable, and helpful. The character of Lisa (Angelina Jolie) influences Susanna to be more of a rebel, but later in the film Lisa runs away from the hospital. During Lisa's absence, Susanna decides to trust the hospital staff and engage in treatment. She recognizes that the staff have things to offer her, and she benefits significantly from her therapy sessions. At the time of her admission, Susanna is still a teenager and would be expected to have opinions that differed from the authority figures around her. A typical course for patients with borderline personality disorder is much rockier than Susanna's experience as portrayed in the film. For example, repeated suicidal gestures, interpersonal turmoil, and sabotage of the staff would have been more consistent with this condition. Given that Susanna cooperated with treatment, improved, and didn't indicate that she needed ongoing treatment, the course of her illness is more consistent with an episode of depression. The diagnosis of borderline personality disorder can be difficult to distinguish from a mood disorder, particularly bipolar mood disorder (see page 74).

The possibility that Susanna suffers from depression is addressed in the film. At the beginning, she asks a rhetorical question of the viewer as to whether or not *"you've ever been blue."* Susanna acknowledges that she is sad and needs a rest. Her father, in the interview with one of her psychiatrists, wonders how long Susanna needs to be hospitalized for depression. Susanna manages to get an unauthorized look at her medical chart. The diagnoses listed there are:

On admission: Psychoneurotic Depressive Reaction
                       Personality Pattern Disturbance
                       Rule out (R/O) Undifferentiated Schizophrenia
Established Diagnosis: Borderline Personality Disorder

For the reasons listed above, Susanna's difficulties as portrayed in *Girl, Interrupted* are more consistent with a **depression with mood-congruent psychotic features** than with borderline personality disorder.

66

The Wrong Man

This 1956 movie, directed by Alfred Hitchcock, is based on the novel called *The True Story of Christopher Emmanuel Balestrero*. In this film, Manny Balestrero (Henry Fonda) is an honest, hardworking musician who is a devoted husband and father. In order to raise the amount of money needed for his wife's dental work he plans to arrange for a loan against her life insurance policy. While he is at the insurance company's office, he is mistakenly identified as the man who has committed a series of neighborhood robberies. Balestrero is summarily charged and jailed, but is released on bail. His wife, Rose (Vera Miles), hires lawyer Frank O'Connor (Anthony Quayle), and the couple undertakes the task of documenting their alibi as part of Manny's defense.

Unfortunately for Manny and Rose, two of the witnesses that could place them miles away from the scene of the crime have since passed away. When Rose learns of the death of the second man, she becomes overwhelmed and makes a few nonsensical statements. After this scene, her psychological difficulties become much more pronounced. Rose believes that her inability to economize was what started the sequence of events that led to Manny's arrest (**feelings of guilt**). She also derides herself for not being a good wife (**feelings of worthlessness**).

In the second meeting with O'Connor, Rose stares ahead blankly and is so listless (**psychomotor retardation**) that she barely moves. She loses track of the conversation even though it centers on something that is vital to her husband's defense (**diminished ability to concentrate**). In this scene Rose comes across as detached, sullen, and utterly unable to rally herself despite the generally optimistic tone of the meeting (**depressed mood**).

Manny works so late that by the time he arrives home the milk has already been delivered. When he enters the bedroom, he finds Rose sitting by the side of the bed with a vacant stare (**insomnia**). Manny expresses his concern that her difficulties are becoming insurmountable, and has also noticed that she hasn't been eating (**diminished appetite**) and has lost interest in everything (**anhedonia**).

Later in this scene, we find out how far Rose's depression has progressed. She believes that it is pointless to care about the outcome of the trial because everything is fixed against them. She intends to keep her family at home, and will lock the doors to keep "them" out. She then launches into a tirade of accusations and denouncements, building to the point where she assaults Manny. Rose's ideas about powerlessness, doom, and relentless persecution qualify as **mood-congruent psychotic features**.

When Rose explains her difficulties to a doctor, she is convinced that she is the guilty party. She believes that she let her family down, and that Manny was arrested because of her failings. Rose is hopeless and helpless, fearing punishment that she views as inevitable.

The doctor gives a tidy summary of Rose's difficulties, making many references to darkness:
- *"Her mind is in an eclipse."*
- *"Her beliefs darken the whole world for her."*
- *"She's living in another world. . . a frightening landscape that could be on the dark side of the moon."*
- *" . . . monstrous shadows that say hateful things"*

Rose's difficulties clearly exceed the level of care available for her at home. By the time Rose is taken to a hospital, she is an automaton who can barely muster a goodbye. Although it is not addressed overtly in the film, Rose appears to be at risk for either harming herself or others because of what she views as punishment that is both justified and inevitable. Overall, this is an excellent portrayal of depression, and in particular, one that progresses to the point where psychotic features have developed.

Ordinary People

We are introduced to the Jarrett family after they have endured two tragedies. First, their eldest son Buck drowned in a boating accident. Then, their youngest son Conrad (Timothy Hutton) made a suicide attempt and required hospitalization for four months.

Conrad is depressed for most of the movie. Either he's suffered a relapse since discharge, or he left the hospital without his episode of depression being fully treated. Within the first few minutes of the film, we can see that Conrad suffers from the following symptoms:

- Insomnia — including distressing dreams
- Decreased appetite
- Diminished ability to concentrate — mainly on school work
- Lack of enjoyment (**anhedonia**) — this was made clear by the coach of the high school swim team

In his first meeting with Dr. Berger (Judd Hirsch), Conrad denies that he feels depressed. It is possible to suffer from an episode of depression and not actually endorse feeling down. In such instances, a pervasive lack of interest or pleasure must be present. Also, the observations of others regarding a patient's mood can satisfy this diagnostic criterion. Conrad describes his mood prior to his suicide attempt in the following manner: *"It was like falling into a hole, except falling into a hole that keeps getting bigger and bigger, and you can't get out. And then, all of a sudden, it's inside and you're the hole. And you're trapped and it's all over. . .it's not really scary, except it is when you think back on it. . ."*

The principal undercurrent in this film is Conrad's unstated guilt that he survived and his brother didn't (sometimes called the **survivor syndrome** or **survivor guilt**). We learn towards the end of the film that Conrad was able to hang on to the capsized boat while his brother was overcome by the waves. This revelation comes about in an interesting manner. Conrad calls Dr. Berger at home in the evening. Conrad has just learned that one of his friends (from his admission to the hospital) committed suicide. Dr. Berger is able to get Conrad to experience the boating accident as if it was actually happening all over again. This process is called **abreaction**, and is defined as follows: *"A process by which repressed material, particularly a painful experience or a conflict, is brought back to consciousness. . .in this process, the person not only recalls but relives the repressed material, which is accompanied by the appropriate emotional response"* (Kaplan & Sadock, 2000).

This session has a noticeably cathartic effect on Conrad, who seems quite relieved after coming to realize that the only thing he did "wrong" was to hang on to the boat.

In what has become known as the **classical theory of depression**, Sigmund Freud and Karl Abraham focused on two key elements: **anger turned inwards** and **loss**.

When Conrad is reliving the accident with Dr. Berger, he says *"screw you, you jerk"* in response to Berger (as Buck) saying that he simply got tired and let go. Despite his obvious love for Buck, Conrad "hates" his brother for dying and abandoning him. Since Conrad cannot openly express these feelings, they are turned inward and fuel his guilt and self-loathing. Historically, depression was subclassified on the basis of the presence of an external precipitant. If a clear cause for an episode of depression was present, this was called a **reactive depression**. If no precipitant was present, it was termed an **endogenous depression**. This distinction is no longer used because the losses causing a depression can be fantasied or symbolic.

Of note, this film contains one of the few positive portrayals of a psychiatrist. The first American film that depicted a psychiatrist was released in 1906 and was called *Dr. Dippy's Sanitarium*. A detailed and enlightening resource describing the depiction of psychiatrists in film is Gabbard & Gabbard's *Psychiatry and the Cinema, Second Edition* (1999).

Dysthymic Disorder

Understanding the Condition

Dysthymic disorder, also called **dysthymia**, literally translated means "ill-humored." Depression is diagnosed in the DSM-IV as either a **major depressive episode** (single occurrence) or **major depressive disorder** (two or more occurrences). Dysthymic disorder is a more chronic but less severe disturbance than a major depressive episode. See page 90 for a diagram illustrating various types of mood disorders. The APA (at the time of writing) is considering a **minor depressive disorder**, but this still would be a diagnostic entity separate from dysthymic disorder. In the past, dysthymic disorder was called **depressive neurosis** (the term neurosis no longer appears in psychiatric diagnostic terminology).

Making the Diagnosis

One of the principal distinctions between dysthymic disorder and depression is the time course. Depression can be diagnosed if the symptoms are present for all or most of a two-week period. Dysthymic disorder must be present for at least two years, with no remission of symptoms for more than two months. The diagnostic criteria for dysthymia are as follows:

i. *Changes in appetite* — can be either increased or decreased
ii. *Sleep changes* — can be either increased or decreased
iii. *Decreased energy*
iv. *Low self-esteem*
v. *Poor concentration or indecisiveness*
vi. *Feelings of hopelessness*

This constellation of symptoms includes the same changes in sleep, appetite, and energy (called **vegetative symptoms**) seen in depression. However, two of the criteria included here are different than in depression: low self-esteem and hopelessness. These characteristics certainly can be seen in depressed patients, but appear more prominently in dysthymic disorder.

71

The Hospital

Dr. Herbert Bock (George C. Scott) is a departmental chief in a major New York City hospital. At the beginning of the film, he is living in a hotel, having made a permanent separation from his wife. His performance at work has noticeably declined. He dwells on suicide and has considered a method that will avoid detection so his family can still claim his insurance benefits.

He does have enough of an awareness of his difficulties to seek help. While giving his life narrative, he admits to having felt depressed for a period of years, possibly extending back to college. He is struggling with the administrative responsibilities of his job, and decides to seek an impromptu appointment with a psychiatrist as his secretary reads him a list of departmental problems. He seems beaten down by his situation, and walks slowly with his head hanging down.

Unfortunately (for this portrayal), Dr. Bock uses alcohol heavily throughout the movie. This complicates his situation, and in fact he almost attempts suicide when he is drunk in his office. He makes no mention of sustained changes in his sleep or appetite. His **energy level** seems down, but he still meets the demands of his job (even after drinking a bottle of vodka the night before). His potent sense of anger at the events in the hospital seems to focus his thinking. His mental abilities are difficult to gauge, though in one scene he confides to a medical student that he's glad that they are discussing tuberculosis because that was the only condition he read about before giving a teaching session.

Dr. Bock does seem to have **diminished self-esteem** and **hopelessness**. He vents his feelings and discloses his impotence to a patient's daughter, Miss Barbara Drummond (Diana Rigg). Having nowhere else to go, he stays in his office to get drunk and attempt suicide. He gives serious consideration to leaving his post to work in a grass-roots clinic in the mountains of Mexico.

While this character does have some symptoms of depression, the duration of at least two years would be an indication that he probably has dysthymic disorder. If we ignore the influence that alcohol has on his situation, he may have acutely developed a depression on top of his dysthymic disorder, which is called **double depression**. His mood and outlook on life improve considerably when he has a tryst with Miss Drummond. He also decides to soldier on in his position at the hospital when he sees that he can still be useful there.

We don't know how long his renewed sense of purpose will last. Most people with depression don't improve this quickly or dramatically, and are much more affected by their symptoms. This depiction is more consistent with dysthymic disorder than with depression because of the time course of this illness, Bock's ability to seek help (indicating that he has some energy to look after himself), and the lack of other depressive symptoms.

Finding Forrester

William Forrester (Sean Connery) wrote "the great novel" and then became a recluse in a New York City apartment building. He slowly befriends a gifted neighborhood high-school student, though in the process reveals himself to be irascible, oppositional, and dour. He demonstrates some of the features of dysthymic disorder, particularly the time course (years) and presence of some depressive symptoms (arguably **low self-esteem**, **hopelessness**, and **decreased energy**).

Complicating this portrayal is that Forrester could qualify for at least three other diagnoses: **alcohol abuse** (amply demonstrated by his continual drinking, and in particular, his need to calm his nerves by imbibing); **agoraphobia** (he usually only leaves his apartment to wash his windows, though he will go outside when persuaded to do so); and a mood disorder due to his physical illness (specifically called a **mood disorder due to cancer, with depressive features** — see Chapter 18).

Mania/Bipolar Disorder

Understanding the Condition

Mania, also known as a **manic episode**, is largely the opposite mood state to that of depression. Mania causes people to seem as if they are speeded up. Common symptoms are extreme excitation, distractibility, and a fast rate of speech. Someone may appear manic after winning a prize (particularly a large lottery). Unlike periods of elation that most people have experienced, mania doesn't subside after a short period of time, and patients don't usually have something to be deliriously happy about. Most people who experience episodes of mania also have periods of depression. Because of the transition between the poles or extremes of mood states, this condition is called **bipolar disorder** or **manic–depressive illness**. Some patients have very brief and mild episodes of depression that can be difficult to recognize. A small number of people who experience manic episodes do not seem to suffer from any periods of depression.

Most episodes of bipolar disorder start with a bout of depression. It is not possible to distinguish on clinical grounds major depressive disorder from the depressed phase of bipolar disorder. Five to ten percent of patients who have major depressive episodes ultimately go on to develop bipolar disorder.

Bipolar disorder affects men and women in equal numbers. It is rarer than depression, with the lifetime chance of developing this illness in the range of 1%. Bipolar disorder frequently starts in the 20's, but can occur in either childhood or in adults over fifty.

There is stronger evidence for a genetic factor involved in bipolar disorder than in major depression. If one parent has bipolar disorder, the chance of his or her child developing a mood disorder is around 25%. This risk can increase up to 75% if both parents are affected with a mood disorder. The prognosis for bipolar disorder is less favorable than for major depressive disorder.

Making the Diagnosis

Because many people have periods in their lives when they feel exhilarated, "on top of the world," or highly charged, it is crucial to determine whether someone's mood state is indeed impairing his or her ability to function in social or occupational roles. The symptoms of a manic episode are as follows:

i.   *Grandiosity* — significantly elevated self-esteem
ii. *Diminished need for sleep* — feel rested with 3 or 4 hours
iii. *Hypertalkativeness* — appear driven to keep talking
iv. *Increased thought production* — feeling as if one's thoughts are racing; rapid shifts are made from one idea to the next with identifiable connections between ideas
v.   *Distractibility* — in spite of having a flood of ideas and boundless energy, mania (as it gets more severe) causes people to lose interest in the task at hand, often because something more interesting around them caught their attention
vi. *Increased level of activity* — this can involve either working towards a goal, or involve purposeless over-activity (**psychomotor agitation**)
vii. *Engaging in high-risk behaviors* — having little regard for the consequences to one's health, finances, reputation, etc.

Making an accurate diagnosis of mania can be a challenge. Manic episodes are frequently complicated by psychotic symptoms (such as hallucinations, delusions, or catatonia). Furthermore, it is common for bipolar patients to have some co-existing symptoms of depression while they are manic and to swing rapidly between excitation and hopelessness (**mood lability**).

The DSM contains a diagnosis called a **hypomanic episode**. This differs from mania in the following ways: people are less impaired in their social or occupational roles; hospitalization is not necessary; and there are no psychotic symptoms. Patients whose mood states ranges up to full mania have **bipolar I disorder**. Mood states that range between depression and hypomania qualify for the diagnosis of **bipolar II disorder**.

Cinematic depictions of the symptoms of a manic episode are portrayed in the following movies:

Mad Love

(Illustrating Grandiosity, Psychomotor Agitation, and Distractibility,)

This movie was made in 1995 and is neither a remake of the 1923 nor the 1935 version. Casey Roberts (Drew Barrymore), a new student at the local high school, catches the eye of Matt Leland (Chris O'Donnell). Casey demonstrates a **grandiose sense of self-worth** in a variety of ways. As she gets to know Matt, she is animated, opinionated, and intrusive. Casey is also abrupt, walking away from Matt until he formally asks her on a date. She then ends their evening together after becoming impatient. After inviting him to "call her sometime," she arrives unexpectedly during school hours and persuades Matt to skip a chemistry lab. Later, Casey interrupts Matt's SAT exam by pulling the fire alarm because she isn't able to get his attention. She tells Matt that she thinks she is sometimes the center of the universe (after he pointedly tells her that she isn't and that her intrusion is unwelcome). Casey's reason for interrupting his exam is that one of her favorite photographers was doing a book signing, and she wanted company when she went to the bookstore.

In the scene where Casey and Matt go out for dinner, she provides a good example of **distractibility** — she can't focus on her conversation with Matt, and similarly can't screen out the events happening around her, even when they aren't very interesting. At dinner, Casey also gives a good demonstration of **psychomotor agitation** — she constantly scans the room, exaggerates her mannerisms, shifts frequently in her seat, and fumbles with her cigarette (butting it and needing it re-lit by the waiter). Casey plays a game with Matt where she holds her hands over his eyes while he's driving on a tortuous stretch of highway. This eventually leads to an accident where their vehicle is wrecked and they narrowly miss being seriously injured.

Good Morning, Vietnam

(Illustrating Pressure of Speech and Flight of Ideas)

Robin Williams portrays military DJ Adrian Cronauer in this comedy/drama. The main character does not have a mood disorder, but his loud, rapid, and amusing on-air performances are good examples of the speech and thought patterns in mania. Cronauer's first broadcast reads as follows:

"Good Morning Vietnam. This is not a test — this is rock 'n roll! Time to rock it from the Delta to the DMZ. Is it me, or does that sound like an Elvis Presley movie? Viva Da Nang, oh Viva Da Nang. Da Nang me, Da Nang me, why don't they get a rope and hang me? Hey! Is it a little too early for being this loud? Hey too late! It's 0600h — what's the 'O' for? Oh, my God it's early!" He then goes on to incorporate many other features into his broadcast such as *The Twilight Zone, The Wizard of Oz*, and impersonations of *Gomer Pyle.*

Another of his soliloquies is worth examining. After sitting through an impromptu meeting replete with acronyms, Cronauer says the following: *"Seeing as how the VP (Vice-President) is such a VIP, shouldn't we keep the PC (press conference) on the QT? Because if it leaks to the VC (Viet-Cong), he can end up an MIA (missing in action), and then we'll all be put on KP (kitchen patrol)."*

Cronauer's speech is rushed (**pressure of speech**) as if he is compelled to keep talking. He switches topics often and quickly, though his ideas are linked together but take off (**flight of ideas**) into many new areas. Like many patients with mania, Cronauer can seemingly talk for hours and include jokes, puns, and amusing irrelevancies in his monologue. People who are manic make word associations faster than they can when they are euthymic. Furthermore, people who have **bipolar II disorder** (sometimes referred to as the **soft bipolar spectrum**) and are able to harness the desirable qualities (increased energy, critical thinking, self-confidence, and eloquence) may do very well in leadership or creative roles — an excellent presentation can be found in *Manic-Depressive Illness* by Goodwin & Jamison (1990).

The Snake Pit

(Illustrating Pressure of Speech, Flight of Ideas, and Distractibility)

A number of minor characters provide accurate portrayals of psychiatric conditions. On Ward 8, the banter at the dinner table is illustrative of one aspect of mania. One woman, upon hearing the word "hello" divides it and says, *"Hell is low, heaven is high."* Another woman picks up on this, and takes the idea of "two" or "divisibility" further by saying that she would speak out of the other side of her face (i.e. being two-faced). The woman in the patient/visitor lounge appears to be manic. She is gregarious and jovial, speaking continuously to whomever is within earshot. She misapplies her make-up and doesn't care when someone points this out to her. She seems driven to catch the attention of a man, and refers to one fellow as both her husband and her boyfriend, not realizing that discretion would be a wiser strategy (thus displaying poor judgment).

The Butcher Boy

(Illustrating Increased Goal-Directed Activity)

Aisling O'Sullivan plays Annie Brady, the mother of the main character. She doesn't receive a lot of screen time in this movie, owing to her lengthy hospitalization and eventual suicide. However, she does have bipolar disorder, and illustrates the symptom of increased goal-directed activity very well. Mrs. Brady requires hospitalization for depression, and is clearly hypomanic when she is discharged. In order to prepare for the holiday season, she bakes (and bakes and bakes) until every flat surface in her kitchen is covered with buns and cakes.

Mr. Jones

(Illustrating Excessive Involvement in Activities with a High Potential for Painful Consequences)

Mr. Jones, while manic, withdraws his savings and spends all of his money within a few days (giving lavish tips to people).

Mr. Jones

Mr. Jones (portrayed by Richard Gere) rides his bicycle one morning to a construction site where he charms the foreman into letting him work for one day. Mr. Jones is highly attuned to the nuances of those around him — he gets the OK to work because he picks up on the foreman's Upstate New York accent. Mr. Jones seems to be **grandiose** — he claims he can do the work of two men, and offers to work free for the first day, but expects to be paid double for his second day. By the third day, Jones predicts that he will have taken over the foreman's job.

We see that Jones is highly **distractible** shortly after he starts working. While hammering nails with a co-worker, he starts a counter-rhythm to the other man's strikes. Every time a plane flies overhead (they are very close to a runway), Jones becomes fascinated by it and tries to calculate whether the speed of a crosswind might actually allow him to fly. Jones soon walks out on a perch, necessitating a rescue that ends up with him getting taken to a psychiatric facility for an involuntary admission.

The psychiatrist, Elizabeth Bowen, prior to interviewing Mr. Jones sees a woman named Amanda (Lauren Tom), who, in relating how she got her name, gives a good demonstration of **pressured speech**. Her ideas are logical, but flow at a rate almost too fast for her to keep up with. Amanda also gives an excellent portrayal of the **mood lability** seen in mania. She smiles engagingly for a couple of seconds and then slips into despair. For this reason, the psychiatric nomenclature changed from calling these conditions affective disorders to mood disorders. Amanda's affect changes considerably, but against a background mood of excitement and effervescence. Some people experience a **mixed episode**, in which their moods alternate very quickly and they suffer from the symptoms of a mania and depression almost simultaneously. These episodes are very unpleasant to endure and are often accompanied by thoughts of suicide.

After a brief stay in the hospital, Jones no longer meets the grounds for involuntary committal and is released. He goes to his bank and is disarming and seductive enough to convince the teller (Susan) to join him for the day. He withdraws over $12,000, which he fully intends to spend frivolously. This is a good example of criteria seven — **excessive involvement in activity that will likely result in painful consequences**. Jones likes to give away $100 bills. He gives one to his co-worker, another to the teller, and still another to a hot dog vendor (to purchase only two hot dogs). He manages to get rid of all his money in just a couple of days, indicating a self-destructive pattern of spending.

At this point in the movie, Jones is fun to be around. He is confident, daring, and charismatic. Manic patients often have an contagious quality to their moods, and lift the spirits of those around them. They quickly become the center of attention, and seem to thrive on making others around them more animated.

Jones seems clairvoyant in guessing how many children his co-worker has. He notices that Dr. Bowen has an area on her ring finger that is less tanned than the rest of her hand, and immediately gleans that she has suffered a "recent emotional setback." During manic or hypomanic episodes, many patients have finely honed powers of observation and deduction. They have an uncanny ability to pick up on people's weaknesses or areas of sensitivity. Because their energy levels are increased and inhibitions have all but disappeared, it is common for such patients to go on to exploit their discoveries. Frequently, this manifests itself in testing the limits of those around them. Manic patients can make reasonable restrictions seem arbitrary and absurd.

Jones' passion for music overwhelms him to the point where he launches himself on stage during a performance to wrest control from the conductor because he thinks the piece should be played faster. This civil disruption lands Jones in hospital again. Shortly after readmission, Jones spirals into a depression. First, we see him lose his lightning ability with numbers (**decreased**

80

concentration). Then he becomes listless, sullen, and morose. He wanders around the city finding no joy in things that usually appeal to him (**anhedonia**). He moves slowly (**psychomotor retardation**), looks lost, and ultimately accepts help after he realizes that he *"can't stop the sadness"* (**depressed mood**). He becomes so apathetic that he can't even wash himself (**anergia**).

Then, his mood starts to escalate again. His speech picks up tempo, and he shows a mocking sense of humor when he invents a story about never having had a headache since taking an overdose of acetaminophen. Instead of his previous qualities of expansiveness or elation, Jones now exhibits a distinct quality of **irritability**, which is particularly pronounced during a ping-pong game he plays with Amanda.

Mr. Jones gives his psychiatrist a tidy summary of his life. At age three he started to play Mozart, by twelve he had read *"everything,"* and at eighteen he was the *"center of the universe."* And then one day he woke up and he was in a mental institution. He improves from depression to an even mood state (**euthymia**). Jones tells his psychiatrist that he is a junkie — he really needs his highs in order to enjoy life. He says of euthymia that he *"doesn't like living down here any more."* Jones admits that he never feels more alive than during his manic episodes, and prefers to have them even with the significant problems he endures (e.g. occupational, financial, interpersonal, or legal).

Within the span of the movie, we see Jones shift from mania to depression and back to mania again. One variant of bipolar disorder is called **rapid cycling**. This describes a pattern where four or more mood episodes occur within a 12-month time span. An episode is defined as a mood disturbance that has either a full recovery or switches to the opposite polarity. Up to 15% of patients with bipolar disorder experience rapid cycling. Other than the compressed time frame, the episodes of mania and depression are no different than in the non-cycling type.

The Mask

Stanley Ipkiss (Jim Carrey) is a meek, mild, and somewhat repressed bank employee. One night, after a long string of unfortunate events, he discovers a mysterious artifact in the form of a green mask. When he puts the mask on, it magically transforms him into a whirling dervish. This new character, initially the alter ego of Stanley, is so full of energy that he can't contain himself and sets about righting the slights that were heaped upon Stanley earlier that day.

On his next outing, the Mask wants to go to a nightclub, but realizes that *"you can't make the scene if you don't have the green"* (manic patients sometimes speak in **rhymes**, **puns**, or choose words for their sounds instead of their meaning — these abnormalities of speech are globally referred to as **clanging** or **clang associations**). He then proceeds to rob his own bank, a demonstration of the **impaired judgment** and **impulsivity** that frequently accompany manic episodes. The Mask's outlandish style of dress, proclivity for nocturnal forays, and utter conviction in his pursuits are consistent with a manic episode.

The Mask carries on a running monologue (in a variety of voices) of mockery and repartée. He re-enacts movie scenes to demonstrate his wit and belittle those around him who would thwart his activities. Manic patients frequently run into difficulties with authority figures, and will vigorously seek to undermine any limits imposed on them. They cannot foresee the likely consequences of their actions, and often engage in financial, sexual, or substance-related indulgences. Manic patients shift the responsibility for their actions onto others and can often make superficially convincing arguments to support their plans. People who are unfamiliar with the symptoms of mania (including inexperienced clinicians) can be amused and entertained by the antics of patients — something hilariously illustrated in this movie when the S.W.A.T. team (sent to apprehend the Mask) start a conga line and sing a chorus of *Cuban Pete*.

The Mosquito Coast

One of the many challenges that face mental health professionals is where to draw the line between illness and individuality. Making a psychiatric diagnosis does involve an element of subjectivity (e.g. when the patient and clinician are from different cultural backgrounds). The DSM has gone a long way to delineate specific criteria that must be present for a certain period of time in the absence of medical complications or substance abuse problems. Furthermore, for a "disorder" to exist, the symptoms must cause *"significant distress or impairment in social, occupational, or other important areas of functioning."* A key consideration is **adaptation**. Are the person's symptoms interfering with his or her ability to lead a healthy, balanced, and productive life? While an all-encompassing definition of mental health remains elusive, Freud's contribution of "to work and to love" is certainly a good starting point.

In *The Mosquito Coast*, Allie Fox (Harrison Ford) is a mechanical genius who is opinionated, passionate, and talented. Though he has four children, he chooses to indulge his interest in inventing and ignore his job as a farm hand. Right from the beginning of the film we see Allie ranting to his eldest son about what he views as society's failings. Allie invents a refrigeration machine that is efficient and useful. However, his employer has asparagus rotting in a field and dismisses Allie's contraption because it does not solve any immediate need. Allie makes a snap decision to pursue his dream and abandons his employer (and the asparagus).

In an instant, Allie combines his romanticized view of the migrant workers' homeland, the farmer's rejection of his invention, and his own distaste for North American society. Allie decides that a more worthy pursuit (or test of his abilities) would be to live in a Central American jungle and create his own society, complete with a much larger ice-making machine. His family, apparently use to indulging Allie's whims, packs up on short notice with no questions asked about why, where, how long, etc.

Allie is an inspiring force. Confident, determined, and intelligent, he charms almost everyone around him and gives the impression that he's always on the right path. He purchases a small village and within a few minutes maps out where certain buildings will go and what amenities to design. Allie then doggedly pursues his vision, acting as a catalyst to those around him as he invents and builds, pushing himself almost to the point of exhaustion.

A string of misfortunes befall Allie and his family. Their original village is leveled by an explosion, and later the materials they can salvage from a beach are washed away by heavy rains. As their possessions dwindle and their safety becomes threatened, Allie becomes fanatical about heading even further into the jungle. Towards the end of the film he becomes more obviously disturbed and exhibits marked paranoia. Given the unfortunate outcome, one cannot help but wonder if he was ill for the entire movie.

Psychiatrists would be providing a disservice by applying diagnoses to those who are simply rebellious, eccentric, or strongly individualistic. Allie has many valid criticisms about contemporary society. He has a desire to provide his children with practical knowledge and for them to learn things that can't be taught on a farm. However, the adaptive value of what Allie plans to do is certainly lacking. The following factors indicate that Allie suffers from at least some type of psychiatric problem:
- Three of Allie's four children are under the age of ten, have received little formal education, and are too young to benefit from the experience
- There is no compelling need to provide refrigeration for remote areas of Central America (somehow, they've managed)
- Allie does not need to flee for legal or financial reasons
- His fanatical drive repeatedly endangers his family
- Most of what he teaches his children can be taught at home
- If Allie loves America (as he claims he does), then he could devote his considerable talents to improving the aspects of society that upset him

84

At the end of the film, we are left with the following situation:
- Allie sets fire to a chapel, endangering the lives of many people
- Despite being without food, possessions or fuel, he wants to relocate to an even more remote area of the jungle
- After being shot, he still expects to be taken further inland
- He sharply accuses his wife of "*always being against him*" when she has been entirely supportive of his passions and whims
- He rejects any form of assistance from others for either himself or his family

The most prominent behaviors that Allie displays are primarily symptoms of bipolar disorder:
- **Restlessness** and **talkativeness** — reported in the narration by his eldest son in the first few minutes of the film
- **Pressured speech** — this is particularly evident in the first few scenes in the film
- **Increased goal-directed activity**
- **Grandiosity**
- **Excessive involvement in activities that have a high potential for painful consequences**
- **Mood lability** — ranging from elated to irritable

This qualifies him for the diagnosis of a manic episode. However, he also displays some psychotic features, specifically paranoid thoughts about his wife and children. Allie also has a persistent belief that America is either imminently faced with, or has been involved in, a nuclear war. These psychotic features are not typical themes for mania, so a more correct diagnosis would be a **manic episode with mood-incongruent psychotic features**. This movie is a good illustration of how an episode of mania progresses. Allie becomes increasingly intense, driven, and irritable as the movie progresses. Many patients who experience episodes of mania escalate in the severity of their symptoms when they get even mild amounts of stimulation (such as interacting with others, attempting to complete work or school assignments). Allie's mood can be seen as soaring in response to meeting the challenges he faces in creating his new "society."

Creativity and Mental Illness

Two of the movie characters described in this chapter were notably creative. Mr. Jones improvised an enchanting piano solo while deciding which instrument to buy, and Allie Fox registered several patents and had more pending.

The link between "creative genius" and "insanity" is a long-standing romantic notion. In this century, this association has been studied more intensively by a number of researchers. Because the list of creative people who also suffered from severe mental illnesses is extensive, it has been speculated that creativity may be a benefit that accompanies certain psychiatric conditions. Dr. Nancy Andreasen, one of America's most prominent psychiatrists, published a study in 1987 that was based on fifteen years' worth of interviews with creative writers. These writers were asked about their personal experiences with psychiatric illness. They were also asked about the presence of mental illness and creative endeavors in immediate family members. Prior to Dr. Andreasen's publication, it was thought that schizophrenia was the condition that was most highly associated with creativity, possibly due to the unusual perceptions that this illness causes. The results of her study found a strong correlation with mood disorders (80% of the writers), and with bipolar disorders in particular (43%). None of these writers had schizophrenia (Andreasen, 1987). Of the bipolar disorders, it seems likely that bipolar II is the most likely to enhance creativity. As mood increases in this condition, thought processes speed up, confidence is enhanced, and energy levels increase. People whose moods don't increase beyond the level of hypomania may be able to harness these benefits and become successful in business or leadership roles. Periods of melancholy are often valuable for the introspection they foster and allowing an incubation time for ideas. Such periods may also be a benefit because people have less energy to expend on other pursuits and can focus their efforts on new ideas. Extremes of mood may foster creativity, though it is likely that the ideas generated during such periods can't be developed until a period of greater stability is reached.

Cyclothymia/ Cyclothymic Disorder

Cyclothymic disorder is the mildest form of bipolar disorder. In this condition, mood changes in a cyclic pattern over at least a two-year span. What distinguishes cyclothymia from **bipolar I and II** is that the symptoms of mood disturbances, even when they are at their most pronounced, are not severe enough to meet the criteria for either hypomania or depression. Specifically, the number, duration, pervasiveness, or severity of symptoms falls short of meeting the grounds for either hypomania or depression.

The DSM stipulates that for this disorder to be diagnosed, there must be numerous periods of time where symptoms of hypomania alternate with symptoms of depression. The period of time between mood cycles is usually much shorter than in bipolar disorder. The changes between high and low moods can occur within hours and at irregular intervals. Interestingly, up to one-third of patients with cyclothymic disorder go on to develop bipolar II disorder.

Previous descriptions of cyclothymia (DSM-I, APA, 1952; DSM-II, APA 1968) classified this condition as a personality disorder, possibly because it typically starts in early adulthood and has an insidious onset. One of the founders of descriptive psychopathology, Emil Kraepelin, provided the following description (which is well illustrated in the movie *Mad Love*): *"They are easily offended, hot-headed, and on trivial occasions become enraged and give way to outbursts of energy. Ordinarily the patients are serene and self-assertive, but ill-controlled. Periods occur in which they are cross and sullen"* (adapted from Kraepelin, 1913).

Cyclothymic disorder is more common in women by a factor of around 3:2. About one-third of patients with this disorder have extended family members with depression or bipolar disorder.

87

Mad Love

This movie was made in 1995 and is neither a remake of the 1935 nor the 1923 version. Casey Roberts (Drew Barrymore) is a young woman whom we first see taking a jet ski for an inspired midnight ride. The next night, she dances frenetically when she's alone in her room. As she gets to know Matt Leland (Chris O'Donnell) she is animated, opinionated, intrusive, and observant. She is abrupt with him, walking away until he formally asks her on a date, and then ends their evening together when she suddenly gets impatient.

After inviting him to call her "sometime," she shows up unexpectedly during school hours and persuades Matt to skip a chemistry lab. Casey shows a significant level of **distractibility** when she drives erratically through traffic, and ultimately heads out of the city without any idea where she's going.

Casey interrupts Matt's SAT exam by pulling the fire alarm because she isn't able to get his attention. She demonstrates a **grandiose sense of self-worth** by telling Matt that she thinks that sometimes she *is* the center of the universe (after he pointedly tells her she isn't and that her intrusion is unwelcome).

When her parents try to discipline her for pulling the alarm, Casey spins out of control. Fleeing her parents in the living room, she throws objects around her bedroom, climbs off the balcony, and then plunges into the lake.

After being suspended by her school and summarily grounded by her parents, Casey's mood crashes and she attempts to take her life with an overdose. After Matt sneaks her out of the hospital, they embark on a romantic odyssey. Once free from the confines of the hospital and her parents' supervision, Casey's mood rebounds dramatically. She plays a game with Matt where she holds her hands over his eyes while he's driving past an eighteen-wheeler on a tortuous stretch of highway. Casey has difficulty adapting to the small town where they stop — earlier in the film she said she felt at home with rudeness, noise, and danger. Her mood changes perceptibly in the scene where she has to wait for Matt to make a purchase. Casey begins to decompensate, starting with her inability to shut out the activity around her. She then displays **persecutory delusions** when she cuts out hundreds of pictures of eyes from magazines because she thinks that this will provide protection for her and Matt.

The next day, Casey and Matt go out for dinner, and here she provides an excellent example of **psychomotor agitation**. Casey constantly scans the room, can't focus on the conversation with Matt, and fumbles with her cigarette (butting it and needing it relit by the waiter). Her distractibility is again marked — she can't screen out the events happening around her, even when they aren't very interesting.

Casey displays some of the symptoms of hypomania, specifically
* **Inflated self-esteem**
* **Distractibility**
* **Psychomotor agitation**
* **Excessive involvement in activities with a high potential for self-harm**

She also experiences the following symptoms of depression:
* **Depressed mood**
* **Diminished ability to think or concentrate**
* **Thoughts of death/suicidal ideation**

The diagnosis of cyclothymia is applicable in this movie because Casey doesn't fully meet the criteria for hypomania or depression, though she certainly does have marked mood swings. Her mood changes do not last long enough, are not severe enough, and change too quickly for her to qualify for the diagnosis of **bipolar I** or **II disorder**. Though Casey's diagnosis is revealed to be "clinical depression" later in the film, this doesn't account for her mood state for most of the time that we see her.

Mood Disorder Patterns

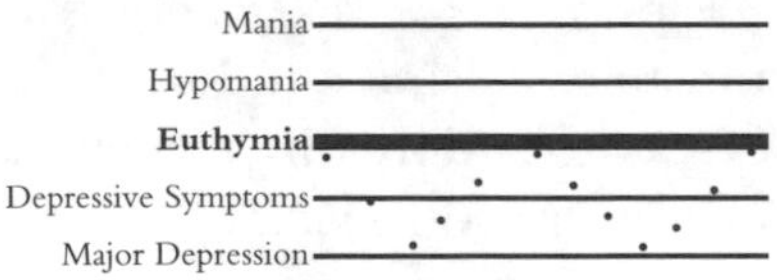

Major Depressive Disorder
Depressive symptoms are of significant intensity and duration; the usual course is a full recovery, but many people have recurrent episodes (the example shows 2 episodes of depression).

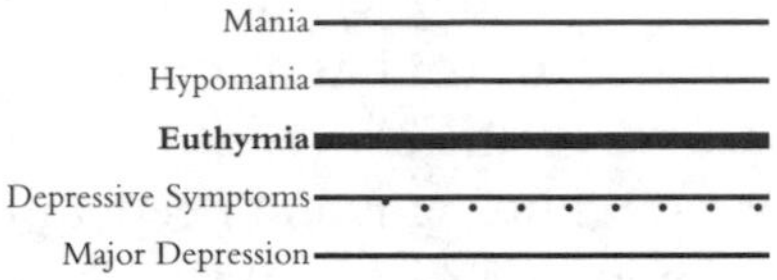

Dysthymic Disorder
Depressive symptoms are present for at least 2 years, but not as severe as in a depressive episode; **double depression** is a major depressive episode complicating dysthymic disorder

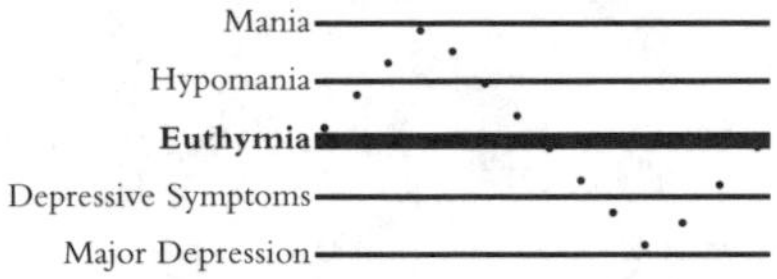

Bipolar Disorder Type I
- Presence of full mania and depression
- Depression can be brief, mild, or in some cases, non-existent
- There is no separate diagnostic category for unipolar mania

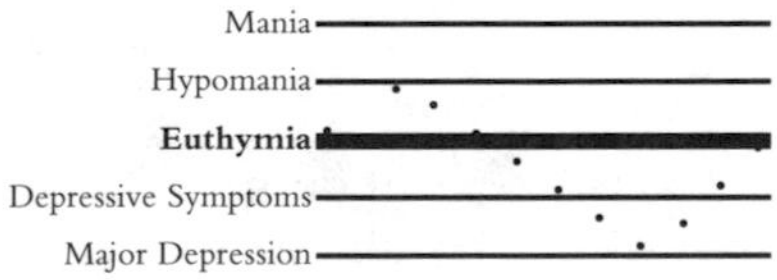

Bipolar Disorder Type II
- Presence of hypomanic episodes and depression; the implications of the distinction from Bipolar I are not clear at this time

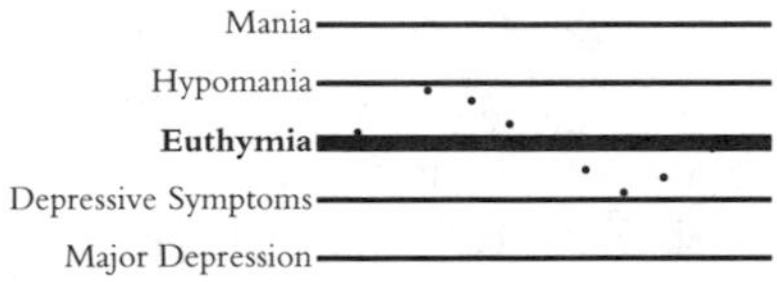

Cyclothymic Disorder
Depressive symptoms do not necessarily meet the criteria for a dysthymic disorder and are not as severe as in a depression; the highs can be hypomanic in intensity (but not full mania)

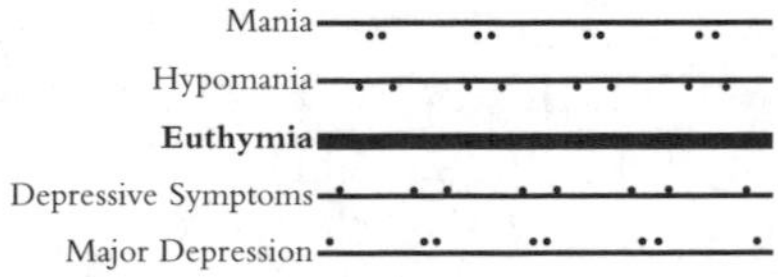

Rapid Cycling Type
4 plus episodes of mania, hypomania, mixed episode, or major depression in 1 year; must have a recovery of 2 months between episodes, or a switch of mood to the opposite polarity

Movie	Feature/Diagnosis
Girl, Interrupted	Alexithymia; Depressed mood; Decreased energy; Mood–congruent psychotic features; Recurrent thoughts of death or suicide; visual hallucinations
Good Morning, Vietnam	Flight of ideas; Pressure of speech
Finding Forrester	Decreased energy, Low self-esteem, Hopelessness
Hope Floats	Appetite changes; Decreased energy; Depressed mood; Diminished interest in activities; Sleep changes
Mad Love	Delusions (persecutory); Depressed mood; Distractibility; Excessive Involvement in pleasurable activities that have a high potential for painful consequences; grandiosity; inflated self-esteem; psychomotor agitation; Thoughts of death/suicide
Mr. Jones	Affective lability; Anergia; Anhedonia; Excessive involvement in pleasurable activities that have a high potential for painful consequences; Decreased concentration; Depressed mood; Distractibility; Euthymia; Grandiosity; Irritable mood, Mixed episode; Pressure of speech; Psychomotor retardation; Rapid cycling
'Night Mother	Recurrent thoughts of death or suicide

Ordinary People	Anhedonia; Appetite changes; Concentration difficulties; Insomnia
Patch Adams	Depressed mood; Guilt; Psychomotor retardation; Recurrent thoughts of death or suicide
The Butcher Boy	Increased goal-directed activity
The Hospital	Decreased energy; Decreased self-esteem; Double depression; Hopelessness
The Mask	Clanging/clang associations; Impaired judgment; Impulsivity; Puns; Rhymes
The Mosquito Coast	Grandiosity; Excessive involvement in activities that have a high potential for painful consequences; Increased goal-directed activity; Mood fluctuations; Mood-incongruent psychotic features; Pressured speech
The Snake Pit	Distractibility; Flight of ideas; Pressure of speech
The Wrong Man	Appetite changes; Decreased concentration; Depressed mood; Guilt; Insomnia; Mood-congruent psychotic features; Psychomotor retardation; Worthlessness

Chapter 7

Anxiety Disorders

Panic Attack/Panic Disorder

Understanding the Condition

Imagine that you are a pedestrian trying to cross a multi-lane highway. The traffic is heavy, but you are determined to get to the other side as soon as possible. Just as you cross to the halfway point, a tractor-trailer that you hadn't seen before bears down on you with its horn blaring and tires squealing. In response to this impending threat, you would likely experience the following symptoms: pounding heart, shortness of breath, sweating, and trembling. This reaction is very similar to what a panic attack feels like — except that there is no truck.

The **autonomic nervous system** controls reactions which are not under voluntary control. It is divided into sympathetic and parasympathetic branches. The sympathetic branch activates a variety of functions characterized as the **flight, fright, or fight response** to emergencies. Here, our body reacts to deal with danger, and a simplified view of a panic attack is that of a false alarm triggered in the sympathetic nervous system.

A panic attack (PA) is an episode of intense fear or discomfort that occurs when no threat is present. PAs cause a wide variety of symptoms that can be subdivided into four categories: cardiovascular, gastrointestinal, neurological, and psychological. PAs occur in a number of psychiatric and medical conditions.

The distinction between a PA and panic disorder (PD) is explained on the next page. There is more accurate epidemiologic data available for PD, which affects around 2% of the population. It can begin at any age but has two peaks of onset — adolescence and the mid-30's. Women are affected with PD between two and three times as often as are men.

There is clear evidence to support a genetic link in people who have PD, particularly those who develop it earlier in life.

Making the Diagnosis

A panic attack consists of an intense episode of fear or discomfort during which the following are experienced:

Cardiovascular Symptoms

i.   *Palpitations, pounding heart, or accelerated heart rate*
ii. *Sweating*
iii. *Chest pain or discomfort*
iv. *Shortness of breath or feeling smothered*
v.   *Choking sensation*
vi. *Chills or hot flushes*

Gastrointestinal Symptoms

vii. *Nausea or abdominal distress*

Neurological Symptoms

viii. *Feeling dizzy, unsteady, lightheaded, or faint*
ix.   *Numbness or tingling (**paresthesias**)*
x.   *Trembling or shaking*

Psychological Symptoms

xi.   *Feeling detached from one's self (**depersonalization**) or the environment (**derealization**)*
xii. *Fear of losing control or going crazy*
xiii. *Fear of dying*

A PA can occur unexpectedly (**uncued**), as a likely consequence in certain situations (**situationally predisposed**), or an almost certain outcome of being exposed to something (**situationally bound** or **cued**). PAs becomes PD when the attacks are unexpected and at least one of the following conditions is met:

•   There is persistent concern about having more attacks
•   The person is worried about the consequences of an attack
•   Significant behavior changes occur because of the attacks

Panic attacks reach their peak within ten minutes of the onset of symptoms and usually subside in less than thirty minutes.

Cinematic depictions of the various symptoms of panic attacks/ panic disorder are portrayed in the following movies:

What About Bob?

(Illustrating various symptoms of Panic Attacks)

Bob Wylie (Bill Murray) is a man who recognizes that he "has problems." In the first few minutes of his initial session with his new psychiatrist, Dr. Leo Marvin (Richard Dreyfuss), Bob says this about himself, "*I have a real big problem moving. . . As long as I am in my apartment, I'm OK. But when I want to go out, I get 'weird'.*"

A cataloging of Bob's symptoms shows that most of them are consistent with a panic attack:

Symptom	Category
Cold sweats	Cardiovascular
Hot sweats	Cardiovascular
Difficulty breathing	Cardiovascular
Difficulty swallowing	Gastrointestinal
Nausea	Gastrointestinal
Pelvic discomfort	Gastrointestinal
Blurred vision	Neurological
Dead hands	Neurological
Dizzy spells	Neurological
Finger nail sensitivity	Neurological (possibly)
Involuntary trembling	Neurological
Numb lips	Neurological
Fever blisters	None

Bob doesn't mention any of the psychological symptoms of a panic attack. The episodic nature of his symptoms isn't clear, although things seem to get worse for Bob both when he is alone or when he has to leave his apartment. Bob appears to have a brief surge in anxiety in the scene where he is walking down a country road and suddenly realizes that he is by himself.

Analyze This

(Illustrating various symptoms of Panic Attacks)

Paul Vitti (Robert De Niro) is the capo of a New York gang. He narrowly escapes being assassinated by one of his rivals, and shortly afterwards begins to develop panic attacks. The emergency room doctor who diagnoses Vitti with anxiety attacks gets physically assaulted for his efforts because he insinuates that wiseguys might actually "panic."

Vitti reluctantly seeks treatment from a psychiatrist and gives the following list of symptoms:

Symptom	Category
Can't breathe	Cardiovascular
Chest pains	Cardiovascular
Feels dizzy	Neurological
Thinks that he's going to die	Psychological

Flooding

(Illustrating various symptoms of Panic Attacks)

Joyce Calloway (Brenna Gibson) watches her husband get murdered while she is taking his photograph. She almost instantly becomes a recluse, and is not able to attend the funeral. We soon learn that she hasn't set foot outside of her home for six months, and except for one neighbor and a man who delivers her groceries, she is walled off from society.

Joyce's parents enlist the help of psychologist Dr. Hank Thornton (Jack Turturici). In trying to establish a diagnosis, he elicits the following panic symptoms from Joyce:

Symptom	Category
Hyperventilation	Cardiovascular
Nausea	Gastrointestinal
Depersonalization	Psychological

The Sopranos

In the first scene of the first episode of the first season, Tony Soprano (James Gandolfini) sits in the waiting room of Dr. Jennifer Melfi (Lorraine Bracco). Soprano has been referred to her because he collapsed while he was barbecuing. Prior to his blackout, he felt as if he had ginger ale in his skull, became short of breath, clutched his chest, and then fell unconscious. He has another one of these spells while taking a tour of a retirement home with his mother. In the second episode he becomes overwhelmed, develops shortness of breath, and sees white spots in his field of vision. While Dr. Melfi diagnoses these spells as panic attacks, only Soprano's shortness of breath can be considered a typical symptom.

Fearless

Max Klein (Jeff Bridges) walks away from a plane crash in which many people perish. Though Max's reaction to this event is more in keeping with posttraumatic stress disorder, there are two scenes where his behavior is consistent with that seen in panic disorder.

First, Max is inundated by reporters seeking to interview him about the plane crash and his miraculous survival. Overwhelmed by their questions, he bolts and runs down the street. Later in the film, Max's lawyer tries to persuade him to alter his recollection of events in order to obtain a larger settlement from the airline. Again, Max becomes intensely distraught, flees the office and runs up to the roof.

While there is no mention made of panic symptoms in this movie, Max's abrupt departures are consistent with what people do when they are experiencing a panic attack. The fear of dying or going crazy is very disturbing, and often people feel as if they must immediately get out of the place or situation that they are in at the time their symptoms develop.

Analyze This

Mob boss Paul Vitti (Robert De Niro) is facing mounting pressure as the date for a meeting with other mafioso approaches. The murder of Dominic, one of his father's friends, sets off a chain reaction that culminates in Vitti experiencing panic attacks. In one scene where Vitti tries to work out the politics behind Dominic's hit, he abruptly becomes uneasy and restless. As the attack progresses he becomes sweaty, choked up, and short of breath. Fearing that he is having a heart attack, he speeds to the emergency department for an evaluation. He tells the doctor that he's had *"8 heart attacks in the last three weeks."*

Later, when Vitti seeks treatment with psychiatrist Dr. Ben Sobol (Billy Crystal), he describes discrete periods of anxiety where he can't breathe, feels dizzy, has chest pains, and thinks that he's going to die. Vitti has had persistent concerns about having more attacks and experiences significant behavioral changes, most notably his aversion to violence during an interrogation. Since Vitti does not seem to avoid certain places or situations, his primary diagnosis would be **panic disorder without agoraphobia**. Panic disorder often co-exists with other anxiety disorders, and Vitti also displays some features of a **generalized anxiety disorder** (presented later in this chapter).

It is not uncommon for people to experience their first panic attack at times of stress, particularly when there is an actual or threatened loss. Examinations, illnesses, deaths, travel, and relationship terminations are often reported as precipitating factors. Even mildly stressful situations can act as triggers, though many people are initially unaware of such connections.

It is also typical for patients to go to emergency departments during or after their first panic attack. Often patients fear that they are suffering from a heart attack, particularly because there are many overlapping symptoms.

Agoraphobia

Understanding the Condition

Agoraphobia, literally translated from Greek, means "fear of the marketplace." The DSM-IV-TR defines it as: *"Anxiety about being in places or situations from which escape might be difficult or embarrassing, or in which help may not be available in the event of having a panic attack or panic-like symptoms."*

Phobic disorders, or phobias, are presented later in this chapter. In these conditions, there are identified objects or situations that people either avoid or endure with considerable distress. Many people with phobias can lead reasonably normal lives because they minimize their exposure to the specific object(s) or situation(s). Agoraphobia is listed here because of its almost universal connection to panic disorder. Agoraphobia is widely considered to be the most debilitating of the phobias because people can end up housebound in order to avoid being separated from their sources of security.

Places or situations often avoided by agoraphobic patients include: crowded areas, standing in line-ups, middle seats in theatre rows, backseats of vehicles, airplanes, elevators, tunnels, and bridges. The ICD lists four particularly problematic situations for agoraphobic people: crowds; public places; traveling alone; and traveling away from home.

In practice, many patients with panic disorder have at least a mild degree of agoraphobia and are particularly hesitant about places or situations where they have previously had a panic attack. They may be able to manage by persuading friends or family members to accompany them. Agoraphobia is often a progressive illness, with a patient's level of comfort outside of his or her home slowly diminishing over time.

Agoraphobia without panic attacks is rare, and little is known of its course. It is thought to be more common in women.

Making the Diagnosis

The criteria for determining if agoraphobia is present are:

I. Anxiety about being in places or situations where help is not easily obtainable, or escape would be difficult or embarrassing

II. Patients avoid places or situations described above, endure them with marked distress, or require a companion to be present as a source of comfort

Agoraphobia itself is not listed as a distinct disorder in the DSM-IV-TR. It is diagnosed in one of two ways, **panic disorder with agoraphobia**, or **agoraphobia without history of panic disorder**. Patients who have the latter condition, while not clearly meeting all the criteria for PA, nevertheless experience many panic-like symptoms. They may also feel embarrassed or incapacitated by their anxiety and are afraid of doing something like vomiting or losing bladder control.

In cases where there is an associated general medical condition, the level of anxiety endured is in excess of what would usually be associated with that condition. For example, people with mild asthma would be expected to avoid going into a dusty attic, but could do so if it was really necessary and would not experience overwhelming anxiety or demand that someone accompany them.

There are three permutations for diagnosing PD and agoraphobia:
* Panic disorder without agoraphobia
* Panic disorder with agoraphobia
* Agoraphobia without history of panic disorder

Associated Features
* **Catagelophobia** is the fear of ridicule or humiliation in social situations
* **Agyrophobia** is the fear of streets or crossing the street
* In addition to the presence of a companion, other reassuring interventions are: sitting near doors, refocusing thoughts elsewhere, and taking a dog or baby carriage along

I Am Sam

Sam Dawson (Sean Penn) is a mentally retarded man who is suddenly left with the responsibility of raising his daughter after her mother abruptly departs. Sam's neighbor Annie (Dianne Weist) is very helpful in supervising his parenting skills, which are somewhat lacking at the beginning of the film. Through an unfortunate misunderstanding Sam's ability to raise his daughter is questioned and a custody hearing is scheduled. Annie is one of Sam's few friends with normal intelligence and the only one who can attest to his diligence as a parent. Her testimony at the hearing becomes pivotal, yet she is extremely reluctant to attend.

We soon learn that Annie spent 28 years "in the real world" and the rest of her time in her apartment. When Sam first needs help with his daughter Lucy (Dakota Fanning), Annie curiously cannot cross the walkway between their apartments. All subsequent interactions between Sam, Lucy, and Annie take place in her apartment.

When Annie is finally able to summon the courage to leave her apartment, she wears sunglasses to the courthouse, which is something that many agoraphobic patients do to reduce their anxiety. After testifying, Annie is terrified to leave Sam's lawyer's car and it takes an extended period of time for her to feel comfortable making the short walk back to her apartment. She shrieks when the car door is opened for her before she has summoned the courage to leave.

The history behind Annie's seclusion is not revealed in the movie. Based on her extreme reluctance to go outside, Annie would appear to meet the criteria for agoraphobia. Because there is no history of panic disorder mentioned, the diagnosis that she most clearly portrays in this film is **agoraphobia without history of panic disorder**. This portrayal would be more accurate if the source of Annie's fears was revealed.

Copycat

Agoraphobia is the central theme in this movie. Helen Hudson (Sigourney Weaver) is a mental health professional who has made a career out of studying serial killers. She is a high-profile lecturer, expert witness, and author. Her testimony in one trial helped convict Daryll Lee Cullum (Harry Connick, Jr.), ostensibly because she proved that he did not suffer from a mental illness. Cullum subsequently escapes and viciously attacks her, but is disarmed by a police officer and re-arrested.

Helen suffers severe anxiety symptoms because of the attack and becomes housebound. We see her have a panic attack and then recite a chronological list of presidents' names in order to distract herself. She manages to quell her anxiety with medication, alcohol, and an on-line support group for people with anxiety problems.

The extent of Helen's agoraphobia is demonstrated in the scene where she must retrieve a newspaper. It has been dropped in the hallway just out of arm's reach. When Helen can't reach it with a broom, she becomes highly distressed just walking a couple of feet to pick it up. Later in the film, Helen chooses to stay in her apartment even when an intruder is there.

When Helen is asked to lend her expertise and consult on a series of murders, she has a panic attack when she is abruptly given a stack of pictures from the crime scenes. Overwhelmed, she hyperventilates and ultimately loses consciousness. Her assistant Andy (John Rothman), places a paper bag over her mouth and nose to help her get through the attack. It is unusual for people to pass out because of a panic attack. More typically, they may feel like they are going to die, lose control, or go crazy. Helen would meet the diagnostic criteria for the following disorders: **panic disorder with agoraphobia**, **posttraumatic stress disorder**, and **alcohol dependence**.

Posttraumatic Stress Disorder

Understanding the Condition

Posttraumatic stress disorder (PTSD) consists of a constellation of symptoms that occur after someone has been exposed to, or witnessed, a life-threatening situation. PTSD has historically been described under a variety of names, usually having something to do with warfare: soldier's heart, shell shock, combat or war neurosis, and battle fatigue.

Events that commonly lead to PTSD are: accidents, assaults, fires, natural catastrophes, torture, and wars. It was initially thought that the symptoms of PTSD would be more severe if the causative experience were more egregious. It has since been established that symptom severity is a highly individual matter, and it is the subjective meaning of the trauma to the person that determines how significantly he or she will be affected.

The onset of symptoms in PTSD can occur weeks, months, or even years after the traumatic event. The symptoms can also be disguised as being suggestive of other conditions, such as substance use, mood disorders, or other anxiety disorders.

The lifetime risk for developing PTSD is approximately 8%, with women having a twofold higher prevalence than men. This is thought to occur because women are more likely to be exposed to traumatic events, and afterwards, are more likely to develop PTSD. It is estimated that one-third of Vietnam veterans had clear symptoms of PTSD, with another one-third suffering from muted or subclinical symptoms.

Young adults appear to be the most vulnerable for developing PTSD. Another key risk factor is social isolation. Lone survivors of traumatic events are more likely to develop **survivor guilt**, and are more prone to developing PTSD. There may be some genetic vulnerability for developing PTSD.

Making the Diagnosis

The traumatic event has two key characteristics:

* The person experienced, witnessed, or was confronted with an event that involved actual or threatened death or serious injury, or a threat to the physical integrity of others
* The person's response involved intense fear or helplessness

Three clusters of symptoms develop as a result of PTSD:

Persistent Reexperience of the Traumatic Event

i. *Intrusive and distressing recollections of the event*
ii. *Recurrent distressing dreams of the event*
iii. *Acting or feeling as if the event were recurring*
iv. *Intense distress upon exposure to anything reminiscent of the event*
v. *Physiological reactions to anything reminiscent of the event*

Avoidance of Stimuli Associated With the Event

vi. *Avoiding thoughts, feelings, or conversations associated with the traumatic event*
vii. *Avoiding activities, places, or people that are reminiscent of the event*
viii. *Inability to recall important aspects of the trauma*
ix. *Markedly diminished interest in significant activities*
x. *Feeling detached or estranged from others*
xi. *Restricted range of emotions*
xii. *Sense of a foreshortened future*

Feelings of Increased Arousal

xiii. *Difficulty falling asleep or staying asleep*
xiv. *Irritability or outbursts of anger*
xv. *Difficulty concentrating*
xvi. *Hypervigilance*
xvii. *Exaggerated Startle Response*

These symptoms must be present for at least one month for PTSD to be diagnosed. **Acute stress disorder** (**ASD**) is diagnosed when the above symptoms are present anywhere between two days and four weeks. ASD can also involve: **depersonalization**, **derealization**, **amnesia**, and emotional detachment.

In Country
(Illustrating various symptoms of PTSD)

Emmett Smith (Bruce Willis) is a Vietnam veteran who lives with his niece Samantha (Emily Lloyd), her mother having remarried and moved elsewhere. This arrangement allows Samantha to complete high school with her friends.

At the beginning of the film, Emmett is attending Samantha's graduation ceremony. The steely voice of the man giving the commencement address reminds him of an officer's farewell he listened to when he shipped out to Vietnam. In response, Emmett tunes out his niece's graduation (**markedly diminished interest in significant activities**) and has trouble summoning any real enthusiasm for her achievement (**restricted range of emotions**).

Samantha's father died in Vietnam before she was born. She develops an increasing curiosity about his life and wartime experiences, particularly because she has been told so little about him. Emmett socializes primarily with three other vets — Tom (John Terry), Pete (Stephen Tobolowsky), and Earl (Jim Beaver) — all of whom have symptoms of PTSD. Collectively, they avoid talking about their experiences or even answering Samantha's questions (**avoiding thoughts, feelings, or conversations associated with the traumatic event**). At a diner, Samantha reveals that Emmett has persistent problems with his sleep (**difficulty falling or staying asleep**).

Emmett experiences combat flashbacks during a thunderstorm (**intense distress upon exposure to anything reminiscent of the event**). When Samantha visits Tom to test drive a car, he exhibits an **exaggerated startle response**. At a dance arranged to honor veterans, Earl picks a fight with Pete (**irritability or outbursts of anger**). Anita, a nurse with an interest in Emmett, has difficulty getting him to dance with her (a sense of **feeling detached or estranged from others**).

106

Behind the Lines/Regeneration
(Illustrating various symptoms of PTSD)

Dr. William Rivers (Jonathan Pryce) works in a W.W.I. Scottish hospital rehabilitating soldiers. Siegfried Sassoon (James Wilby) is a decorated soldier-cum-poet who, in his first interview with Dr. Rivers, indicates that he has **recurrent distressing dreams of events** from the war. When he opens his eyes, the horrific images do not disappear, giving him **intrusive and distressing recollections** of his experiences. Sassoon has no plans or wishes, and in this way demonstrates a **sense of foreshortened future**. He mourns the loss of a comrade, and in this way pays his respects because his slain friend can no longer realize his dreams.

Billy Prior (Jonny Lee Miller) is an officer also receiving treatment. In his meeting with Dr. Rivers, Prior indicates that he can neither speak of nor remember what happened to him (**inability to recall important aspects of the trauma**). Later in the film, he has recurrent and distressing dreams of the fate of the soldiers under his command, and wishes to **avoid thoughts, feelings, or conversations associated with this event**.

Other soldiers in the hospital are affected by their experiences, and **act or feel as if the event were recurring** and demonstrate **physiologic reactions** to their reminiscences, such as sweating, trembling, and hyperventilating. One runs after Dr. Rivers wondering if Sassoon is a German spy, thus demonstrating **hypervigilance**.

Sassoon does not ultimately suffer from PTSD, though he has some symptoms. Prior would be most accurately diagnosed with a **conversion disorder**, which is presented in the *Somatoform Disorders Chapter*. The best single depiction of PTSD in this film is the character of Burns (Rupert Proctor), who landed head first in the abdomen of a disemboweled German soldier and becomes severely affected by this experience (Burns is the soldier depicted in the haunting forest scene of this movie).

107

Scream 2

Sidney Prescott (Neve Campbell) survives the two serial killers from the first Scream, permitting this franchise to be serialized. In this movie, she has enrolled as a drama major at Windsor College and has earned the lead role of Cassandra in their annual production. During the practice of *Act 3, The Fall of Troy*, Sidney is surrounded by a mob intent on stabbing her because she foretold of certain disasters. As the crowd descends upon her, Sidney mistakes one of them for her nemesis and has a flashback to her harrowing experiences, illustrating **distressing recollection of the event**, **feeling as if the event were recurring**, and **suffering intense distress**.

 ## Fearless

Max Klein (Jeff Bridges) is one of only a handful of survivors of a major airline crash. Depicted as a somewhat anxious man before the accident, Max comes to terms with his mortality during the plane's descent and is prepared to die upon impact. After the crash, it seems as if Max has undergone a radical change, not only in personality, but because he can now eat strawberries without suffering his previous serious allergic reaction. The title of the film stems from Max's new sense of invincibility.

Max displays several features of PTSD after the crash:
- He has **recurrent and distressing recollections** and **dreams** of the crash (that is, he is troubled by intrusive memories both while he is awake and asleep)
- He feels **intense distress on being exposed** to questions from the media and being forced to rehash the events in his lawyer's office; on both occasions he flees the scene
- He becomes **irritable** and has **outbursts of anger** with others, most notably his son and the psychiatrist (John Turturro) hired by the airline to provide grief counseling
- He is **detached and estranged** from his wife, with whom he had a very good relationship before the crash

The Deer Hunter

The Deer Hunter centers on the lives of three young men who leave their jobs as steel workers to serve in combat roles in Vietnam. Each one becomes irreversibly affected by the war.

Michael (Robert De Niro) survives the war physically intact, but seems to have lost his soul upon his return home. He purposefully avoids the party arranged for him, demonstrating an **avoidance of thoughts, feelings, and conversations** associated with his experiences. Michael also seems to have a **restricted range of emotions** and **diminished interest in significant activities**. An avid and capable deer hunter, he is unable to kill a buck after his wartime experiences.

Steven (John Savage) decompensates dramatically when he is taken prisoner. His captors force all the POWs to play Russian roulette, and if they refuse, they are placed in a bamboo cage that is almost entirely submerged in a river. Michael rescues him, but Steven becomes an amputee who lives in a Veterans' Administration (VA) hospital upon his return home. Steven cannot bring himself to return to his wife and doesn't even want his friends to know where he is hospitalized.

Nick (Christopher Walken) is also forced to play Russian roulette when he is captured, as are Michael and Steven. Michael devises a plan to kill the captors, but needs Nick to play one round in order to get more bullets added to the revolver. This experience is so devastating for Nick that he has trouble even saying his parents' names when he is later treated at a hospital. Unfortunately, for the sake of this portrayal, Nick doesn't indicate if he has persistent reexperiences of his time as a prisoner of war.

Later, Nick exhibits a response called a **counterphobic attitude**, where instead of avoiding stimuli associated with Russian roulette, he remains in Vietnam and plays on a regular basis, sending his winnings back home to Steven.

Vertigo

Vertigo is an Alfred Hitchcock film starring James Stewart as John "Scottie" Ferguson. At the beginning of the film, Ferguson is a detective involved in a rooftop pursuit of a felon. Ferguson is unable to make the leap between two buildings and slides down an incline until he is barely able to hold onto an eavestrough. Another police officer tries to come to his rescue, but instead slips and falls to his death. After this event, Ferguson chooses to retire from the force because he develops dizziness and disorientation when he encounters a situation where he must take more than a few steps off the ground.

The term vertigo used in this context of the movie is a misnomer. The medical definition involves the sensation of moving, particularly spinning, when one is actually remaining still. This is not what Ferguson experiences. The event causing his difficulties is certainly severe enough to qualify for PTSD. After taking his medical leave from the police force, he indicates that he is having **recurrent, distressing dreams of the event**.

Other symptoms of PTSD that Ferguson exhibits are:
* **Intrusive and distressing recollections of the event** — Ferguson has a flashback to his near fatal rooftop slip when he climbs to the third step of a tall chair in Midge's (Barbara Bel Geddes) apartment
* **Intense distress** upon being exposed to anything reminiscent of the event, particularly heights
* **Physiologic reactions** to reminders of the event — dizziness and disorientation when he climbs a steep incline
* **Diminished interest** in significant activities — he has no particular plan for his future and has to be cajoled by an old friend into doing some investigative work
* **Feelings of detachment from others** — he rebuffs the romantic interests of Midge and leaves her apartment after brief stays on several occasions

110

Born on the Fourth of July

Ron Kovic (Tom Cruise) volunteered to serve in the Marine Corps during the Vietnam War. While planning an assault on a village, some members of his squad disregarded his orders to wait and began firing a machine gun at the thatched huts in a small village. The gunfire kills several adults in one area, leaving a baby to fend for itself when a counterattack is launched. In the ensuing chaos of seeking cover, Ron accidentally shoots an American soldier. The image of the slaughtered civilians with the orphaned baby and the knowledge that he was responsible for the death of a comrade haunts him for years.

Once he is back home, Ron is invited to speak at his town's Fourth of July celebration. He flinches repeatedly when firecrackers are set off during the parade, demonstrating an **exaggerated startle response**. When Ron is giving a speech, the sound of a baby crying causes him to experience a **distressing recollection** of the events in the village. In response, he **loses his concentration** and feels as if the **experience were recurring**. Ron is prone to **outbursts of anger** and becomes progressively more **detached from his family**. Though he does not explicitly state that he has a sense of a foreshortened future, he doesn't make any plans for his future, even though he does have some options (**markedly diminished interest in significant activities**). Ron shows a **restricted range of emotions** for several months after he returns home, and seems to gain some peace of mind only after apologizing to the parents of the slain soldier. He also has **recurrent dreams** of his experiences in Vietnam.

It is very difficult to disentangle the symptoms of PTSD from the continual sacrifices and adjustments that Ron has to make in being a paraplegic. He constantly has his dignity stripped away from him and lapses into alcohol abuse to numb the pain he feels when even some of his family members disagree with America's involvement in Vietnam.

Obsessive-Compulsive Disorder

Understanding the Condition

Obsessive-compulsive disorder (OCD) has a very similar name to another psychiatric condition, obsessive-compulsive personality disorder (OCPD). These conditions are distinct and share fewer features than their names might suggest. Furthermore, neither condition is a prodrome or a consequence of the other. In other words, someone who develops OCD does not typically have OCPD first, nor does it develop later.

OCD can be understood as consisting of everyday thoughts and actions that are carried to extremes. For example, checking to see that the stove is turned off, washing one's hands, and keeping one's home tidy are typical activities for many people. People with OCD experience repeated, intrusive, and unwanted thoughts and spend much of their time dealing with matters such as checking locks, warding off contamination, or having to arrange their possessions in a symmetrical manner.

OCD is diagnosed if patients suffer from either obsessions or compulsions, though in most cases both are present. Obsessions are recognized as being a product of the person's own mind, in contrast to **thought insertion**, a symptom of a psychotic disorder in which patients have the experience of thoughts being placed in their minds from somewhere else. Many people suffer from the symptoms of OCD for several years before seeking help even though they recognize that the obsessions and compulsions are excessive and unreasonable.

OCD is an illness that usually begins between adolescence and early adulthood. Men seem to develop the illness earlier (between the ages of 6 and 15 years), whereas in women it typically starts in the 20's. The sexes are equally affected, with the lifetime prevalence being around 2%. Interestingly, some children develop OCD after certain types of bacterial infections.

Making the Diagnosis

An **obsession** is diagnosed when the following features are present:

i. *Recurrent, persistent thoughts, impulses, or images that are intrusive and inappropriate, and that cause anxiety or distress*

ii. *The thoughts, impulses, or images are not simply excessive worries about actual problems*

iii. *The person attempts to ignore, suppress, or neutralize the thoughts*

iv. *The person recognizes that the thoughts are a product of his or her own mind*

A **compulsion** is diagnosed when the following features are present:

i. *Repetitive behaviors or mental acts that the person feels driven to perform in response to an obsession*

ii. *The behaviors or mental acts are aimed at reducing or preventing distress or some dreaded event, but are not connected in a realistic way with decreasing anxiety or warding off disaster, e.g., washing one's hands repeatedly will not reduce the risk of developing skin cancer or prevent a flood from occurring*

Common Obsessions
• Contamination
• Need for order or symmetry
• Lucky and unlucky numbers
• Pathological doubt
• Aggressive impulses
• Being scrupulous about religious matters out of keeping with the person's background

Common Compulsions
• Washing
• Checking
• Ordering or arranging
• Asking or confessing
• Hoarding
• Counting
• Touching
• Opening and closing

In some situations patients develop their own rituals as a way of reducing the distress caused by their intrusive thoughts. The DSM-IV-TR refers to these as *"rules which must be applied rigidly."*

Cinematic depictions of the symptoms of OCD are portrayed in the following movies:

The Color of Night

Dr. Bob Moore (Scott Pakula) runs a group therapy session that consists of people with a smorgasbord of illnesses. One of his patients, Clark (Brad Dourif), is a mild-mannered lawyer who is correctly diagnosed in the film as having OCD.

Clark has two major manifestations of OCD. When we are introduced to him, he is counting the books in Dr. Moore's group room. Other members of the group call out numbers to distract him from this task and tease him about whether he knows the number of pages in the current edition of the newspaper. When Clark finds out that Dr. Moore was murdered — and knifed in particular — his **obsession** to find out how many stab wounds were inflicted supercedes any utterance of grief or surprise. Later in the film Clark goes into some detail in explaining his obsession with numbers. He said that he initially only paid attention to "relevant" numbers (such as phone numbers) but this gave way to a growing focus on "irrelevant" numbers such as the number of pages in a deposition. Clark eventually became consumed by OCD and was placed on medical leave from his law firm, with a request that he not return to work. While they aren't demonstrated in the film, Clark would appear to have a number of rituals or **rules that must be applied rigidly** regarding his behavior and how he manages in situations without becoming incapacitated.

Clark also suffers from an **obsession** regarding contamination. In response to this, his compulsion is to use a handkerchief when he touches things and then constantly wipe his fingers with it. In one scene, he refuses to shake hands with Dr. Bill Capa (Bruce Willis) for fear of the consequences of becoming contaminated. In another scene, Clark devotes considerable effort to cleaning his fingernails instead of paying full attention to the group discussion.

As Good As It Gets

Melvin Udall (Jack Nicholson) is a writer suffering from OCD. As soon as he enters his apartment, he begins to display his **compulsions**:

- Clicking his locks five times before feeling satisfied that they are set properly
- Turning his light switch on and off five times before entering the bathroom
- Wearing a new set of gloves every time he leaves his apartment; he discards them once they are worn
- Washing his hands in uncomfortably hot water as soon as he returns home
- Using a new bar of soap every time he washes his hands; Melvin christens the soap by touching it on the bathroom mirror before unwrapping it
- Tapping his toes over each other three times before putting on his slippers
- Avoids walking on cracks or lines on the sidewalk

Melvin's compulsions and rituals dominate much of his activity outside of his apartment. He patronizes the same restaurant everyday, sits in the same seat, and orders breakfast from Carol (Helen Hunt). In order to reduce his anxiety about contamination, Melvin brings his own plastic utensils wrapped in a transparent bag. Any departure from this routine is very upsetting for Melvin, though his anxiety is expressed as derision, sarcasm, and impatience. For much of the film, Melvin's personality can be described as abrasive, insensitive, and condescending. These features are not consistent with OCD. However, some people with this illness may appear to be controlling, rigid, or even hostile when an event triggers one of their obsessions or interferes with the carrying out of a compulsion. For example, when Melvin is touched by others, he becomes upset because they don't appreciate the extent of his obsession for cleanliness or the extensive and time-consuming rituals he engages in to cleanse himself.

Generalized Anxiety Disorder

Understanding the Condition

Generalized anxiety disorder (GAD) is characterized by excessive anxiety that is difficult to control and that causes a variety of physical symptoms. Before a stressful event such as an examination, many people feel tense, sleep poorly, can't focus on anything except the exam, and feel joyless. GAD is similar to this constellation of stressful reactions except that it isn't due to any identifiable event. In other words, it is like having to prepare for an exam every day of one's life.

Anxiety is a significant component of many other psychiatric illnesses. Conditions such as depression, psychotic disorders, substance use, and certain personality disorders among many others often involve prominent and persistent anxiety. GAD is probably the condition that most frequently coexists with other psychiatric diagnoses, usually another anxiety disorder. When two or more psychiatric conditions are present at the same time, they are said to be **comorbid**. Because GAD causes chronic physical symptoms, many patients focus on the manifestations of this illness and see medical specialists rather than psychiatrists.

In common parlance, patients with GAD are referred to as "worry warts" and often need to be coaxed by friends and family members to set aside their apprehensive expectations to be able to just enjoy some of life's basic pleasures.

GAD is thought to affect between 3 to 5% of the population. It typically starts early in life, with the majority of sufferers indicating that they have felt excessively anxious their whole lives. GAD appears to afflict women more frequently than men, with approximately 60% of patients being female. As with many psychiatric disorders, genetic factors are thought to be contributory but have yet to be clearly established. A link to depression has also been reported in some studies.

116

Making the Diagnosis

GAD is diagnosed when the following features are present:

i.   *Excessive anxiety that occurs more days than not and involves a wide number of concerns*

ii. *The anxiety is difficult to control*

iii. *Some of the following physical symptoms are present:*
   * *Feeling restless, keyed up, or edgy*
   * *Becoming easily fatigued*
   * *Difficulty concentrating*
   * *Irritability*
   * *Muscle tension*
   * *Disturbed sleep*

iv. *The focus of worry is not limited to the symptoms of another illness (e.g. someone who has panic disorder being worried about having a panic attack) and does not occur only in the context of another illness (e.g. someone feeling anxious only when he or she is depressed)*

One of the crucial points in diagnosing GAD is that the focus of someone's worry is about life circumstances such as: health, finances, job performance, family members, etc. The things that patients worry about are multiple and change with time. If a person's worry is focused only on one concern, GAD is unlikely to be the correct diagnosis. For example, patients with hypochondriasis worry about their health, paranoid patients focus on humiliation, and anorectic patients on weight gain. Cinematic depictions of some of the symptoms of GAD are portrayed in the following films:

Analyze This

(Illustrating restlessness, irritability, disturbed sleep)

Paul Vitti (Robert De Niro) suffers from panic disorder in this film. In between the attacks however, he lists the following symptoms: falling apart, crying for no reason, difficulty sleeping, and feeling uneasy around his friends to the point where he has to get away from them. This is a typical constellation of symptoms for people suffering from GAD.

117

Annie Hall

Woody Allen has made a career out of playing angst-ridden, neurotic, nebbish characters. In Annie Hall, he plays the role of comedian Alvy Singer, who struggles to maintain a relationship with Annie Hall (Diane Keaton). Alvy is so filled with self doubt that he has spent 15 years in psychotherapy, but is willing to give his analyst one more year to help get him on track. In the opening few minutes of the film, Alvy admits that he has a nervous personality with a hyperactive imagination, and that he is prone to confusing fantasy with reality.

Alvy very clearly meets the first two criteria for GAD, which are: **excessive anxiety that occurs more days than not and involves a wide number of concerns** and that the **anxiety is difficult to control**. A cataloging of just some of Alvy's multitudinous concerns is as follows:

- Rampant anti-Semitism
- The possibility of a conspiracy in the JFK assassination so absorbs him that he can't be intimate with his first wife
- Everything that his parents told him was good (sun, milk, red meat, college) he deems to ultimately be bad for him
- He wants to kiss Annie early during their first date so that he will be less anxious and better able to digest his dinner
- He refuses to shower in front of other men
- He keeps a first aid kit, insect spray, and a fire alarm handy so that he can be prepared for emergencies
- He panders to the audience and passers-by to show that he is being maligned, or to try and enlist their assistance in deciding what is "normal"
- He becomes defensive and irritable around accomplished, successful, or famous people
- He asks many questions about Annie's past relationships and then is envious about her past experiences
- He pays for Annie's analysis, and then gets jealous because she makes progress at a faster rate than he does

Alvy suddenly becomes dizzy, nauseated, and has a queasy stomach when he is scheduled to give an award on television. Rather than a physical manifestation of anxiety or social phobia, this appears to be due to Alvy's objection to having his artistic integrity compromised (he thinks people should be working instead of attending award ceremonies).

Alvy provides a reasonably good example of someone with GAD. Compared to most people, Alvy is more light-hearted about his various worries, and seems to have a reasonable perspective on his role in perpetuating them. Furthermore, he doesn't mention many of the physical manifestations of GAD, such as muscle tension or easy fatiguability.

In this picture, a good example of GAD is given by Alvy's second wife Robin (Janet Margolin), though she has only two scenes in the movie. We see her parading Alvy through a room of some of New York's intelligentsia. She is so focused on making a proper impression that she misses his rather humorous comments. Later, when she and Alvy are being intimate, Robin is so distracted by the sound of a siren that she cannot continue and instead begins to search for a bottle of tranquilizers. Alvy laments that Robin is so edgy that background sounds (e.g. airplanes and car horns) have interrupted their physical relationship.

Manhattan

Woody Allen plays Isaac Davis, a character who is quite similar to Alvy Singer but appears to be a little **edgier and more keyed up**. In one scene, Davis abruptly quits his job because of creative differences with other staff members. In another scene he has **difficultly sleeping**, though this is partly due to the noises his neighbors are making. Rather than expressing his angst in the physical symptoms typical of GAD, Davis feels that it wells up inside him and might be producing a tumor, which is more typical of a **hypochondriac** (see the chapter on *Somatoform Disorders*).

Specific Phobia

Understanding the Condition

Specific phobias encompass the familiar fears that people have of objects or situations such as: heights, animals, needles, storms, etc. This condition has previously been called **simple phobia**.

The concerns that people have as a result of these phobias are twofold. There is the apparent concern about falling from a height, being bitten by animals, etc. However, some people with specific phobias also fear the physical and psychological reactions they experience upon exposure to certain objects or situations. Some of the more common reactions are similar to those that occur in a panic attack: increased heart rate with palpitations, shortness of breath, losing control, fainting, etc. Exposure of phobic individuals to blood or injections typically brings on a fainting or near-fainting episode. Patients who fear specific situations such as tunnels or bridges seem to be particularly concerned about screaming or losing control of themselves.

As with social phobia, insight is preserved in that patients recognize that their fears are excessive and unreasonable. Since many people are able to avoid the objects and situations that they fear, they are able to lead relatively normal lives and do not usually seek medical or psychiatric assistance.

Specific phobias usually begin in childhood. Accurate estimates of the prevalence of specific phobia have been difficult to obtain, with reports varying between 5 and 10%. Certain types of specific phobias are more common than others and have different typical age ranges when they start. The categories of specific phobias are listed on the next page. In contrast to social phobia, a higher percentage of females suffer from specific phobia and the person is usually aware of a precipitating event. Specific phobias seem to have a strong genetic basis, particularly the fear of blood, injection, or injury.

Making the Diagnosis

i.   *Marked and persistent fear that is unreasonable, excessive, and cued by the presence or anticipation of an object or situation*
ii. *Exposure to the object or situation almost invariably provokes an immediate anxiety response, which may lead to either* **situationally bound** *or* **situationally predisposed panic attacks**
iii. *The person recognizes that the fear is excessive or unreasonable*
iv. *The phobic object or situation is avoided if possible; if it must be encountered the person suffers intense anxiety or distress*

The subtypes of specific phobias are as follows and are listed in order from most to least common:
*   Situational — tunnels, bridges, elevators, driving, flying, etc.
*   Natural Environment — storms, heights, water, thunder, etc.
*   Blood, Injection, or Injury
*   Animal — usually involves mammals (e.g. rodents) or insects

Heights, spiders, mice, and insects have been reported to be the most common specific phobias. Less common phobias are:
*   Anginaphobia — fear of narrowness
*   Anuptophobia — fear of staying single
*   Cherophobia — fear of good news
*   Dementophobia — fear of insanity
*   Ergophobia — fear of work
*   Gelophobia — fear of laughing
*   Genuphobia — fear of knees
*   Iatrophobia — fear of doctors
*   Kainophobia — fear of newness
*   Kenophobia — fear of empty spaces
*   Kleptophobia — fear of stealing
*   Logophobia — fear of words
*   Methyphobia — fear of alcohol
*   Myxophobia — fear of slime
*   Panphobia — fear of everything
*   Pentheraphobia — fear of mother-in-law
*   Phobophobia — fear of fear itself
*   Polyphobia — fear of many things

High Anxiety

This movie spoofs at least a half dozen of Alfred Hitchcock's films, though it focuses primarily on *Vertigo*. The title of this film is a pun referring to both the main character's general level of nervousness and his particular fear of heights. Dr. Richard Thorndyke (Mel Brooks) is a psychiatrist who becomes the administrator of the *Psycho-Neurotic Institute for the Very, Very Nervous*. Thorndyke's aversion to heights is evident throughout the movie because he is unable to avoid situations such as taking airplanes or riding in elevators. Even his office overlooks a sheer cliff face. Thorndyke develops clear symptoms of anxiety when exposed to heights, particularly when an old friend insists that he take in the panoramic view from his office by standing on the edge of a cliff.

Towards the end of the movie, the cause of Thorndyke's phobia is linked to a memory he has from early childhood. He clearly recalls his parents openly expressing their dissatisfaction with him. Shortly afterwards, Baby Thorndyke topples over in his high chair. When he is reminded of this event, Thorndyke instantly comes to the realization that it is not heights he has problems with — it is his parents.

While this isn't a typical event for causing a fear of heights, it does illustrate three factors that are relevant to the mechanism by which phobias develop:
- There was a direct cause (**precipitating event**) for his phobia
- The real conflict was not dealt with directly, instead it is transferred to a different situation or object; this process is called **displacement**
- The feared object or situation is often linked to the real conflict, which is called **symbolization**

Because he was unable to deal with his parents' rejection directly, Thorndyke instead displaced his anxiety into a fear of heights, symbolized by the chair from which he fell.

Vertigo

John "Scottie" Ferguson (James Stewart) is a detective who learns of his fear of heights after nearly plummeting to his death from a rooftop while pursuing a criminal. After his near fall, Ferguson develops a constellation of symptoms that are more consistent with PTSD than simply a fear of heights. Most people with specific phobias do not experience vertigo-like symptoms. Shortness of breath, palpitations, sweating, and trembling are more typical experiences.

The name of the movie derives from the dizziness and disorientation Ferguson develops upon climbing even a couple of steps, which is graphically illustrated in the film.

However, Ferguson also suffers from **acrophobia** (fear of heights), which is what made him feel so paralyzed when he was hanging from the eavestrough, and necessitated the intervention of an officer who fell to his death while providing assistance.

Arachnophobia

Ross Jennings (Jeff Daniels) is a physician who relocates his family from a big city to a small town. Jennings has a vivid and disturbing memory from childhood about being powerless to fend off a spider, and since that time has had a phobia of them. In one scene, he encounters a household spider and clearly expresses his distress while waiting for his wife to remove it.

Like many people who have specific phobias, Jennings is able to lead a normal life as long as he can avoid spiders. Later in the film, a group of mutant spiders with highly toxic venom infiltrate the town and Jennings has a showdown with the leader, a large aggressive Venezuelan arachnid. In these situations, a phobia would not be diagnosed because there is an actual threat present and his reaction is neither unreasonable nor excessive.

Social Phobia

Understanding the Condition

Phobia is derived from the Greek word for fear. Phobias are marked and persistent fears of objects, places, or situations that people understand as being irrational. For example, being wary of large, strange dogs is a sensible precaution. Leaving the room in a terrified state to avoid an eight-week old Labrador retriever puppy is phobic avoidance.

Phobias, also called phobic disorders, are divided into three categories in the DSM-IV-TR:

Agoraphobia — presented on page 100
Social Phobia — fear of social or performance situations where embarrassment may occur
Specific Phobia — fear of discrete objects or situations

Social phobia, also called **social anxiety disorder**, can have a significant cultural component. In some cultures, eye contact, the order in which people speak within a group, and visible signs of deference come into play in social exchanges. In Japan, a culturally distinct phobia called **taijin kyofusho** renders people intensely fearful that their body parts or functions are inherently offensive to others by way of odors, appearance, movements, or facial expression.

Social phobia typically begins insidiously and not after a discrete humiliating event. Epidemiologic studies have been difficult to conduct accurately. Many people are anxious before speaking in public or are self conscious when doing something in crowds, and it has been a challenge to define precisely where an expectable reaction ends and a disorder begins. Social phobia appears to be equally prevalent in males and females and affects somewhere in the range of 2 to 5% of the population. This condition typically starts in adolescence or young adulthood. A strong heritability has been shown for social phobia.

Making the Diagnosis

Social phobia is diagnosed when the following features are present:

i.   *Marked and persistent fears in social or performance situations where a person feels that he or she will do something that is humiliating or embarrassing, or will show clear symptoms of anxiety*

ii. *Being exposed to the feared social situation (e.g. public speaking) almost invariably provokes anxiety, which may lead to either* **situationally bound** *or* **situationally predisposed panic attacks**

iii. *The fear is recognized as being unreasonable and excessive for the circumstances*

iv. *The situation is either avoided altogether or endured with great anxiety or distress*

People with social phobia are afraid of doing something in front of an audience that will cause others to think that the person is incapable or silly. They are fearful of having their trembling hands or halting voice betray their keen sense of humiliation or embarrassment. In addition to public speaking, other activities that are commonly problematic in social phobia are: eating, drinking, reading, writing, playing a musical instrument, and using a public restroom. Social phobia can cause people to decline job promotions (to avoid conducting meetings and making presentations), educational opportunities, and relationships.

Adults with social phobia recognize that their fears are excessive and unreasonable. When this insight is not present, the same set of fears would likely be diagnosed as a different condition. For example, a man who felt that people were scrutinizing him for signs of nervousness and were seeking primarily to embarrass and humiliate him would be diagnosed with a paranoid personality disorder or delusional disorder.

Common uneasiness about social situations, such as performance anxiety, stage fright, shyness, and butterflies in the stomach does not qualify for the diagnosis of social phobia.

Little Voice

Little Voice, abbreviated to LV in this film, is the name of the character played by Jane Horrocks. LV lives in a quiet seaside town in England. She is a recluse, rarely leaving her house and at times doesn't even answer the phone. LV adored her deceased father who ran his own record store. As a tribute to him, she listens to the albums of his favorite female singers: Judy Garland, Marilyn Monroe, and Shirley Bassey. As her only connection to her father, LV learns to mimic these divas with remarkable accuracy.

LV speaks in a soft, high-pitched voice but sings with the fullness and gusto of the star she is impersonating. She considers her tributes to be "private" and sings in front of a picture of her father. LV's life changes when Ray (Michael Caine), both a scoundrel and a talent scout, overhears her singing and manipulates her into performing for an audience.

The scene in the movie most consistent with social phobia is LV's initial night club performance. She has to literally be pushed out onto the stage. The microphone looms in front of her with a menacing quality and she freezes instead of being able to sing, even though there is a sparse and largely disinterested audience. She cannot begin until the house lights have been turned off, needs to be cued by Ray, and then sings only a few lines from a few songs. This scene would have been a more accurate depiction if LV did not have such a reclusive lifestyle (because she is socially awkward), and if she hadn't expressed her clear wish to sing only for her father's memory (because she didn't really want to be there in the first place).

The other character in the film that exhibits some features of social phobia is Billy (Ewan MacGregor). Although quite taken with LV when he meets her, he needs considerable encouragement and a contrived situation to feel comfortable in making contact with her again. When he sees her, he is visibly anxious, awkward, and embarrassed.

Movie	Feature/Diagnosis
Analyze This	Cardiovascular symptoms of panic attacks; Disturbed sleep (GAD); Gastrointestinal symptoms of panic attacks; irritability (GAD); Psychological symptoms of panic attacks; Panic disorder; Restlessness (GAD)
Annie Hall	Anxiety which is difficult to control (GAD); Excessive anxiety (GAD)
Arachnophobia	Specific phobia
As Good As It Gets	Compulsions (OCD)
Behind the Lines/ Regeneration	Avoidance of stimuli associated with the event (PTSD symptom cluster); Feelings of increased arousal (PTSD symptom cluster); Persistent reexperience of the traumatic event (PTSD symptom cluster)
Born on the 4th of July	PTSD symptom clusters (all 3)
Copycat	Panic disorder with agoraphobia; Posttraumatic stress disorder
Fearless	PTSD Symptom clusters (all 3); Psychological symptoms of panic disorder
Flooding	Cardiovascular symptoms of panic attacks; Gastrointestinal symptoms of panic attacks; Psychological symptoms of panic attacks
High Anxiety	Specific phobia

I Am Sam	Agoraphobia without history of panic disorder
In Country	Avoidance of stimuli associated with the event (PTSD symptom cluster); Feelings of increased arousal (PTSD symptom cluster); Persistent reexperience of the traumatic event (PTSD symptom cluster)
Little Voice	Social phobia
Manhattan	Difficulty sleeping (GAD); Edginess and feeling keyed up (GAD)
Scream 2	Persistent reexperience of the traumatic event (PTSD symptom cluster)
The Color of Night	Obsession with numbers; Obsession with contamination; Rules that must be applied rigidly (OCD Symptom)
The Deer Hunter	Avoidance of stimuli associated with the event (PTSD symptom cluster)
The Sopranos	Cardiovascular symptoms of panic attacks
Vertigo	Avoidance of stimuli associated with the event (PTSD symptom cluster); Persistent reexperience of the traumatic event (PTSD symptom cluster); Specific phobia
What About Bob?	Cardiovascular symptoms of panic attacks; Gastrointestinal symptoms of panic attacks; Neurological symptoms of panic attacks

Chapter 8

Somatoform Disorders

Hypochondriasis

Understanding the Condition

Translated from Greek, somatoform means "body like." As a group, the somatoform disorders are conditions where patients express their psychological difficulties in terms of physical symptoms. These symptoms are often suggestive of medical conditions, yet no satisfactory explanation can be found even after repeated physical examinations or laboratory tests.

Probably the best known of the somatoform disorders is hypochondriasis, with the person suffering from this illness being referred to as a hypochondriac. The name of this disorder stems from the medical term **hypochondrium**, meaning "below the cartilage" and was so named because patients with this condition have a high frequency of abdominal complaints.

The central feature of hypochondriasis involves a person who believes that he or she has, or will soon contract, a serious illness. In many cases, patients have their complaints investigated by a number of physical medicine specialists. It is only after some period of time and repeated negative test results that physicians can eliminate physical causes for the patient's symptoms and determine that a somatoform disorder is present. Hypochondriasis is often seen accompanying mood or anxiety disorders.

Hypochondriasis can start at any age, but most commonly starts in the 20's. Surveys estimate that from 1 to 5% of the general population suffers from hypochondriasis, with an equal ratio of men and women affected.

Serious illness in childhood and exposure to others who are very ill are thought to be important causative factors. Transient hypochodriacal features are commonly seen in people who suffer the loss of a loved one, particularly due to protracted illnesses.

Making the Diagnosis

Hypochondriasis is diagnosed when the following symptoms are present:

i. *Preoccupation with the fear of having a serious illness*
ii. *Medical evaluation and reassurance have not diminished this fear*
iii. *This belief is not of delusional intensity*

One of the ways of understanding hypochondriasis is to consider it as being a misinterpretation of bodily functions. For example, occasional palpitations can be a normal occurrence but to a hypochondriac they would signify serious heart disease. Patients can also amplify minor symptoms into hypochondriacal proportions, such as a mild cough being clear evidence that the person might have tuberculosis or lung cancer. Lastly, some patients list vague symptoms which are not specific for any illness (such as fatigue) and think that these experiences are early indications of more serious illnesses.

In some cases, patients focus their concerns mainly on the presence of a serious illness even though they are experiencing few symptoms. The DSM-IV-TR criteria stipulate that the hypochondriacal beliefs are not of delusional intensity. In practice, this means that patients are at least willing to accept the possibility that they will not develop a serious illness. If, for most of the duration of the illness patients demonstrate excessive and unreasonable concerns, then a specifier called "with poor insight" is added to the diagnosis. If patients have absolutely no capacity to see that their concerns may not be warranted, then a **delusional disorder, somatic type** would be diagnosed.

Hypochondriacal patients remain focused on having a serious illness, but the actual malady of concern can change over time.

Hypochondriasis is not diagnosed if the person's concerns focus solely on some aspect of appearance. This condition is called **body dysmorphic disorder** and is presented later in this chapter.

Bandits

Terry Collins (Billy Bob Thornton) states that his *"body chemistry is extraordinarily sensitive to suggestion and any symptom can be manufactured given the right circumstances, and that, by the way, doesn't mean that it isn't real."* Diagnostically, Collins is an amalgamation of a number of conditions. While his two most prominent diagnoses are **hypochondriasis** and **conversion disorder** (presented in the next section), he also suffers from **specific phobias** (antique furniture, black & white movies, etc.) and **obsessive-compulsive disorder** (he must press button A-1 on jukeboxes). The features of hypochondriasis that Collins displays are:

- Listening to the Merck Manual on tape while driving his car (this manual is an authoritative source on physical illnesses)
- Saying that he doesn't want to live outside of the U.S. because he has *"sanitation issues"*
- Getting upset that the warden banned fresh garlic from the commissary because it is a miracle drug that is helpful in preventing hypertension, emphysema, arthritis, cancer, and allergies; Collins follows this up by saying that he has "symptoms regardless of what the prison doctor says" and clearly can't be reassured that he doesn't have a serious illness

Hannah and Her Sisters

Mickey Sachs (Woody Allen) is the prototypic hypochondriac. Neurotic, plaintive, and blessed with an active imagination, much of his role centers on his enduring health concerns. A screen labeling Mickey as a hypochondriac is shown before we even see him.

Mickey is on the way to see his doctor. In contrast to other visits, this time he feels that he really has something wrong with him, something that is slowly ruining his health — possibly an ulcer. He had previously been concerned that his adenoids were causing problems for him, but withdrew this complaint when he was reminded that they'd already been removed. Mickey acknowledges that while he often imagines that he has something seriously wrong with him, it is his father who is the real hypochondriac in the family.

Mickey narrows down his physical complaints to dizziness and some loss of hearing, but has trouble deciding which ear is affected. He is startled to learn that he actually does have some high-frequency hearing loss in his right ear, especially since he can't account for why this might have happened. His physician wants Mickey to have more tests, but doesn't specify which illnesses he is concerned about investigating. Mickey contacts another physician by telephone and learns that a brain tumor is a remote possibility for causing hearing loss in one ear.

A gray spot on a tomogram (a type of X-ray) prompts yet another round of investigations and it is too much for Mickey to bear. He wakes up from his sleep absorbed in morbid thoughts about his health. . . *"I'm dying, I'm dying, I knew it. There's a spot on my lungs. [calm inner voice: Take it easy, it's not on your lungs, it's on your ear]. It's the same thing, isn't it? I can't sleep. Oh God, there's a tumor in my head the size of a basketball. Now I keep thinking that I can feel it every time I blink."*

Mickey then has a morbid fantasy about the gray spot on the tomogram in which an unempathic, robotic specialist tells him that it is an inoperable tumor. Of course, this notion is quickly dispelled when the specialist actually does enter the room and tells Mickey that the spot is nothing to be concerned about.

Mickey is prone to quickly escalating a minor event into a life-threatening crisis. In another scene, his co-worker Gail (Julie Kavner) reminds him of the time that he thought he had a melanoma because he had a new black spot on his back that others pointed out. The spot was actually on his shirt. This portrayal is an excellent one, particularly because the viewer is party to Mickey's private thoughts as he goes through the ordeal of not knowing whether or not has a serious illness.

Conversion Disorder

Understanding the Condition

In conversion disorder (CD), psychological trauma or conflict becomes "converted" into a physical symptom. In contrast to the other somatoform disorders, CD usually occurs in a rapid, dramatic fashion and the trauma or conflict is usually easily identified. A common example of CD would involve a person who suddenly becomes blind or mute after catching his or her spouse in an act of infidelity.

The symptoms in CD primarily involve the nervous system, particularly sensation and voluntary movement. Symptoms limited to pain or sexual dysfunction are usually due to a different somatoform disorder. The deficits reported in CD don't conform to the anatomical pathways of nerves. For example, it is not possible to suddenly lose one's sense of touch on only the surface of both hands and both feet (**glove and stocking anesthesia**).

Breuer, a contemporary and collaborator of Freud's, treated a woman with **hysteria** in which CD was one of the components of her illness. Breuer referred to the patient as "Anna O" and described her situation as follows, *". . .she is an intelligent woman of 21 years who presented a plethora of hysterical symptoms in association with her father's fatal illness. . .including serious disturbances of sight and speech, inability to ingest food, paralysis of three extremities with contractures and anesthesias, and a nervous cough."*

CD occurs more commonly in the following groups: rural populations, lower socioeconomic strata, those with fewer years of formal education, and people with lower IQs. It usually begins after the age of 10 and before thirty-five. CD affects women to a much greater extent, with estimates ranging between factors of 2:1 to 10:1. Interestingly, in women the physical symptoms usually occur on the left side of the body. CD in men is often seen in the context of an industrial accident or due to combat.

Making the Diagnosis

The following are the criteria used to diagnose CD:

i. *One or more of the symptoms or deficits affecting voluntary movement or sensation suggests a neurological or general medical condition*

ii. *Psychological factors are deemed to be associated with the onset of the symptom or deficit*

iii. *The symptom or deficit is not being intentionally produced*

iv. *The symptoms or deficits cannot be explained by a general medical condition, the effects of a substance, or by culturally sanctioned experiences*

v. *The symptom is not limited to pain or sexual dysfunction*

Two other features of CD are:

- **La belle indifférence** — in spite of usually rather marked neurological problems, patients seem unconcerned about their symptoms
- **Identification** — patients may model the symptoms of someone close to them who had a serious illness (such as a stroke)

The most common symptoms seen in CD are:

Sensory Symptoms/Altered Sensation
- Anesthesia (loss of sensation)
- Loss of special senses (e.g. vision and hearing)
- Paresthesia (unpleasant sensations, such as tingling)
- Dizziness

Motor Symptoms/Altered Movement
- Gait disturbances, falling
- Paralysis, but reflexes and muscle bulk remain intact
- Tics, tremors, involuntary movements
- Weakness
- Muteness (**aphonia**)

Seizure Symptoms/Convulsions
- Seizure-like movements, but without true seizure activity and the resulting physiological changes

Bandits

Terry Collins (Billy Bob Thornton) and partner Joe Blake (Bruce Willis) make an unlikely pair of bank robbers. Blake is smooth and confident in contrast to Collins' perpetual ranting about his health concerns. Collins' quote about his susceptibility to the symptoms of other people is included in the hypochondriasis section.

When the pair approach bank manager Lawrence Fife (Richard Riehle) and inform him that they intend to rob his bank, Fife immediately collapses. Mrs. Fife (Micole Mercurio) gives Collins a succinct and accurate account of her husband's **narcolepsy**. Sure enough, during the robbery the next morning, Collins has fallen asleep while leaning against a wall, a move which jeopardizes a safe and timely egress from the bank.

Later in the film, Collins and Blake are joined by Kate Wheeler (Cate Blanchett), who is fleeing her self-absorbed husband. Kate initially falls for Blake, but in the confusion arising after a bank job, is forced to flee with Collins. Over the span of two weeks, she falls for him, making for an uneasy reunion with Blake.

Blake, in order to take out a measure of revenge against Collins for attempting to steal his girl, invents a story about a fictitious brother with a brain tumor. Blake says that his brother suffered from headaches, and as the symptoms of the tumor became more pronounced, started to smell burning feathers all the time. This story strongly affects the suggestible Collins who, while in the middle of another robbery, asks a bank employee to check to see if his pupils are unequal. Shortly afterwards, Collins believes that he too smells burning feathers and then develops numb lips and weakness on the right side of his body. In doing so, he demonstrates the following signs of CD:

- His symptoms are suggestive of a neurological condition
- The emotional conflict stemming from his affections for both Kate and Blake is expressed in physical terms
- Collins is not faking his symptoms

- Collins is identifying/modeling the symptoms of Blake's brother
- Collins does not have a tumor; after being informed that Blake never had a brother, the symptoms remit completely

Behind the Lines/ Regeneration

In this film, Craiglockart is a Scottish hospital dedicated to the treatment of W.W.I soldiers. Dr. William Rivers (Jonathan Pryce) is one of the staff physicians assigned to treat patients with psychological difficulties arising from combat. Billy Prior (Jonny Lee Miller) is an officer who is sent to the hospital. In his interview with Dr. Rivers, Prior indicates that he has lost his voice (**aphonia**). This is a classic CD symptom for the following reasons:

- Aphonia is suggestive of a medical or neurologic disease
- As we later learn, Prior is haunted by the fate of the soldiers under his command, clearly indicating that a psychological factor was responsible for his muteness
- Prior is not malingering (faking his symptoms)
- The aphonia developed rapidly
- Prior suffers from no physical injury

Rivers himself begins to develop stuttering as a conversion symptom. The sad irony of his efforts — healing men so that they can return to the horrors of war — takes a toll on Rivers and he requires a brief leave of absence.

While there is no identification or modeling involved in either of Rivers' or Prior's symptoms, one can reasonably see that being an officer and having to issue orders that may cost men their lives could cause a conflict that would be manifested as a problem with speaking. In this way, the physical symptom (aphonia) achieves the **primary gain** of attaining a psychological resolution to their conflict.

Somatization Disorder

Understanding the Condition

Somatization Disorder (SD) is another condition distilled out of the original concept of **hysteria**. The brief description of Anna O's symptoms listed on page 134 indicates involvement of visual, speech, respiratory, gastrointestinal, nervous, and musculoskeletal systems, which is beyond the description provided for CD. SD has also been called **Briquet's syndrome** after the French physician who accurately described the symptoms and course of the illness in 1859.

SD is characterized by physical complaints that involve multiple systems within the body that have no demonstrable medical cause. SD is distinguished from hypochondriasis in that patients with SD focus on multiple symptoms and less on the possibility of having a serious or life-threatening illness. SD differs from conversion disorder in that patients with SD have at least eight unexplainable symptoms from 4 body systems. In CD, the complaints are usually neurologic in nature. Furthermore, patients with SD are usually quite focused on, and troubled by, their symptoms. In CD patients can appear to be unconcerned about their symptoms (**la belle indifférence**).

SD is found to occur primarily in women and starts before the age of 30. The lifetime prevalence of SD in women is estimated to range between 0.2% and 2%. It is found in less than 0.2% of men but may be more common outside of North America. SD is thought to have a significant genetic component, with up to 20% of the first-degree female relatives of female patients being affected. Male relatives of females with SD appear to have a higher incidence of **antisocial personality disorder** and **substance related disorders**. It has been hypothesized that in certain cultures, it is more common or acceptable to express emotions in physical terms, an indication that social or ethnic factors may have a role in the development of SD.

Making the Diagnosis

SD is diagnosed on the basis of the following criteria:

i. *Multiple physical complaints that have no demonstrable physical basis*

ii. *If a general medical condition exists, the symptoms are in excess of what would typically be expected*

iii. *The physical complaints are present for many years*

iv. *The physical complaints begin before age 30*

v. *Each of the following types of complaints must have been present at some time during the illness:*
   - *4 pain syndromes (at different sites in the body)*
   - *2 gastrointestinal syndromes*
   - *1 sexual symptom*
   - *1 pseudoneurological syndrome*

- Common pain syndromes are: back pain, abdominal pain, chest pain, painful urination or intercourse, joint pain
- Common gastrointestinal syndromes are: nausea, vomiting, bloating, diarrhea, intolerance of many types of foods
- Common sexual symptoms are: sexual indifference, erectile or ejaculatory dysfunction, irregular menses
- Common pseudoneurological syndromes are: muteness, anesthesia, lump in throat, blindness, deafness, amnesia

No Movie Example Available

Body Dysmorphic Disorder

Understanding the Condition

Dysmorphic means that something is physically deformed or has an abnormal appearance. Body dysmorphic disorder (BDD) is a preoccupation with an imagined defect in appearance, usually involving the head or face. BDD is also diagnosed if a slight abnormality is present but the patient's reaction is markedly excessive. This condition, also known as **dysmorphophobia**, is frequently accompanied by anxiety or depressive disorders. Common complaints involving the face and head center on: hair, shape, symmetry, color, scars, disproportion, wrinkles, etc. While patients may be concerned about any body part, they usually focus their complaints on a single feature. The prevalence of BDD has not been accurately established, with data on sex ratios being similarly inconclusive. At times, patients can be so embarrassed by their perceived defect that they are reluctant to even discuss the matter. Many patients with BDD seek treatment from dermatologists and cosmetic surgeons.

Making the Diagnosis

In this condition, beliefs about appearance are not of delusional intensity, on some level patients can agree that their perceptions are distorted. If this degree of insight is not present, then a **delusional disorder, somatic type** would be diagnosed.

Red Dragon

Francis Dolarhyde (Ralph Fiennes) has a cleft lip which was surgically repaired, leaving him with a scar on his upper lip and a slight speech impediment. Although there is more affecting Dolarhyde than BDD, he demonstrates many of the common characteristics of this condition. Dolarhyde is quite shy, and probably chose to work in a photographic laboratory because of the isolation it provides. Reba McClane (Emily Watson) is the only woman he feels comfortable with because she is blind. Even still, he doesn't like

140

her touching his face and he doesn't respond favorably when she comments on his slight speech impediment. Dolarhyde engages in strenuous body building to compensate for, or distract from, his "defect." All the mirrors in Dolarhyde's house are smashed, as are those in the homes where he commits violent crimes. He has a huge tattoo of a red dragon on his back, but it is unclear if this was done for the purpose of distraction. What is missing from this portrayal is Dolarhyde's account of his symptoms, which are not revealed. Also, there is clearly a psychotic component to Dolarhyde's illness which is not typically present in BDD.

Pain Disorder

This condition is diagnosed when a patient's difficulties are exclusively due to complaints of pain. Psychological factors are thought to play an important role in the onset, severity, or maintenance of the sensation of pain. The prevalence of pain disorder has not yet been accurately determined, but is thought to occur about twice as often in women. Pain disorder can occur at any age but begins most commonly in the fourth and fifth decades. A significant genetic factor is likely involved in this disorder. The most common complaints are: headache, back pain, pelvic pain, and facial pain.

No Movie Example Available

Movie

Feature/Diagnosis

Bandits

Ideas about ill health are not of delusional intensity (Hypochondriasis); Medical evaluation does not alleviate concern about serious illness (Hypochondriasis)

Preoccupation with fears of having a serious illness (Hypochondriasis); Physical injury is not present (CD); Psychological factors are deemed to be associated with the onset of symptoms (CD); Symptoms affect the voluntary nervous system (CD)

Behind the Lines/ Regeneration

Physical injury is not present (CD); Psychological factors are deemed to be associated with the onset of symptoms (CD); Symptoms affect the voluntary nervous system (CD)

Hannah and Her Sisters

Ideas about ill health are not of delusional intensity (Hypochondriasis); Medical evaluation does not alleviate concern about serious illness (Hypochondriasis); Preoccupation with fears of having a serious illness (Hypochondriasis)

Red Dragon

Markedly excessive preoccupation with slight defect in appearance (BDD)

Chapter 9

Factitious Disorder and Malingering

Factitious Disorders

Understanding the Condition

The principal feature in factitious disorders is that symptoms are intentionally produced in order to assume the "sick role." Symptoms are feigned or invented in order to facilitate care in a medical setting, usually as an inpatient. In extreme cases, patients with factitious disorders go from hospital to hospital faking a variety of illnesses in the hope that they can convince doctors to investigate and treat their symptoms. Factitious disorders are commonly referred to by the following names:

- Professional patient syndrome
- Peregrinating patients
- Hospital hoboes
- Polysurgical addiction

Pseudologia fantastica, a feature of factitious disorders, is defined as *"an extreme form of pathological lying consisting of telling stories without adequate motive and with such zeal that subject may become convinced of their truth"* (Campbell, 1996). False and conflicting accounts of illness and personal information are mixed with the patient's fantasies, such as being connected to someone famous or highly accomplished.

Another term often used synonymously with factitious disorders is **Münchausen's syndrome**, named after a character in Gottfried August Bürger's book. Münchausen was a German soldier and raconteur who lived in the 18th century. This term is really a misnomer since Münchausen didn't fake illness, instead he told fanciful tales. Some of his exploits are portrayed in the film, *The Adventures of Baron Münchausen*. **Münchausen's syndrome by proxy** denotes a parent who simulates or induces an illness in his or her child for the purpose of repeated investigations, hospitalizations, sympathy, attention, etc.

Limited information is available on the epidemiology of factitious disorders. Some studies estimate a prevalence of 1% of inpatients in a general hospital setting.

Making the Diagnosis

Factitious disorders are diagnosed on the basis of the following criteria:

i. *Intentional production or feigning of symptoms*
ii. *The motivation for feigning symptoms is to assume the sick role*
iii. *External incentives for feigning symptoms are absent*

The DSM-IV-TR specifies three subtypes of factitious disorder:
• Predominantly psychological signs and symptoms
• Predominantly physical signs and symptoms
• Combined psychological and physical symptoms

Patients with factitious disorders will go to dramatic lengths to feign having an illness, such as: taking medications surreptitiously, injecting themselves with substances that cause infection, manipulating diagnostic tests, and placing thermometers in hot drinks to fake having a fever.

Don't Say a Word

Elisabeth Burrows (Brittany Murphy) saw her father, a bank robber, get brutally murdered in a subway station. For the next ten years she found ways to get admitted to psychiatric institutions by imitating almost 20 different diagnoses. Dr. Nathan Conrad (Michael Douglas) pieces together the inconsistencies from her medical record and recognizes that her catatonic symptoms (**waxy flexibility**) are not real. Elisabeth was able to mimic a wide variety of psychiatric conditions, apparently for the purpose of staying in hospitals. Later in the film, this is shown to be largely an adaptive strategy for Elisabeth because she is being pursued by her father's killers.

This portrayal is less than ideal because Elisabeth clearly does have a reason for wanting to "assume the sick role" and would be most accurately diagnosed with malingering (see page 146). Also, Elisabeth has some symptoms of PTSD because of the trauma she experienced in seeing her father murdered.

Malingering

Malingering is the conscious, intentional production of physical or psychological symptoms for the purpose of obtaining some external incentive. Malingering differs from factitious disorder in that there is a clear "real world" advantage to the person mimicking the illness. These external advantages are called **secondary gain**. Primary gain was defined in the section on conversion disorder in the chapter on *Somatoform Disorders*. Examples of secondary gain include:

- Financial incentives (e.g. due to stress or disability)
- Avoiding prosecution, military service, work, etc.
- Obtaining prescription medication, often pain killers
- Receiving sympathy or attention from others

At times, it is difficult to distinguish factitious disorder from malingering. Making an accurate distinction is based on the obviousness or transparency of the secondary gain. Since malingerers don't actually have anything wrong with them psychiatrically, this condition is not considered to be an actual diagnosis and appears in the DSM-IV-TR under the heading *Additional Conditions Which May Be a Focus of Clinical Attention*. Psychiatric symptoms are often favored by malingerers because they don't need to have a physical abnormality or lab test to help persuade doctors that there is something wrong. Malingering has been reported to occur more frequently in men, though accurate statistics are difficult to obtain.

The diagnosis of either factitious disorder or malingering is a difficult one for even seasoned clinicians. Some textbooks providing detailed information on malingering are:

- *Clinical Assessment of Malingering and Deception*, by Richard Rogers
- *Malingering and Deception in Adolescents: Assessing Credibility in Clinical and Forensic Settings*, by Joseph T. McCann
- *Legal Neurology and Malingering: Cases and Techniques*, by Warren F. Gorman

Primal Fear

In Chicago, Archbishop Richard Rushman (Stanley Anderson) is savagely murdered in his quarters. The police arrive within minutes and notice a young man hiding in the trees outside the building. They give chase, and take into custody Aaron Stampler (Edward Norton), who is covered in the Archbishop's blood.

Stampler's case gets the immediate attention of defense attorney Martin Vail (Richard Gere). Vail has just been featured on the cover of a Chicago magazine and is pleased to offer his services on a pro bono basis in exchange for the media attention he'll receive. Vail immediately gets to work on Stampler's defense.

In Stampler's first meeting with Vail, Aaron indicates that he has had "spells" or periods of time for which he has amnesia. These episodes of lost time have been affecting Stampler since he was 12 years old but haven't been medically assessed.

As part of the preparation for Stampler's defense, a neuropsychologist is hired to conduct an evaluation. Dr. Molly Arrington (Frances McDormand) videotapes her sessions, and makes a chilling discovery. When she started to press Stampler to talk about a woman he cared for, his stutter worsened, he became confused and agitated, and started to develop a headache. Seconds later, his facial expression, tone of voice, and demeanor all changed as his alter personality Roy emerged. Perhaps this is only fitting, since Aaron Stampler was an altar boy in Archbishop Rushman's congregation.

Stampler goes on to give a convincing portrayal of dissociative identity disorder, fooling Vail and Judge Miriam Shoat (Alfre Woodard). A mistrial is called and Stampler is to be sent instead to a psychiatric forensic ward. In a compelling last scene, Stampler informs Vail that the personality of Aaron was manufactured for the purpose of avoiding prosecution.

The Royal Tenenbaums

Royal Tenenbaum (Gene Hackman) is a man seeking forgiveness for being a lousy husband and father for over thirty years. At the beginning of the film, he is evicted from the hotel where he's been living for decades. Broke, lonely and homeless, he seeks to rekindle his relationship with his estranged family.

Unfortunately, Royal was so nasty to his own family that he needs yet another scheme to even allow him to make contact with them. He decides to announce that he has stomach cancer and has only six weeks left to live. The ploy works, particularly on his ex-wife Etheline (Angelica Houston). The power that an illness has on a family is nicely illustrated in the scene where he first tells her that he's dying. She radiates sympathy and caring, and embraces him despite his many years of irresponsible behavior.

Royal is immediately allowed to move back into the family home. He has a bedroom to himself, a personal attendant, and an impressive array of medical machines, ostensibly to ease his suffering and prolong his life. When confronted with a difficult issue, Royal slowly falls to the ground and puts a spoon between his teeth as if he is expecting to have a seizure. He asks for a barbiturate by name, giving an air of authenticity to his illness.

Soon, Royal is found out. The doctor who makes a house call after the fall is revealed to be an imposter. The hospital garments that Royal wears are from an institution that folded years ago. His pills are revealed to be breath mints.

If Royal had feigned stomach cancer solely to gain admission to a hospital, this would have been an example of **factitious disorder with predominantly physical signs and symptoms**. However, he clearly wanted the attention and absolution of his family, which qualifies as meeting the grounds for **secondary gain** and therefore his correct diagnosis is malingering.

148

The Usual Suspects

Roger "Verbal" Kint (Kevin Spacey) is ostensibly a small time con man. He is rounded up with four higher profile criminals when the police are investigating the hijacking of a truck. Once he makes the acquaintance of these other men, he becomes increasingly involved in their exploits.

Within a few weeks, the group of five is presented with an offer they can't refuse. They have all inadvertently crossed an almost mythical criminal mastermind who demands that they attack a docked ship on his behalf, and then their trespasses will be forgiven. Their assignment is virtually a suicide mission.

Verbal is the only survivor of the group, and is interviewed at a police station before he is released. Verbal is shown for most of the movie to have a left-sided paralysis. He is unable to use his left arm, which he either protects by holding it or putting his hand in a pocket. Verbal's left foot is rotated inward to such a degree that he walks slowly and with a noticeable limp. He also appears to be dim-witted and easily intimidated. In the last scene of the film, Verbal straightens up, lights a cigarette with his left hand, and walks normally, proving that his physical problems were feigned.

M*A*S*H

Corporal Max Klinger (Jamie Farr), later promoted to Sergeant, was a character in the TV series that ran from 1972 to 1983 and is available on DVD. Klinger was fixated on obtaining a discharge from the army on a "Section 8," which was for psychiatric reasons. He tried a wide variety of ploys to obtain his release, most notably dressing up in women's clothes. When the unit was visited by psychiatrist Dr. Sidney Freedman (Alan Arbus), Klinger's antics were intensified as he became even more determined to show how "crazy" he was.

Movie

Feature/Diagnosis

Don't Say a Word

Conscious production of psychological symptoms in order to assume the sick role (Factitous Disorder)

M*A*S*H
(TV Series)

Conscious production of psychological symptoms in order to obtain secondary gain (Malingering)

Primal Fear

Conscious production of psychological symptoms in order to obtain secondary gain (Malingering)

The Royal Tenenbaums

Conscious production of physical symptoms in order to obtain secondary gain (Malingering)

The Usual Suspects

Conscious production of physical symptoms in order to obtain secondary gain (Malingering)

Chapter 10

Dissociative Disorders

Dissociative Identity Disorder

Understanding the Condition

The central feature in dissociative disorders is an alteration in consciousness, identity, and memory. **Amnesia** is a loss of memory for personal details which has a psychological cause, as opposed to dementia where the memory loss involves a wider range of information and has a medical cause.

Dissociative Identity Disorder (DID) was formerly called **multiple personality disorder** and is still commonly referred to by that name. The essential feature of this condition is that two or more distinct identities recurrently take control over a person's behavior. DID can be quite dramatic, with various personality states speaking different languages, having different accents, and fighting for control with other identities.

The average number of personality states ranges from 7 to 11, with half of the reported cases having about ten identities, called **alters**. The usual arrangement involves a primary identity who frequently appears to be passive, quiet, masochistic, or dependent. This primary personality often complains of significant gaps in memory for both recent and remote events. Some people have referred to this as "losing time." In some instances, patients rely on others to tell them what they were doing during these intervals. In other situations, patients are able to discover or reclaim these memories. Most of the patients who have DID also meet the criteria for other psychiatric conditions.

DID is the subject of considerable controversy among psychiatric experts. Estimates of its prevalence vary widely depending on the study conducted. It is reasonably well established that DID is much more common in women (75% to 90% of cases). It usually starts in childhood, but has been seen to begin in people in their 40's. Women appear to manifest an average of 15 alters, twice as many as men.

Making the Diagnosis

DID is diagnosed on the basis of the following criteria:

i.   *Two or more distinct identities or personality states (**alters**) are present*
ii.   *At least two of the alters recurrently take control of the person's behavior*
iii. *The amnesia is too extensive to be considered ordinary forgetfulness*

In some cases, the alters have reciprocal arrangements with each other. Two common pairings are aggressive and dependent, or protector and innocent. In other situations, the victim, perpetrator, and witness to a traumatic event are all internalized in the arrangement of alters.

Transition between personality states usually takes place in a matter of seconds, but can be gradual. Switches are usually triggered by stressful situations. Typically, the emerging personality is unaware of the one it is taking over from. A hostile or worldly identity may emerge to deal with a situation that the principal personality didn't feel equipped to handle. Angry and depressed are the two most common dispositions of alter personalities.

The degree to which alters have their own characteristics can be striking. Features such as handedness, symptoms of medical illnesses, brain wave patterns, and allergies can all be unique to the different identities. They can encompass different ages, sexes, races, and families of origin.

The primary personality may or may not be aware of all the alters. Usually the alters have proper names, but in some cases they are known by their functions (such as teacher, protector, or observer). It has been reported that a delay of six or seven years is not unusual before patients seek psychiatric assistance.

Events that typically bring DID patients to clinical attention are: finding unfamiliar possessions, having unfamiliar people speak to them as if they are friends, and having memory gaps for significant periods of their personal history.

Fight Club

Fight Club is based on the novel written by Chuck Palahniuk. The main character/narrator Jack (Edward Norton) is a lonely, working-class insomniac whose empty, consumer-driven lifestyle finally becomes too much for him. While there is no particular trauma or crisis, Jack focuses on the meaninglessness of his life during his return flight from a business trip. From this void emerges Tyler Durden (Brad Pitt), who is the antithesis of Jack. Slick, confident, and dangerous, Tyler recruits a cabal of bored, frustrated young men to carry out acts of sabotage against corporate America.

The viewer is unaware that Tyler is a manifestation of Jack's psyche until well into the film. Tyler and Jack appear on the screen simultaneously, which of course wouldn't happen in a real case of DID. The reciprocal awareness between Jack's activities and Tyler's isn't adequately portrayed. Perhaps the most inconsistent aspect of DID in this film is that one of the alters can be removed by some physical means, which Jack does by shooting himself to remove Tyler. Tyler's identity does not reside in a discrete area of Jack's brain, thus it is not possible to make an immediate and complete removal of Tyler's personality.

 The Three Faces of Eve

This movie is based on the book by the same name written by Drs. Corbett Thigpen and Hervey Cleckley. The patient on whom the book was based, Chris Costner Sizemore, wrote a personal account of her illness in a book called *I'm Eve*.

Eve White (Joanne Woodward) is a dowdy, sullen woman who is referred to psychiatrist Dr. Luther (Lee J. Cobb). She had been experiencing splitting headaches, which preceded a "spell" lasting several hours, and for which Eve had no recollection (**amnesia**). After the initial visit with Dr. Luther, Eve has a period of several months where these episodes do not recur. Then one day several dresses and pairs of shoes are delivered to her home, purportedly ordered by Eve. However, she can't recall purchasing these luxuries and her husband Ralph (David White) not only didn't buy them as surprise gifts, but he becomes furious with Eve because the clerk at the store remembers her trying them on before arranging delivery.

When Eve returns to see Dr. Luther, she confides that she has been hearing voices for several months. Further exploration reveals that it is only one voice, and Eve thinks that it might be her own. The prospect of having a mental illness is so upsetting for Eve that she dissociates and an alter emerges, Eve Black. This personality state is aware of everything that happens to Eve White, but does not have the ability to emerge on her own. Eve Black is allergic to her nylons, smokes cigarettes, likes to dance, and is rather flirtatious. None of these traits are shared by Eve White. Eve Black feels that she is gaining strength, and hopes to soon become the dominant personality.

When alters are not the dominant personality, they can gain access to consciousness by causing sensory stimuli that are perceived as **auditory** or **visual hallucinations**. The more hostile or controlling personalities often have more complete memories, so that Eve Black knows everything that happens to Eve White. Eve White, however, is totally unaware of Eve Black. On one occasion, Eve White becomes suicidal, but the pain of one self-inflicted cut on her wrist brings out Eve Black, who acts as the protector and stops the cutting.

Under hypnosis, yet another personality emerges who is more stable than the others but lacks any personal memory and doesn't even have a name. She chooses to call herself Jane, and after her initial appearance comes out on a regular basis. This further confuses Eve White, who is now dominant for even less of the time. Eventually Eve White and Eve Black are reintegrated with Jane, whose memories are returned, and after two years is reported to have no further episodes of dissociation.

Sybil

This movie is based on the novel written by Flora Rheta Schreiber. It was originally a TV movie with a running time of 198 minutes. Edited versions with run times of 122 and 132 minutes are available for sale and rental. Sybil (Sally Field) is a young woman who lives in New York City and is struggling to complete her M.A. She is having increasing difficulty concentrating on her studies, and supports herself by working as a substitute teacher.

In the opening scene of the edited version, Sybil is distracted by the squeaking of a swing as a white-haired woman pushes her grandchild. Sybil has a flashback to an episode of abuse from her childhood where she was bound and raised by a winch. The sound of a swing triggers this memory. Sybil disconnects from her surroundings for a few seconds and has to ask a woman near her to repeat what she had just said.

As Sybil walks closer to the white-haired woman and the swing, she has a more prolonged dissociative episode. She emerges from it several minutes later wading in a pond and mumbling to herself. After returning home, the sound of a piano playing torments her to the point where she again dissociates and is brought back to reality when she pushes her hand through a window and cuts her wrist on the shards.

At the hospital, Dr. Cornelia Wilbur (Joanne Woodward) examines Sybil and tests her vision. Sybil speaks in a little girl's voice and has both tunnel vision and poor acuity. When the "little girl voice" is addressed by Dr. Wilbur, Sybil snaps out of it, changing her voice and demeanor, as well as regaining normal vision. The smell of disinfectant causes yet another episode of lost time from which Sybil emerges in the private office of Dr. Cornelia Wilbur, who now recognizes that Sybil has DID. At one point, Sybil reveals that there is a two year period for which she has no recollection.

Soon, other personalities begin to emerge:
- Vicky — age 13, speaks French and exudes confidence
- Peggy — age 9, attention-seeking and sulky
- Mary — older woman; thinks she's in heaven
- Marsha — focused on committing suicide
- Vanessa — sings and plays the piano

In contrast to the flamboyant identities that emerge during the film, Sybil is quiet, shy, sullen, and afraid of interacting with others. The alters are correctly identified early in the film as being different aspects of Sybil, as opposed to being completely unrelated. DID is a failure to integrate the various aspects of memory, identity, and consciousness. Together, Sybil's alters contain all of her memories, abilities, and social skills. An appropriate metaphor for the arrangement of Sybil's alters is that they were developed or recruited, much like the various implements on a Swiss Army knife. The alters have specific abilities or functions that helped Sybil survive the prolonged and repeated abusive situations that she faced as a child. Vicky makes calls to Dr. Wilbur when Sybil is in trouble, and also makes sure that she keeps her appointments. Vanessa is the one who is confident enough to go out on a date with Richard (Brad Davis) when Sybil is too afraid to leave her apartment.

Sybil shifts seamlessly between personality states, usually in response to either stimuli that remind her of her horrendous history of abuse, or due to the questions or clarifications arising out of her interviews with Dr. Wilbur. Common clues to shifts in personality states are: blinking, changing facial expression or voice, or an interruption in train of thought. In her therapy sessions, Sybil recounts not only the events from her past, but also the emotions that accompanied them. This process is called **abreaction**. Where *The Three Faces of Eve* depicted more of an episodic course of DID, *Sybil* demonstrates a continuous cycling between up to 17 distinct personality states.

Dissociative Fugue

Understanding the Condition

This condition, previously called **psychogenic fugue**, involves sudden, unexpected travel away from one's usual daily routine, coupled with an inability to recall important personal information. Fugues states are usually caused by an overwhelmingly stressful or traumatic event. Wars, accidents, and natural disasters are common precipitating events.

Dissociative fugues are thought to affect around 0.2% of the general population. This condition is more common during time of upheaval or calamity. Fugue states can occur at any age, but most cases are reported in adults. Men and women have been reported to be affected in equal numbers.

In some instances, patients with dissociative fugue travel for periods of several months, establish new residences, and engage in well-integrated social practices that are not indicative of the presence of a mental disorder.

Making the Diagnosis

Dissociative fugue is diagnosed when the following are present:

i.   *Sudden, unplanned travel away from home or one's customary place of work*
ii. *The unplanned travel is accompanied by an inability to recall one's past*
iii. *Confusion about personal identity is present*
iv. *Partial or complete assumption of a new identity*

Dissociative fugue differs from DID in that during fugue states people are confused about who they are and their new identity is usually incomplete. In DID, each alter has a distinct identity, and a clear but fragmented memory of events. In fugue states people do not cycle through various identities, and usually do not behave in a way that draws attention to themselves.

Paris, Texas

Travis (Harry Dean Stanton) disappeared into the night and wasn't heard from for over four years (**sudden, unplanned travel away from home**). After trudging northward from Mexico, he collapses from heat exhaustion in a south Texas gas station. Aside from a dusty suit and baseball hat, his few possessions contain a contact number for his brother Walt (Dean Stockwell). Walt immediately leaves from California to reunite with Travis, but the reception he receives is anything but encouraging.

Travis is mute, intent on continuing his journey, and indifferent to everyone around him. He seems to understand Walt's requests and generally cooperates with them but takes a considerable amount of time to answer questions. When Travis does speak, he says that he wants to go to Paris, Texas but can't remember why. There are significant gaps in Travis' personal memory. He forgets things like his mother's maiden name, sister-in-law's name, and a vacation that he took with his wife Jane (Nastassja Kinski) and son Hunter (Hunter Carson). On this basis, Travis meets the criterion for **unplanned travel accompanied by an inability to recall one's past**. Because of Travis' mutism, it is difficult to determine if he is confused about his identity when he is reunited with Walt. The film also does not reveal if Travis assumed a different identity when he was in Mexico, or why he decided to return to the U.S.

Travis eventually finds Jane and tells her what happened. He became morbidly jealous of her and abused alcohol to deal with his feelings. One night he tied her up inside their trailer to prevent her from leaving. A fire started and Travis barely escaped, throwing himself on the wet ground to douse the flames. He didn't look back at the fire and just started to run. The aspects of this portrayal that make it less than ideal are the unknowns listed above, as well as Travis' alcohol abuse, which could cause some of his dissociative experiences.

Nurse Betty

Betty Sizemore (Renée Zellweger) is a waitress in a small town in Kansas. Her husband Del (Aaron Eckhart), finding that the used car business isn't profitable enough, unwittingly tries to sell stolen drugs back to the organization from where they were taken. Two assassins are sent to recover the goods, and in the process Del is murdered in his own home in front of Betty.

Betty is a devotee of a soap opera, and is enamored of one of its stars, Dr. David Ravell (Greg Kinnear). Overwhelmed by the brutal slaying of her husband, Betty almost instantly develops amnesia. She psychologically replaces the loss of her husband with the latest plot twist in the soap opera, which becomes her new reality. She is correctly diagnosed at the police station as being in a dissociative state, and at this point in the film would be diagnosed with **dissociative amnesia** (see next page). Betty recognizes that something has gone wrong in her marriage, and the day after Del's death she writes him a letter announcing their separation. Betty then heads off to Hollywood to help her beloved Dr. Ravell through his crisis.

Betty now believes that she is both a nurse and Dr. Ravell's ex-fiancée. With her **unexpected travel away from home** and **assumption of a new identity**, she meets the criteria for a dissociative fugue. She still identifies herself as Betty Sizemore, states that she hails from Kansas, and that she was married to Del. Through a string of coincidences, Betty actually gets to meet Dr. David Ravell, or more precisely, the actor who plays that role. She so impresses him with her earnestness and persistence that he gets her a small part on the show. Betty becomes overwhelmed, botches her lines, and can't continue. The tirade directed at her by the Dr. Ravell character is so stressful that she snaps out of her dissociative state and her memory returns. This depiction is accurate in that recovery from fugue states tends to be spontaneous and rapid.

Dissociative Amnesia

This condition is the inability to recall important personal information, usually as a result of a traumatic experience. The memory loss can involve either a single gap or series of gaps and is in excess of what would be expected by ordinary forgetfulness. The time period of events for which the person is amnestic can range from minutes to years. The amnestic episodes themselves last for a variable period of time, with the majority reported as lasting less than one week. The onset of amnesia is usually abrupt, and patients are often aware that they've lost their memories.

Depersonalization Disorder

This condition involves persistent or recurrent experiences of feeling detached from either one's body or thought processes. Common descriptions of depersonalization are that people feel as if they are automatons or are in a dream, often being an external observer to their thought processes or bodies. Depersonalization itself is not an uncommon phenomenon. It can occur in people without a psychiatric illness, as a result of substance use, or in conjunction with other conditions such as schizophrenia, panic disorder, or PTSD.

No Movie Examples Available

161

Movie	Feature/Diagnosis
Fight Club	Amnesia; Two or more distinct identities are present who recurrently take control of the person's behavior (DID)
Nurse Betty	Amnesia; Confusion about personal identity; partial or complete assumption of a new identity; Unplanned travel from home or place of work that is accompanied by an inability to recall one's past (Dissociative Fugue)
Paris, Texas	Amnesia; Confusion About personal identity; Unplanned travel from home or place of work that is accompanied by an inability to recall one's past (Dissociative Fugue)
Sybil	Amnesia; Two or more distinct identities are present who recurrently take control of the person's behavior (DID)
The Three Faces of Eve	Amnesia; Two or more distinct identities are present who recurrently take control of the person's behavior (DID)

Chapter 11

Sexual
and
Gender Identity
Disorders

Sexual Dysfunctions

Sexual dysfunctions include disturbances in sexual response or pain associated with intercourse. A list of these disorders is as follows:

Sexual Desire Disorders
- Hypoactive Sexual Desire Disorder
- Sexual Aversion Disorder

Sexual Arousal Disorders
- Female Sexual Arousal Disorder
- Male Erectile Disorder

Orgasmic Disorders
- Female Orgasmic Disorder
- Male Orgasmic Disorder
- Premature Ejaculation

Sexual Pain Disorders
- Dyspareunia — genital pain associated with sexual intercourse; can occur in males and females
- Vaginismus — involuntary spasm of the muscles of the vagina that interferes with sexual intercourse

These disorders are further subdivided into the following types:
- Lifelong type
- Acquired type
- Generalized type
- Situational type

Sexual dysfunction can be due to psychological factors alone, or a mixture of both psychological and medical reasons.

A catalogue of movie examples and a discussion of sexual dysfunctions are not included in this chapter for two reasons: these conditions are relatively self-explanatory, and examples are difficult to find in mainstream commercial films.

Paraphilias

Literally translated from Greek, paraphilia means "beside love." Paraphilias are defined as recurrent, intense sexually arousing fantasies, urges, or behaviors generally involving:
- Inanimate objects
- A non-consenting partner
- The suffering and /or humiliation of one's self or one's partner.

In order for a particular sexual activity to qualify as a paraphilia, the following conditions need to be met:
- The behavior is considered atypical for the person's culture
- A non-consenting person may be harmed by the activity
- Legal consequences result from the paraphilic interest
- The activity leads to clinically significant distress or impairment (this applies to some of these conditions)

If these conditions are not met, then the behavior is called **non-pathological use of sexual fantasies, behaviors, or objects as a stimulus for sexual excitement**. Many people with paraphilic interests are not troubled by their urges or practices. The only difficulties they encounter stem from the disapproval of others. Considerable effort and expense may be invested into paraphilic interests, such as collecting books, pictures, videos, articles of clothing, etc. A spectrum of necessity for the paraphilic item or situation for sexual gratification exists. In other words, some people are able to engage in conventional sexual activities and still derive pleasure, yet have a desire for their paraphlia. At the other end of the spectrum are those who are unable to become interested in anything but their preferred activity. Most people with paraphilias do not come to medical attention. Indulging interests such as exhibitionism or pedophilia brings people into contact with the legal system and from there possible referral for treatment of these conditions. Accurate statistics have proven to be elusive, though it is known that the great majority of people with paraphilias are male.

Exhibitionism

Exhibitionism is the exposure of one's genitals to an unsuspecting stranger. This condition is also diagnosed if the person has not acted on these fantasies or urges but is distressed by having them.

The principal goal of exhibitionism is to shock or surprise an unsuspecting stranger. There is considerable sexual excitement in the anticipation of this event. In the majority of cases, exhibitionists do not desire further sexual activity, though in some cases they masturbate in view of the stranger. The patient may later develop a fantasy about what might have happened if the stranger had become sexually aroused.

People who engage in exhibitionism are also called flashers. They are almost exclusively men, and their preferred victims are women.

High Anxiety

Dr. Richard Thorndyke (Mel Brooks) agrees to become the director of a prestigious California psychiatric hospital. His flight to the west coast is a harrowing one for him because he suffers from a fear of heights. Upon landing at Los Angeles International Airport Thorndyke is quickly ushered away by a distinguished looking man (played by Robert Ridgley). This man appears to be acting in an official capacity and for the sake of discretion does not say anything publically to Thorndyke, who follows him into the washroom. Then, the flasher opens his coat and exposes his genitals to the unsuspecting doctor, whose bland response isn't what the perpetrator was expecting.

Exhibitionism and pedophilia are the most common paraphilias. The image of the flasher opening his rain or trench coat is a fairly familiar cinematic portrayal.

Fetishism

Fetishism involves the use of inanimate objects for sexual gratification. The most common fetishes are for women's clothes, particularly lingerie and footwear (shoes and boots). Alone, people with fetishes will masturbate while holding, rubbing, or smelling the object. With a partner, they will usually request that the item is worn or somehow used in the sexual activity. Fetishism is not diagnosed if the item is one that was designed for use in sexual activity (such as sexual aids, lotions, etc.). A movie depiction of fetishism can be seen in *Blue Velvet*, presented on page 171.

Frotteurism

Frotteurism almost always involves males who, while remaining clothed, rub their genitals against women. Less often, the male will try to fondle a woman's breasts or genitals through her clothing. Frottage frequently takes place in crowded areas where the unsuspecting stranger will either be distracted or be too embarrassed to say anything. Probably the most common site for frottage is on public transit systems. Here, the crowding and swaying of the bus or subway car are conducive to this activity. Also, the perpetrator can make a hasty exit if he is discovered.

No Movie Example Available

Pedophilia

Pedophilia is defined in the DSM–IV–TR as a recurrent, intense sexual urge that an adult has towards children age 13 years and younger. This diagnosis is applied to people who are at least sixteen years old and 5 years older than the victim. The gray area in the definition of this disorder involves someone in late adolescence who has an ongoing sexual relationship with a 13-year-old. In these situations, the relative maturity of the younger person and the age difference need to be taken into account.

Pedophiles tend to report a fairly specific attraction to children of a certain gender and age range. Those attracted to girls most often have a preference for 8-to-10-year olds, whereas those attracted to boys seem to prefer victims a couple of years older.

Many pedophiles do not feel guilty or conflicted about their fantasies and actions. For this reason, distress or social/occupational impairment is not required for this diagnosis. Acting on these urges is sufficient grounds alone to make this diagnosis.

Pedophiles arrange many of their activities to indulge their attraction to children. Some coach sports teams, take in foster children, or marry single mothers in order to get access to children. Pedophiles often have a certain routine that they prefer with children. It can range from undressing children to virtually any sexual act, though what is most commonly reported is genital fondling or oral sex. The vast majority of pedophiles are males, and describe themselves as heterosexual.

The DSM–IV–TR subdivides pedophilia into the following types:
* Sexually attracted to males
* Sexually attracted to females
* Sexually attracted to both
* Limited to incest
* Exclusive type (desire sex with children only)
* Non-exclusive type (desire children and adults)

The Man Without A Face

Justin McLeod (Mel Gibson) was a teacher who became severely disfigured by burns he received in a car accident. After being dismissed from his job, he moved to a small Maine town to lead a solitary existence. Many rumors circulate about him, one being that he sexually abused a former student. McLeod befriends Chuck (Nick Stahl), a fatherless boy who needs tutoring for a military academy entrance exam. One night Chuck's life falls apart when he learns the true fate of his father and he runs to McLeod's house in a fit of despair. McLeod doesn't have a phone, and when the sheriff finds that Chuck spent the night, suspicions of pedophilia soon follow. McLeod is not a pedophile, but the town is intent on labeling him as one because this situation is typical for how a pedophilic relationship begins.

Sliver

In this movie, all the apartments in a building are wired for sound and video by voyeuristic landlord, Zeke Hawkins (William Baldwin). Hawkins spends much of his time watching and recording the activities of his tenants. In one of the apartments lives Mr. Ballinger (Matthew Faison), his new wife, and step-daughter Joanie (Marne Patterson). In a rather unsettling scene, Joanie discloses to her mother that her step-father has been molesting her. For reasons that are not disclosed in the film, Mrs. Ballinger (Robin Groves) chooses to ignore Joanie's cry for help. Mrs. Ballinger tells Joanie that her step-father is a hard-working man and that she won't hear anything negative about him. Hawkins confirms to his girlfriend Carly (Sharon Stone), who was made aware of the secret cameras, that Ballinger does indeed have his hands *"all over the girl every chance he gets."* There is a telling scene where Ballinger, Joanie, and Carly all get on the same elevator after Carly is made aware of the abuse. Ballinger is squeezing Joanie's hand as if to silence or control her. Joanie looks at Carly with a pleading look, as if she is telepathically asking for help, and Carly glares at Ballinger.

169

Sexual Masochism

The term **masochism** derives from the writings of Leopold von Sacher Masoch (1836—1895). He was an Austrian novelist whose works contained characters who derived sexual pleasure from being hurt, abused, or humiliated. When the term is used in a sexual context it is sometimes called **erotogenic** or **primary masochism**. Masochistic behavior itself is common and not necessarily pathological. Suffering for some greater gain, or for the benefit of others, is a key component of **altruism**.

Sexual masochism involves recurrent, intense, and arousing fantasies, urges or behaviors of being humiliated, beaten, bound, or otherwise made to suffer. Some common masochistic activities include: bondage, blindfolds, whipping, electric shocks, piercing, spanking, beating, being forced to stay in a cage and imitate an animal, etc. Sexual masochism can become lethal when it involves oxygen-depriving activities such as self-strangulation or the use of inhalants with a bag or mask.

Sexual Sadism

The term **sadism** is named after the French writer Marquis de Sade (1740—1814). It was initially used to refer to people who derived erotic pleasure from inflicting pain on others. In a more generalized sense, sadistic behavior involves the enjoyment of inflicting physical violence, pain, humiliation, or harsh discipline on others.

The essence of sexual sadism is that the suffering of the victim is erotically stimulating. When a partner voluntarily engages in sadistic behavior it is commonly referred to as "S&M" or **sadomasochism**. In many cases however, the partner does not participate willingly, and can be subjected to sexual assault, torture, stabbing, mutilation, or even killed. The majority of sexual sadists are thought to increase the severity of their behaviors over time until they are apprehended by the police.

8 mm

Tom Welles (Nicholas Cage) is a private detective hired by the wife of a recently deceased business tycoon. In this man's private safe was found a grainy 8mm film in which a teenage girl is viciously assaulted and then stabbed to death — a so-called "snuff film." The widow is so distraught that she hires Welles to investigate whether or not the film is authentic.

Welles is able to establish the girl's identity and that she went to Hollywood with the hope of becoming an actress. While searching for leads about her activities prior to her death, Welles gains access to black market pornography videos that generally contain depictions of sexual sadism. While the scenes of these videos are displayed briefly, the victims are usually bound and gagged, and subjected to the whims of a leather-bound dominator or dominatrix.

Welles eventually tracks down the maker of the film, Dino Velvet (Peter Stormare) and the masked on-screen sadist, a man known as Machine (Christopher Bauer). This film turns out to be authentic, which enrages Welles to the point where he avenges the girl's death. In the fight sequence towards the end of the film, Machine offers this explanation for his paraphilia after removing his mask, *"What'd you expect — a monster? My name's George, you probably knew that already. Can't get your mind around it, huh? I don't have any answers to give. Nothing I can say that's going to make you sleep easier at night. I wasn't beaten. I wasn't molested. Mommy didn't abuse me. Daddy didn't rape me. I'm only what I am, and that's all there is to it. There's no mystery — the things I do, I do them because I like them. Because I want to. . ."*

Blue Velvet

This movie contains some scenes which are very rich in their psychiatric content. Jeffrey Beaumont (Kyle MacLachlan) becomes intrigued with the unusual events in his town and decides to become an amateur detective. His first step is to sneak into the apartment of Dorothy Vallens (Isabella Rosellini). He makes a noise while hiding in the closet, and Dorothy arms herself with a knife and then orders him to explain what he is doing. Thus begins a series of three erotic couplings that portray a variety of paraphilias.

In the first portrayal, Dorothy orders Jeffrey to strip at knifepoint. She insists that he not look at her as she kneels in front of him with the intention of performing fellatio — while she is still holding the knife. Dorothy is alternating between being dominant/sadistic and submissive/masochistic in this scene.

Dorothy and Jeffrey are interrupted by the unexpected arrival of Frank Booth, who is an aggressive sadist. He takes immediate control over Dorothy by yelling at her and insulting her. They then begin a ritualized scenario where she sits in front of Booth and opens her night gown. Booth focuses primarily on her vagina, a paraphilia called **partialism** where sexual activity is concentrated on one part of the body. When Dorothy looks at Booth directly, he admonishes her verbally and then punches her. It is after the first blow that Dorothy appears to take any pleasure in the encounter. She then places a swatch cut out from her blue velvet robe in Booth's mouth, illustrating **fetishism**. Booth then engages in **infantilism** (a type of masochism) where he wants to be called "baby" to Dorothy's "mommy."

After Booth leaves, Dorothy becomes needy and submissive and seeks solace from Jeffrey (who watched everything from the closet). As their intimacy is resumed, Dorothy asks and literally begs Jeffrey to hit her. It is only at this point that the viewer is made aware of the extent of her masochistic desires. In this encounter, Jeffrey is unable to bring himself to strike Dorothy and she is unwilling to proceed. In a later meeting, Dorothy cajoles, taunts, and entices Jeffrey into striking her, at which point their lovemaking reaches a new level of intensity.

Quills

Quills is a fictionalized account of the last few months of the life of Marquis de Sade. It takes place in Napoleonic France and when the movie begins, de Sade has already been imprisoned and spends his time writing lewd novels that have a distinctly sadistic tone. Unfortunately, the film doesn't deal with how de Sade earned his reputation, and the brief passages quoted are not directly from his writings.

 The Story of O/Histoire d'O

Dominique Aury wrote this novel under the pen name Pauline Réage. O (Corrine Clery) is a woman who, at the beginning of the movie, is in love with Rene (Udo Kier). To prove her devotion to him, she agrees to enter a countryside mansion where she is trained in the practices of sexual submission. O is given the option to leave the mansion at any time, but chooses to subject herself to a variety of masochistic treatments, such as humiliation, bondage, whipping, forced silence, and punishment for making eye contact with any men (who would all qualify as being sadists).

After O's training is complete, she is "given" by Rene to Sir Stephen (Anthony Steel) to settle a debt. Sir Stephen is also a sadist who requests that O pierce her genitalia, become branded, and submit to him completely. This depiction is interesting in the way that O, through being entirely submissive, gains power over the men around her. She is eventually put in the position of engaging in sadistic behavior herself and later manipulates another woman into entering submissiveness training. In the last scene of the movie, O requests that Sir Stephen demonstrate his love for her by submitting to some of the things that he requested of her. When he agrees, she burns the back of his hand with a cigarette holder, which makes the letter 'O.' What makes this portrayal accurate is that the roles of sadist and masochist can alternate between partners, hence the use of the term **sadomasochism** to describe this type of fetish.

173

Transvestic Fetishism

Also known as **cross dressing**, this condition involves the recurrent, sexually arousing fantasy, urge, or behavior of a male to dress in women's attire. The articles of clothing can range from a single item (such as lingerie) worn under masculine attire to dressing entirely as a woman, including make-up. Transvestic fetishism has been described only in heterosexual men, and needs to be distinguished from **gender identity disorder** (presented later in this chapter). In pure transvestic fetishism, men are comfortable with their gender and do not want it altered.

There are some men with transvestic fetishism who are not entirely comfortable with their gender, and a specifier called "with gender dysphoria" is added to the diagnosis in these situations. In some men, gender dysphoria emerges over time as they get increasingly comfortable in women's attire. Apart from cross dressing, the behavior and mannerisms of men with transvestic fetishism is unremarkably masculine. Some men wear items of clothing alone at home, while others who can imitate women more completely venture out to clubs or bars.

To Wong Foo: Thanks For Everything! Julie Newmar

The title of this movie stems from a signed picture that Julie Newmar gave to a restaurateur. This movie starts with a New York City drag queen contest. Miss Vida Boheme (Patrick Swayze) and Miss Noxeema Jackson (Wesley Snipes) tie for the title and are given the chance to compete in the Drag Queen USA Contest. When they decide to invite Miss Chi Chi Rodriquez (John Leguizamo) along on the journey, Noxeema explains the following to him, *"When a straight man puts on a dress and gets his sexual kicks, he's a transvestite. When a man is a woman trapped in a man's body and he has that little operation, he is a transsexual. When a gay man has way too much fashion sense for one gender, he is a drag queen."* Because the main characters are homosexual, are

174

comfortable being men, and do not cross dress for the purpose of sexual pleasure, they do not meet the criteria for transvestic fetishism.

Just Like A Woman

This movie is based on the novel *Geraldine* written by Monica Jay. Gerald Tilson is an American investment banker working in England. He is handsome, successful, and both a husband and father. His wife and children return early from a trip and Gerald scrambles to get home before they do, but he arrives several minutes too late. Gerald's wife discovers many articles of women's clothing — particularly lingerie — in their home. She assumes that Gerald is having an affair and immediately decides to end their marriage without hearing his explanation.

Gerald has transvestic fetishism, and the clothes are his. He has dressed up as a woman for all of his life but hasn't told his wife and cannot bring himself to tell her even though it might save his marriage. Gerald moves into a boarding home run by Monica (Julie Walters). One evening Monica notices a woman visiting Gerald's apartment and asks him about her.

Gerald and Monica start a romance that seems doomed to fail because a large part of his sexuality is expressed by dressing up as Geraldine, his female identity. He decides to trust Monica with his transvestic interests, and after a short period of adjustment, she accepts Gerald's practices and actually finds it stimulating. Gerald makes it clear in the film that he is strictly heterosexual, and has no difficulty being intimate with Monica when he is able to dress according to his desires. Other than the fact that he plucks his eyebrows and paints his toenails, there is nothing obviously effeminate about him. Gerald regularly visits a dinner club that caters to a clientele of transvestites. Monica accompanies him and is surprised to learn how many men actually share this interest. She is equally surprised to find supportive wives at the restaurant.

Voyeurism

The word voyeur stems from the French verb meaning "to see." Voyeurs, also known as "Peeping Toms" have the recurrent fantasy, urge, or behavior of watching an unsuspecting person disrobe or engage in sexual activity. Voyeurs may engage in masturbation while watching the person, or may do so later after developing a fantasy about what might have happened. In most instances, sexual contact with the observed person is not pursued.

 ## Sliver

The title of this movie refers to the tall, thin high-rise apartment buildings that crop up in big cities. Carly Norris (Sharon Stone) is a New York City book editor who is approved for an apartment in a sliver building so effortlessly that it surprises her. What Carly doesn't realize at the time she moves in is that the building is owned by one of the other tenants, Zeke Hawkins (William Baldwin). Zeke is a voyeur's voyeur, and instead of hoping for a fortuitous glimpse at people's private lives, Zeke has hidden cameras and microphones in each apartment. He spends much of his time in a custom-built, multi-million dollar control room where he monitors and records other tenants' activities. Zeke anonymously leaves a telescope in Carly's apartment, and is delighted to watch her immediately start to scan the other apartment buildings for interesting activities. Carly holds a cocktail party for her co-workers, one of whom delights in using the telescope to find a couple making love with the lights on and curtains open. Many of the guests at the party wait their turn to watch the amorous couple. At the end of the evening, Carly has another look at the couple, and is surprised to find that they are sitting in the nude on their bed scanning other apartment buildings with their own telescope. As a relationship develops between Zeke and Carly, she is eventually given access to his video control room, and after her initial surprise, begins to enjoy the voyeuristic view she has of other people's lives.

Gender Identity Disorder

There are two key aspects to diagnosing this condition:
- A strong and persistent cross-gender identification
- Persistent discomfort with one's assigned sex

Gender identity disorder (GID) in males is manifested as a preoccupation with typically feminine activities. Boys with this condition prefer to wear girl's clothes and engage in traditionally feminine games and pastimes. They have a distinct aversion to activities typical for other boys, such as competitive sports or games with physical contact. Some believe that when they grow up, they will lose their penis and develop breasts and a vagina. Similarly, girls with GID prefer traditionally masculine activities. They dress as boys, have masculine mannerisms, and may ask to be called by a boy's name.

Adults with this disorder often feel tortured by having to live life according to their biological sex. They have an intense desire to acquire the physical characteristics of, and function in society as, the other sex. Many pass convincingly in public as the other sex. Where deemed appropriate, cosmetic surgery, hormone treatments, and sexual reassignment surgery (SRS) are employed to varying degrees to help people with GID make this transition.

GID is usually identified in children between the ages of 2 to 4 years, though it can develop in adolescence or early adulthood. Accurate statistics have been difficult to obtain, but estimates indicate that 1/30,000 males and 1/100,000 females seek SRS.

The DSM-IV-TR includes the following specifiers for GID:
- Sexually attracted to males
- Sexually attracted to both
- Sexually attracted to females
- Sexually attracted to neither

Significant percentages of males with GID fall into all four of the above categories, while almost all women with this condition are sexually attracted to females.

Boys Don't Cry

Hilary Swank won an Academy Award for her portrayal of Teena Brandon, a woman who had GID. The movie begins with Teena already having made her transition to living as a man. She reverses her name and is known as "Brandon Teena" for much of the movie. She reveals little of her past, but says at one point that she was a "girl," then a "boy-girl," and finally decided that she was meant to be a man and changed her appearance.

It is only under dire circumstances that Brandon admits that she is a genetic female. In order to effect the appearance of a man, Brandon has her hair cut in a masculine fashion, binds her breasts with a large tension bandage, and places a sock in the crotch of her jeans to simulate the male anatomy. She wears no make-up, speaks in a passable male voice, and tries to engage in masculine activities such as "surfing" on the back of a pick-up truck.

Brandon's sexual orientation is that she is decidedly attracted to females, and in the short time span that the movie covers has a number of women interested in her. After her evening with a young woman at a roller-skating rink, Brandon kisses her date goodnight. At some point soon after, Brandon is discovered to be a genetic female and is hotly accused of being a lesbian by a group of young men. In Brandon's self-view, she is a man attracted to women, not a woman attracted to women. Until she was sexually abused towards the end of the film, Brandon had not had intercourse with a man.

Brandon is able to function convincingly as a man for quite a span of time. She runs into some difficulty when she has her period and needs to wash the blood from her pants and steal some tampons. She also has intercourse with her love interest Lana (Chloë Sevigny) by not letting Lana touch certain parts of her body and by using an artificial penis that was attached to her with straps. Brandon was considering hormone treatments and SRS but was unable to afford them.

The Adventures of Priscilla, Queen of the Desert

In this Australian film, Priscilla is the name given to the bus used by three performers whose act consists of lip syncing and choreographing a variety of disco hits. The trio consists of Tick (Hugo Weaving), Adam (Guy Pearce), and Bernadette (Terence Stamp). Adam is a gay man, Tick is bisexual, and Bernadette is a transsexual.

Bernadette, formerly Ralph, is shown in a flashback sequence switching Christmas presents with his sister so that he could play with the doll that was intended for her. He then became a she after having SRS (which he calls "the chop") and takes hormones to develop breasts and some feminine sexual characteristics. Bernadette clearly defines herself as a woman, and seeks to engage in heterosexual relationships with men. She expects to be treated like a lady, and accepts the flowers and kind attention of a rugged outback dweller named Bob (Bill Hunter). Throughout the film, Adam and Tick are seen in a variety of outfits, ranging from regular apparel to outlandish show costumes. In keeping with her preferred gender, Bernadette always appears as a woman, wearing a wig, make-up, and feminine clothing.

The Crying Game

Dil (Jaye Davidson) is a genetic male living as a woman in London, England. She works as a hairdresser, dresses and speaks as a woman, and is so convincing that Fergus (Stephen Rea) falls for her. Dil does not appear to be taking hormones and has not had SRS. Dil clearly meets the DSM-IV-TR criterion for strong and persistent cross-gender identification. During the film however, she does not mention anything about being uncomfortable with her sex or expressing a sense of inappropriateness about her gender the way that Brandon Teena and Bernadette do in the other films presented in this section.

Movie	Feature/Diagnosis
High Anxiety	Exhibitionism
Blue Velvet	Fetishism, Sexual Masochism and Sexual Sadism
The Man Without A Face	Pedophilia
Sliver	Pedophilia, Voyeurism
8 mm	Sexual Masochism and Sexual Sadism
Quills	Sexual Sadism
The Story of O/ Histoire d'O	Sexual Masochism and Sexual Sadism
To Wong Foo: Thanks for Everything! Julie Newmar	Transvestic Fetishism
Just Like a Woman	Transvestic Fetishism
Boys Don't Cry	Gender Identity Disorder
The Adventures of Priscilla, Queen of the Desert	Gender Identity Disorder
The Crying Game	Gender Identity Disorder

Chapter 12

Eating Disorders

Anorexia Nervosa

Understanding the Condition

Anorexia nervosa (AN) is a refusal to maintain a generally accepted minimum weight. The term anorexia itself is a misnomer because people with this disorder rarely lose their appetite. The weight loss is achieved primarily through restricting food intake, though other means are used as well.

Other psychiatric symptoms that commonly occur along with AN are:
- Mood changes (depression, irritability)
- Sleep changes (insomnia)
- Social withdrawal and diminished libido
- Obsessive-compulsive behaviors

Symptoms of depression often accompany starvation, and it can be difficult to determine whether a separate diagnosis is warranted. There are a variety of serious medical consequences that accompany starvation, and AN carries with it a significant risk for a number of complications, such as anemia, changes in heart function, and hormone irregularities.

AN is more prevalent in industrialized nations. It is thought that cultural factors such an idealized body shape play a role in the development of this disorder. AN is present in 0.5% of the population. It is far more prevalent in females, with a gender ratio of 10:1. AN also appears to be more prevalent in women who are in certain fields of endeavor, such as gymnastics, ballet dancing, and fashion modeling.

AN usually begins in females between the ages of 14 to 18 years. In some instances, a stressful life event or comment about someone's physique has been associated with the onset of this illness. While the course and outcome of AN is variable, there are studies that have shown up to 15% of sufferers die from the medical complications of this illness.

Making the Diagnosis

AN is diagnosed when the following criteria are present:

i. *Refusal to maintain body weight at least at a minimally expected level (85% of that expected for age and height)*

ii. *Intense fear of becoming fat despite being underweight*

iii. *Distortion in body image such that the person perceives him or herself to be overweight*

iv. *Undue influence of body shape on self-evaluation*

v. *Denial of the serious medical consequences of being underweight*

vi. *Absence of at least three consecutive menstrual cycles (in women who have begun menstruating)*

The DSM-IV-TR further defines the following subtypes of AD:

- **Binge-Eating/Purging Type** (eat in binges and then engages in purging behaviors such as laxative abuse)
- **Restricting Type** (control weight only through reducing intake)

Associated Features

- In order to determine what is a normal weight, pediatric growth charts or life insurance tables are routinely used
- A method of determining a normal weight is **body mass index (BMI)** — weight in kilograms (kg) is divided by height in meters (m) squared; the cutoff is 17.5 kg/m²
- A certain minimum weight and proportion of fat in the female body is necessary for production of the hormones that regulate the menstrual cycle; the body turns this mechanism off in order to prevent further blood loss
- AN has a number of features in common with OCD, but patients with the latter condition do not exhibit the perceptual distortions and denial of medical consequences
- Many patients with AN have obsessive-compulsive personality traits: perfectionism, a strong desire to control their surroundings, and restricted expression of emotions
- In spite of their state of emaciation, anorectic patients maintain a strong interest in food, and will often cook, exchange recipes, work in food preparation areas, etc.

183

The Best Little Girl in the World

This made-for-TV movie is commercially available from a variety of sources and is based on the novel by the same name written by Steven Levenkron. Casey Powell (Jennifer Jason Leigh) is a 17-year-old high school student who at the beginning of the film appears to be bright and well adjusted. She is in good health, exercises regularly, and as we find out later in the film, weighs 108 lbs.

There are a number of factors that influence Casey to focus on her weight. One of her high school friends is being persuaded by her mother to lose five pounds, the reward for which will be a gorgeous dress selected directly from a fashion magazine. Casey's ballet instructor, Madame Seurat (Vivica Lindfors), praises her abilities but advises her to lose a bit of weight if she is serious about dancing. As Casey leaves the studio, Madame Seurat reminds her to not drink any milkshakes. Casey buys the same fashion magazine as her friend and begins to focus on the thinness of the models, and soon after starts to diet and exercise.

Casey constantly evaluates her appearance in a full-length mirror that hangs behind her bedroom door. She has a bathroom to herself and begins to vomit there regularly without being detected. She **drastically reduces her food intake** and begins to **exercise obsessively**, and in one scene is doing an abdominal work-out at 3:30 am.

By Thanksgiving, Casey has starved herself down to 84 pounds. She looks haggard, is morose, and is failing three courses in school. Though her family is aware of her decreased food intake, Casey dresses in layers to disguise her state of emaciation, which is a common thing for anorectics to do. When Casey's sister catches a glimpse of her body, she recoils and immediately tells their parents what is going on. Casey is then taken to Dr. Garrett (David Spielberg) for a physical examination.

Dr. Garrett asks Casey about her **periods** and learns that she hasn't had one for almost two months. He also notes that she has low blood pressure, which is a common complication of AN. Casey **denies that there is anything wrong with her** and thinks that she still has a few flabby spots. She grudgingly agrees to see a psychologist, but her motivation is more to get her parents off her back than any real acknowledgment of a problem.

Her parents become very concerned and search Casey's room. They find a cornucopia of medications that promote weight loss, particularly diet pills and laxatives. In another scene, Casey looks at herself in the mirror and sees a grossly distorted image of herself as being obese, which is a good example of the **perceptual disturbances** that accompany AN. Casey still has an interest in food and in one scene cooks breakfast for her family.

Casey persists with her regimen of dieting and weight loss to the point where she faints and requires hospitalization. Initially only an IV is started, which Casey rips out before going AWOL. She is still so weak that she passes out again on the hospital grounds. Even after she is returned to the ward, she refuses to eat and eventually requires the surgical insertion of a tube into her neck for intravenous nutrition. To reduce the effectiveness of this intervention, she exercises as often as she can.

As her illness progresses, Casey becomes sullen and withdrawn, giving a good portrayal of the **mood changes** accompanying AN. There is also a good depiction of **obsessive-compulsive features** in one of Casey's sessions with her psychologist, Dr. Clay Orlovsky (Jason Miller). Casey has a ritual where she prevents food from touching her lips directly. Later she admits to never sitting on a toilet seat for fear of getting some communicable disease.

This movie provides an excellent overall portrayal of the features and medical complications of AN. Casey does not binge, but she does purge, so neither of the subtypes is accurately depicted.

Dying to Dance

After dancing up a storm, Alyssa Lennox (Kimberly McCullough) gets voted prom queen and in the same week receives an offer to audition for a major ballet company. She barely makes the cut, and in the process is advised to work at improving her technique and to trim five pounds off her already svelte 104 lb. frame.

Alyssa does both, immersing herself in practices and putting herself on a **strict diet**, which consists mostly of vegetables. One of the other dancers suggests that Alyssa should start smoking as a means of **appetite suppression**. She resists, but does try a herbal remedy and later attempts to buy amphetamines.

In several scenes, Alyssa cuts her food into very small pieces. This is a trick often employed by anorectics to give the illusion that they have consumed more food than they actually have. Other ploys include playing with their food, hiding it in their clothing, and feeding it to the dog.

This movie presents the viewer with a dilemma regarding Alyssa's eating and exercise pattern. Is she just a determined young dancer who wants to maximize her chances in the ballet company? She does have a letter from the director encouraging her to lose weight, and most of the other dancers at the initial weigh in were under 100 lbs. Or has Alyssa developed AN and is camouflaging her illness with her devotion to dance?

The answer is found in Alyssa's closet, where her mother is horrified to find many derogatory messages and images about gluttony, clearly indicating a **distorted sense of body image**. Alyssa thinks that the key to success as a dancer is to attain the perfect body shape, but she loses her strength and stamina in this quest. Alyssa eventually requires hospitalization before she can begin recovering. This movie also provides an excellent example of AN, particularly the **restricting type** as there is scant mention of any purging behaviors on Alyssa's part.

For the Love of Nancy

This is a made-for–TV movie and is based on the true life story of Nancy Walsh (Tracey Gold). Nancy's descent into AN is precipitated by the removal of her wisdom teeth, giving her a reason to avoid eating for a prolonged period of time. Over the summer before she is to begin college, Nancy steadily loses weight by restricting her food intake and exercising. She becomes irritable, withdrawn, and downcast, giving a good portrayal of the **mood symptoms** that often accompany AN. In another scene, Nancy tries to scoop off the top layer of fat from a pot of spaghetti sauce and later organizes canned goods according to some arbitrary scheme. Both of these activities are good depictions of the **obsessive-compulsive traits** that can be seen in anorectic patients.

Nancy eventually ends up starving herself to the point where she requires hospitalization. She is past the age of 18 and according to the law in her state is able to refuse medical treatment for herself. Her illness progresses to the point where her life is in constant jeopardy and she no longer appears able to make competent decisions about her care. Her father is left with no alternative but to have her declared incapable to make treatment decisions. This involves taking his daughter to court, which would be an emotionally difficult situation for any family.

There is a common theme in each of the three movies in this section, and that is the issue of control. Seemingly caring, well-intentioned parents are depicted as invalidating the wishes of their children. This "I know what's best for my child" belief is nicely illustrated in this film when Nancy's mother (Jill Clayburgh) arbitrarily decides that Nancy should be in a double room in the college dormitory instead of the single room that she clearly wanted. Nancy's mother finds her a *"nice girl from Philadelphia"* as a roommate, and it takes an angry outburst on Nancy's part and the intervention of her father to reverse this arrangement. Such family dynamics are common in patients with AN but are not present in every single case.

Bulimia Nervosa

Understanding the Condition

Bulimia nervosa (BN) involves binge eating and engaging in a variety of methods to compensate for the caloric intake of the food. The DSM-IV-TR defines a **binge** as: *"eating in a discrete period of time an amount of food that is definitely larger than most individuals would eat under similar circumstances."* A binge is considered to last for less than 2 hours.

Compensatory behaviors are varied and involve four main activities:
- Preventing digestion — self-induced vomiting either manually or with medication
- Speeding up metabolism — abuse of thyroid medication
- Hastening transit time in the digestive system — laxatives and enemas
- Averaging out intake — fasting and exercise are also used to balance out the caloric intake from binge eating; amphetamines may also be taken because of their appetite suppressing effects

Patients with BN frequently also suffer from mood, anxiety, and substance abuse disorders. Borderline personality disorder is also a common comorbid condition. Prior to the onset of BN, a significant number of patients had mild-to-moderate obesity.

BN, similar to AN, is more prevalent in industrialized nations. The vast majority of patients (90% or more) are female. BN usually begins in late adolescence or early adulthood. It is present in between 1 and 3% of the population. A significant proportion of women may engage in binge-eating behavior, but do not go on to meet the full criteria for BN. BN typically has a waxing and waning course. The overall prognosis is better than for AN. When purging behaviors (particularly vomiting) are more common, the long-term outcome of this illness appears to be less favorable.

Making the Diagnosis

BN is diagnosed when the following criteria are met:

i. *Engaging in binge-eating behavior*
ii. *Feeling a lack of control over one's eating during the binge*
iii. *Recurrent, inappropriate compensatory behavior*
iv. *Episodes of binge-eating and compensatory behaviors that occur an average of at least twice per week over a 3 month period*
v. *Self-esteem and self-evaluation are strongly influenced by body shape and weight*

The DSM-IV-TR further defines the following subtypes of AD:
- **Purging Type** (engages in self-induced vomiting, misuse of laxatives, diuretics, or enemas)
- **Nonpurging Type**

Associated Features

- Patients with BN range from being slightly underweight to being obese
- The distinction between AN binge-eating/purging type and BN purging type may be only whether the person's body weight is above (BN) or below (AN) the 85th percentile for age and height
- The DSM-IV-TR also lists a condition called **binge-eating disorder** as a consideration for future study; this condition is similar to BN but involves none of the compensatory behaviors listed above
- Binge-eating episodes often occur in isolation to avoid embarrassment over the amount of food being eaten and the rapidity with which it is consumed
- After a binge, feelings of guilt, disgust, or depression are common and often lead to compensatory behaviors which help reverse these emotional states
- Foods selected for binges are often high-calorie substances chosen more for their consistency than nutritional value, such as: cakes, ice cream, pudding, custard, icing, etc.
- Binges can be brought on by stress, feelings of depression, attempts at dieting, and self-criticism

189

A Secret Between Friends/ When Friendship Kills

This is a made-for -TV movie that is available from a variety of commercial sources. Lexi Archer is a new student at a high school, having been forced to relocate by her parent's separation. She is a good athlete and is able to make the school volleyball team. Lexi develops a fast friendship with the team's star player, Jennifer (Marley Shelton). On one occasion when Lexi is visiting Jennifer's house, they "raid the fridge." The scene depicted afterwards is classic for **binge eating**. There are several empty containers of ice cream, cookies, candy, and potato chips that litter the table top — all of them empty or near-empty. The two girls are reclining next to one another on a couch and are clearly uncomfortable because they've consumed too much food, and appear to have been **unable to stop** before they reached that point. Each of them complains about their full stomachs and at his point, Jennifer lets Lexi in on her secret; she **purges** by going to the bathroom to vomit. Jennifer skips merrily out of the bathroom saying that the Romans had the right idea in having vomitoriums near their dining areas, and in doing so gives an excellent portrayal of the **purging type** of BN.

Jennifer demonstrates both the binge-eating and purging behaviors that constitute bulimia nervosa. She maintains a body weight in the normal range throughout the film. While the frequency of her binge/purge activity isn't explicitly portrayed it appears that Jennifer engages in these behaviors regularly. She is quite conscious about her weight and her appearance in general, and in this way meets the criterion for her self-esteem being influenced by her body shape.

When Lexi eventually reveals Jennifer's secret, Jennifer rejects her completely and goes into a rage that is reminiscent of borderline personality disorder. Close to the end of the movie, Jennifer binges with alcohol much the same way she does with food, indicating a lack of control over her oral intake.

Freeway II:
Confessions of a Trickbaby

Crystal (Natasha Lyonne) got her name because her mother was fond of using crank (methamphetamine). At the beginning of the movie, she is sentenced to a lengthy prison term for a variety of crimes including armed robbery and assault. The judge is aware that she has an eating disorder and sends her to a hospital for treatment after which she will be incarcerated.

In the holding cell, the guards are made aware of Crystal's bulimia and supervise her meals. They don't appear to understand that Crystal is a **binge-eater** and will consume food all too readily. They leave her unsupervised in her cell after her meal, where she is so experienced at **purging** that she can vomit without having to manually trigger her gag reflex. Crystal seems to purge after every meal and easily meets the criterion for vomiting **twice per week over a three-month period**.

Crystal is taken to a hospital for treatment of her bulimia, but her binging and purging catch the attention of other female patients who relish the idea of eating whatever they desire and finding a way to not gain weight. In one memorable scene, several women enter the washroom and vomit simultaneously into toilets that do not have stalls around them. Later during her hospitalization Crystal steals away into a secluded part of the hospital with a number of other patients and engages in ritualized bulimia. They gorge themselves on high-carbohydrate foods like cookies and ice-cream and purge shortly afterwards by vomiting into a pail. They pass the bucket around the circle much like other people would pass around a flask of whiskey or a joint.

This movie is listed here with the strongest of reservations. While the depictions of bulimia are excellent, the characters are coarse and senselessly violent. There are a number of scenes involving sexual situations which many people might find offensive.

Movie	Feature/Diagnosis
A Secret Between Friends/When Friendship Kills	Bulimia Nervosa, Purging Type
Freeway II: Confessions of a Trickbaby	Bulimia Nervosa, Purging Type
Dying to Dance	Anorexia Nervosa, Restricting Type
For the Love of Nancy	Anorexia Nervosa
The Best Little Girl in the World	Anorexia Nervosa

Many of the movies presented in this chapter were made-for-TV productions that are not easily available for rental. Copies of these films can be obtained through various online auctions or sites that sell used videos.

Chapter 13

Sleep
Disorders

In the DSM-IV-TR, sleep disorders are divided into four categories:
- Primary Sleep Disorders — Dyssomnias and Parasomnias
- Sleep Disorder Related to Another Mental Disorder
- Sleep Disorder Due to a General Medical Condition
- Substance-Induced Sleep Disorder

The **American Sleep Disorders Association** published *The International Classification of Sleep Disorders* in 1990. This classification system involves more subtypes of sleep disorders than does the DSM-IV-TR.

The relationship between sleep disturbances and psychiatric conditions is a fascinating one to study. In some psychiatric disorders, changes in sleep patterns occur before other manifestations of an illness and can be useful in predicting relapses. Studies of sleeping patterns occur in a sleep laboratory and are recorded via a process called polysomnography. Sleep labs record a variety of functions including brain electrical activity (electroencephalogram or EEG), eye movements, breathing pattern, muscle tone, and heart activity.

Introduction to the Sleep Cycle

The human sleep cycle is divided into five stages based on rapid eye movements (REM) and characteristic brain electrical activity. The first four stages involve non–rapid eye movement and are abbreviated NREM. Stage 1 NREM sleep is the transition from wakefulness to sleep. Stage 2 NREM comprises about 50% of the time spent asleep. Stages 3 and 4 NREM are called "deep sleep" and together make up about 20% of total sleep time. Progression to REM sleep occurs after deep sleep. REM sleep typically occurs in short bursts, though periods of REM sleep lengthen throughout the night. REM sleep comprises about one-quarter of total sleep time. One of the parameters recorded in polysomnography is the time it takes for someone to have a period of REM sleep. Normally it takes around 90 minutes, but in some psychiatric conditions such as depression this latency is reduced.

Dyssomnias

The term **dyssomnia** refers to difficulty falling asleep, staying asleep, or excessive sleepiness. The disorders are:

- Primary Hypersomnia
- Primary Insomnia
- Narcolepsy
- Breathing-Related Sleep Disorder
- Circadian Rhythm Sleep Disorder

Primary Hypersomnia

Primary hypersomnia is diagnosed when prolonged sleep or excessive daytime drowsiness is present over a one-month period. Impairment in social or occupational roles is directly related to the excessive sleepiness. This condition is not diagnosed if sleepiness is due to a medical condition, substance use, another psychiatric condition, or another sleep disorder. People with primary hypersomnia typically sleep between 8 and 12 hours per night, have trouble waking up and do not feel rested. They fall asleep in situations that aren't mentally or physically stimulating. Daytime naps typically last more than one hour and do not help the person feel refreshed. About 15% of people develop hypersomnia at some point during their lives.

No Movie Example Available

Primary Insomnia

The essential features of primary insomnia are: difficulties spanning at least a one-month period with getting to sleep, staying asleep, or not feeling refreshed after sleeping (**nonrestorative sleep**). The difficulties with sleep then cause problems at work, in relationships, or in social roles. Primary insomnia can be diagnosed only when medical conditions, substance use, other psychiatric disorders, and other sleep disorders are not present. People with primary insomnia often develop habits that further impair their ability to sleep soundly at night, such as daytime napping or erratic attempts at sleeping. Primary insomnia is thought to be present in up to 10% of the general population, increasing to 25% in the elderly.

Bulworth

Jay Bulworth (Warren Beatty) is a California senator seeking re-election. Somewhere during the last week of his campaign he has an emotional meltdown, which occurs before the film begins. When we first see him, he hasn't slept for two nights and is mentally sluggish. Though he has several important decisions to make, Bulworth sits in his office staring blankly at a TV that among other things plays his own commercials. Bulworth then flies cross-country, drinks alcohol and uses marijuana, all of which worsen his sleeping problem. Even without the influence of jet lag and substance abuse, Bulworth is a "sleep drunkard" and acts in an extremely disinhibited manner. He makes poor decisions for himself, alienates many of his supporters, and ruins his reputation. These consequences are good examples of the social and occupational impairment that is specified in the DSM-IV-TR criteria. In this movie, it is difficult to ascribe all of Bulworth's erratic behavior to sleep deprivation. He does get a full night's sleep on the last day depicted in the film and appears to be back to his usual conservative self. There are too many confounding variables in *Bulworth* to make this an accurate depiction of primary insomnia.

196

Narcolepsy

Narcolepsy consists of three elements:
- Irresistible sleep attacks
- Loss of muscle tone (**cataplexy**)
- REM episodes in the transition between sleep and wakefulness

Narcolepsy can be diagnosed just on the basis of sleep attacks with sleep-onset REM episodes, which is recorded in a sleep laboratory. Sleep attacks occur suddenly and are usually irresistible, though some people can ward them off or nap to decrease their frequency. Situations involving low mental or physical stimulation can induce people with narcolepsy to have a sleep attack. These episodes typically last 10 to 20 minutes or longer if the person isn't interrupted. Upon awakening, people often feel refreshed. They usually report that they were dreaming.

Cataplexy is the complete loss of muscle tone. This is an associated feature of narcolepsy that is present in about three-quarters of patients. It varies from subtle, such as a sagging jaw, to profound, where someone may completely collapse. Cataplexy often develops after the sleep attacks. Typical cataplexic episodes last seconds to minutes. Consciousness is preserved and the person can breathe and move his or her eyes during an attack. Sleep deprivation makes people more susceptible to attacks. The expression of strong emotions can trigger cataplexic episodes. REM episodes in narcolepsy occur very soon after sleep begins, usually within 5 minutes. Desynchronized REM cycles can cause perceptual disturbances. If these occur while falling asleep, they are called **hypnagogic hallucinations**, upon waking they are called **hypnopompic hallucinations**. These phenomena occur in 10% of the general population but are two to four times more common in people with narcolepsy. This condition is inherited and a strong association with a specific gene has been found. Narcolepsy is present in approximately 1/1000 people. It can only be diagnosed definitively in a sleep laboratory.

My Own Private Idaho

The opening image in this movie is a dictionary definition of narcolepsy. Mike Waters (River Phoenix) is a troubled young man who makes his living in the sex trade. When we first see Waters, he is stranded on a desolate Idaho highway. No vehicles approach for an extended period of time and he has a narcoleptic episode that leaves him asleep in the middle of the highway. Waters has a sleep-onset REM episode, which is nicely depicted by his eyes moving back and forth as soon as he falls asleep. Narcoleptic episodes can affect people at inopportune moments or even ones where they are in imminent danger, such as Waters falling asleep in the middle of a road.

Waters does not receive treatment for his sleep attacks and he continues to have them on a daily basis. The average number of attacks for untreated patients is between 2 to 6 per day. Waters has them in low-stimulation settings and is shown sleeping in restaurants and other public places. In another scene, he becomes emotionally overwrought while preparing to have sexual relations with a woman and falls to the floor in her bedroom. Waters is taken outside by his friend Scott (Keanu Reeves). Waters is left to sleep on the lawn for the whole night, which is somewhat inconsistent because narcoleptic attacks usually last on the order of an hour if the person isn't interrupted. Otherwise this portrayal of narcolepsy is quite accurate.

Bandits

Two armed robbers invade bank managers' homes, stay overnight, and then have their hostage open up the vault the next morning. When bank manager Lawrence Fife (Richard Riehle), who suffers from narcolepsy, opens his front door to the robbers he has a cataplexic episode and immediately drops to the floor. Since cataplexy itself does not involve a decrease in consciousness, this scene portrays Fife as having both cataplexy and a sleep attack.

Breathing-Related Sleep Disorder

This diagnosis involves sleep problems that are related to inadequate respiration. **Obstructive sleep apnea** is a blockage of the upper airways and is usually caused by being overweight. When the person lays down, the adipose tissue in the neck compresses the trachea and air is unable to pass. After about 30 seconds the respiratory center in the brain causes the person to rouse in order to start breathing again. This is often accompanied by a loud snore, moan, or a jerking motion made by the whole body. People with sleep apnea are typically unaware of the frequent periods of arousal. Their most common difficulty is feeling excessively drowsy during the day, often nodding off in low-stimulation situations. Less common complaints involve insomnia or frequent awakenings. **Central sleep apnea** involves a decreased stimulus from the brain to breathe and is commonly due to cardiac or neurological conditions. In central sleep apnea the airways are unobstructed. Breathing-related sleep disorders have been estimated to affect up to 10% of the population with men being affected two-to-four times as often as women. The obstructive type accounts for 90% of the cases of sleep apnea.

No Movie Example Available

Circadian Rhythm Sleep Disorder

The body has its own internal clock called the **circadian rhythm**. Many body functions follow a cycle, such as secretion of hormones and temperature. Circadian rhythm sleep disorders result from a mismatch between a person's internal cycle and the demands that he or she has to meet. The body's sleep generating functions are not faulty but are thrown out of sync and take time to recover. There are four subtypes of this disorder:

- **Delayed Sleep Phase Type** — this is a time shift sleeping pattern where people stay awake later and wake up later than socially accepted norms
- **Jet Lag Type** — travel between time zones necessitates changes in sleeping patterns; travel eastward where one advances hours is usually a more difficult adjustment
- **Shift Work Type** — shifts that alternate between days, afternoons, and nights are very disruptive; this can be further worsened by social demands that cause people to have to further delay sleep after their shifts are over
- **Unspecified Type** — see the example below

 ## Insomnia

This film was originally a 1997 Norwegian release and was redone in 2002, which is the version presented here. Will Dormer (Al Pacino) is a Los Angeles detective who flies to Alaska to help solve a murder. In northern regions there is sunlight for most of the day during the summer and Dormer has considerable difficulty making this adjustment. He cannot sleep because of the persistent light streaming into his hotel room. Dormer goes for almost six days without sleep and becomes progressively more disorganized and makes a number of errors in his investigation. This portrayal is less than entirely accurate because there are many things plaguing Dormer's conscience would impair his sleep.

Parasomnias

Parasomnias are abnormal behaviors that occur during specific stages of sleep or the sleep-wake transition. There are three types:
- Nightmare Disorder
- Sleep Terror Disorder
- Sleepwalking Disorder

Nightmare Disorder

Nightmares are anxiety-provoking dreams that cause the sleeper to awaken. While many people have nightmares, this disorder is diagnosed when the awakenings lead to significant distress or the inability to function in social or occupational roles. This disorder is not diagnosed if the nightmares occur exclusively during the course of another psychiatric disorder or are due to substance use. Typically, people can recall their nightmares as they happen just before waking up and cause a lingering sense of anxiety. Nightmares are a function of REM sleep. As sleep progresses, REM cycles tend to become longer, so most nightmares occur in the second half of sleep.

Braveheart

The young William Wallace (James Robinson) witnesses some horrific scenes. He attends a meeting of Scottish noblemen with his father and older brother, only to discover that it was an ambush and they have all been hung. When he returns home that night, William has a nightmare that one of the corpses opens his eyes and begins speaking to him. William's father and older brother head off to avenge their countrymen and are slain in battle. William sees their bodies as they are being prepared for burial and again has a nightmare that his father is speaking to him. On both occasions he awakens in an anxious state and appears to recall what he was dreaming. This portrayal falls short of being entirely accurate because the nightmares do not trouble William enough to cause him the degree of difficulty stipulated in the DSM-IV-TR.

Sleep Terror Disorder

Sleep terror disorder is also called **night terrors** or **pavor nocturnus**. It is distinct from nightmare disorder and has the following features:

- Awakening from sleep with a scream or cry
- Sleep terrors occur in the first third of sleep
- Episodes of sleep terror last between 1 — 10 minutes
- During sleep terrors, the person is difficult to rouse
- The person reacts physically to the upsetting events by sweating, breathing faster, and increased muscle tone
- Upon awakening, there is usually no recollection of the upsetting events

This is a disorder of stages 3 and 4 NREM sleep, which explains why there is typically no recollection of events. Sleep terror disorder affects up to 5% of children and begins between the ages of 4 and 12 years. In children, it is more common in boys. Sleep terror disorder is present in less than 1% of adults and has an equal sex distribution. Adults with this condition often have an associated anxiety or personality disorder. There is a strong family history of sleep terror or sleepwalking in the relatives of people with this condition.

No Movie Example Available

Sleepwalking Disorder

Sleepwalking involves complex motor behavior that occurs during stage 3 or 4 of sleep. It doesn't always involve a person getting out of bed; activities such as sitting up in bed or picking at blankets qualifies for this diagnosis. Rarely, complex behavior is seen, such as operating machinery or eating. During an episode of sleepwalking, the person is unresponsive to the surroundings and has a blank stare on his or her face. It is usually difficult to rouse someone who is sleepwalking, but if they do wake up there is typically a period of confusion that lasts several minutes. Whether people wake up while sleepwalking or the next day, they usually do not recall the episode. Sleepwalking often starts in children between the ages of 4 and 8 years, and is present in up to 5% of the population. While adults do sleepwalk, the prevalence of this disorder in older age groups is quite low.

Donnie Darko

Prior to the film beginning, Donnie Darko (Jake Gyllenhaal) has started some type of psychiatric medication and has regular therapy sessions. At precisely midnight Donnie sits up in bed, slowly gets dressed, and leaves the house. He walks down the street and eventually falls asleep on the putting green of a nearby golf course.

Sleepwalking usually occurs in the first third of the night, so Donnie's episode at midnight is consistent with this disorder. He also has no idea the next morning how he got to the golf course. Some people remember fragments of what they were experiencing while sleepwalking but it is more typical to not remember anything. The types of activities that people engage in while sleepwalking are fairly routine. Leaving the house is unusual but is still in keeping with this disorder. There are rather strong signs in this film that Donnie is developing a serious psychiatric illness (most likely paranoid schizophrenia) which in itself could impair his sleep, as could the medication he takes.

Movie	Feature/Diagnosis
Bandits	Narcolepsy (cataplexy and sleep attacks)
Braveheart	Nightmare Disorder
Bulworth	Primary Insomnia
Donnie Darko	Sleepwalking Disorder
Insomnia	Circadian Rhythm Sleep Disorder
My Own Private Idaho	Narcolepsy

Chapter 14

Impulse-Control Disorders

Intermittent Explosive Disorder

Intermittent Explosive Disorder (**IED**) involves discrete episodes of engaging in aggressive activity that is directed at either other people or property. The intensity of the assault on others or the damage to property is grossly out of proportion to the degree of provocation existing beforehand. These outbursts must occur on several occasions and not be due to the effects of another psychiatric condition.

IED is different than someone just having a "bad temper." Prior to aggressive outbursts, people with IED may describe physical sensations such as chest tightness or tremor. After the outburst, they often have a dysphoric mood and feel fatigued. People with IED describe their periods of aggression as very distressing. They often run into personal or occupational problems because of their outbursts.

Punch Drunk Love

Barry Egan (Adam Sandler) is in business selling novelty plungers. While trying to close a deal, he receives a phone call from each of his seven sisters who implore him to attend a birthday party. At the party, Barry is gently ribbed about some of his boyhood antics. Ironically, it is the teasing about previous angry outbursts that causes him to again lose control, and Barry kicks out the glass from a sliding door. Later in the film, Barry meets Lena (Emily Watson), a friend of one of his sisters, and has dinner with her. In order to start the conversation, Lena mentions something she heard about one of Barry's childhood outbursts. He calmly excuses himself and then proceeds to trash the men's washroom before returning to the table. Barry does not have an irritable disposition and doesn't seem to be suffering from another condition that would account for his destructive outbursts.

Kleptomania

Kleptomania is the recurrent theft of items that are not needed for personal use or taken for their monetary value. The items are not stolen for the purposes of revenge or as a result of another psychiatric illness, such as an auditory hallucination telling someone to take an item. Prior to taking the item, the person with kleptomania feels a sense of tension, which can be manifested by chest tightness, palpitations, sweating, or tremors. There is a sense of immediate relief as soon as the item is stolen.

Kleptomania differs from shoplifting in the following ways:
- The item taken is not for personal benefit
- The person usually has enough money to pay for the item
- Items are often discarded when the person leaves the store
- Episodes of kleptomania are not pre-planned

Female Perversions

While this film does have an erotic focus, the title of this movie stems from the "perversity" of having to curtail the expression of one's sexuality to the confines of what is considered socially acceptable. The kleptomaniac in this film is Madelyn Stephens (Amy Madigan), a graduate student who is just days from defending her thesis. She comes from at least an upper-middle class background and has a sister who is a highly successful lawyer.

Madelyn enters a lingerie store and slowly wraps a silk scarf around her neck. Spurred by the excitement of the successful theft of the scarf, she then asks the clerk to look for an item in another color and impulsively steals a garter belt by concealing it in her pants. Madelyn then leaves the store, and staring right back at the entrance, removes the garter and throws it in a garbage can. We later learn that she has taken many items that are not useful to her, such as a dozen hammers and children's clothes.

Pathological Gambling

Pathological gamblers employ this activity in a very similar manner to those who are dependent on substances. In essence, financial risk taking becomes their drug of choice. Pathological gamblers get the same euphoric rush (called "action" in gambling parlance) and will continue to take huge risks in the face of thin odds and dire consequences. Someone is diagnosed with pathological gambling when the following criteria are met:

* Preoccupation with gambling
* The need to gamble with increasing amounts of money to get the same level of excitement
* Repeated, unsuccessful efforts to reduce or stop gambling have been made
* Reducing the frequency of gambling results in dysphoric mood or irritability
* Gambling is used as a means of reducing dysphoric mood or to escape from life's problems
* After losing money, the person will return to try and recover the lost amount (called "chasing" one's losses)
* Deliberately deceives friends, family, and others about the extent of involvement in gambling
* Has committed illegal acts such as forgery, theft, embezzlement, etc. to cover gambling debts
* Has social, occupational, or education difficulties that are directly related to gambling activities
* Financial situation becomes so desperate that the person requires others to provide assistance

Pathological gambling is thought to be present in up to 3% of the population, but accurate statistics are difficult to obtain. It is more common in men by a factor of around two. Men also appear to develop pathological gambling earlier in life than women. There is an increase in the prevalence of this condition in places where gambling is legal. A genetic component to this condition has been found to be present, along with a link to alcohol dependence.

Casino

Casino is based on the novel by Nicholas Pileggi and details the rise and fall of two men who run a casino in Las Vegas, Sam "Ace" Rothstein (Robert De Niro) and Nicky Santoro (Joe Pesci). Rothstein runs the successful Tangiers casino and sums up his view of the gambling world — the house always wins.

One of the Tangier's high rollers is a wealthy man named K.K. Ichikawa (Nobu Matsuhisa). Ichikawa wins two million dollars at baccarat and then intends to fly home on the casino's private jet. Rothstein bribes the pilot into saying that there are mechanical problems and Ichikawa has no choice but to stay over another night. He cannot be content with his winnings and ventures back to the gaming table. Ichikawa's initial bets are far lower than his customary $30,000, but he can't resist the urge to try and recover his initial losses the second time around. By the end of the evening, Rothstein's gamble has paid off nicely. Ichikawa lost all of his winnings and another $1,000,000 of his own.

A more accurate example of pathological gambling is given in the scene with Santoro and a fellow named Al. Santoro is a vicious mob figure who is in charge of security at the Tangiers. His extreme outbursts are reminiscent of IED but at his core, Santoro is a violent man who takes opportunities wherever he can find them. One of his many ventures in Las Vegas is to lend money at exorbitant rates to gamblers who are down on their luck.

In the scene with Al, Santoro chastises him thoroughly for allowing his gambling debts to take money away from paying the rent, heating bills, and supporting his family. Santoro has already lent Al money on one occasion and calls him a *"degenerate gambler."* Santoro reaches into his pocket to remove another stack of bills, but it just as easily could have been a weapon. While many of the criteria for pathological gambling are implied in this brief segment, owing a man like Santoro money indicates that Al's gambling habit is beyond his ability to control.

Pyromania

Pyromania is the intentional setting of fires on several occasions. Other features of this condition are:

- The person feels a sense of tension prior to setting the fire
- After the fire is lit, the person feels a sense of relief, gratification, or pleasure
- The person has an enduring interest in things related to fires, such as flammable substances, people and places that get burned, firefighting equipment, etc.

The fires are not set for financial reasons, because of protest or revenge, or for any clear personal gain. Also, the fire-setting is not better accounted for by another psychiatric illness.

Backdraft

Ronald Bartel (Donald Sutherland) is an imprisoned pyromaniac in this film. Although he did engage in committing arson at some point, he was clearly enamored of fire before hiring out his talents. Bartel keeps track of major fires with the avidity that collectors have for trading cards of their favorite athletes. Bartel instantly recognizes the name of Brian McCaffrey (Stephen Baldwin) from a magazine cover showing McCaffrey as a child at the scene of a fire holding the helmet of his father (who perished in the blaze).

Bartel refers to fire as *"the animal"* and has pathological reverence for it. Bartel is so fixated on fire and its consequences that he admits at his parole hearing that he likes to burn people, and if he had the chance, would burn the whole world. Fire investigator Donald Rimgale (Robert De Niro) tells McCaffrey that fire is alive — it breathes, and eats, and hates. Furthering Rimgale's anthropomorphization of fire, Bartel asks McCaffrey if the fire "looked" at him and is entranced to hear that it did. Bartel spends much of his time reading and thinking about fire and collects any memorabilia that he can dealing with the topic.

Trichotillomania

Trichotillomania involves pulling out one's hair to the point that it results in noticeable hair loss. As with the other impulse-control disorders, people with this condition experience a sense of tension that compels them to pull out their hair. Immediately after doing so, they experience a sense of relief, well-being, and gratification. People with trichotillomania do not usually pull out their hair in front of others. Typically the hair pulling episodes are brief and occur at various times during the day. However, some people engage in this activity for hours at a time. Hair is pulled from a variety of sites: scalp, eyebrows, underarms, forearms, legs, pubic area, eyelashes, etc. Once the hair is pulled, activities such as examining it, twirling it, chewing on it, and swallowing it are common. Human hair is not digestible, and in some cases forms a mass (**bezoar**). Eating hair can cause a variety of medical complications including anemia, abdominal pain, and obstruction which requires surgery to repair. Trichotillomania is quite rare, and accurate statistics on its prevalence have not been recorded. In children, this condition is equally present in both sexes. In adults, trichotillomania is more common in women. Many children transiently pull on their hair in times of stress, which is not considered trichotillomania.

No Movie Example Available

Movie	Feature/Diagnosis
Backdraft	Pyromania
Casino	Pathological Gambling
Female Perversions	Kleptomania
Punch Drunk Love	Intermittent Explosive Disorder

Chapter 15

Personality Disorders

This chapter describes and gives cinematic examples of psychiatric conditions known as personality disorders. What sets this chapter apart from the others in this book is the ease with which one can identify with many of the diagnostic criteria listed here. While many people will not have experienced hallucinations, profound depression, or unremitting anxiety, the descriptions of personality disorders will likely strike a chord of familiarity. A condition known as "medical student's disease" seems to afflict many doctors during their formative years. This condition occurs when the reader of a medical textbook is convinced that he or she suffers from the very illness being studied at that time. When these same students study psychiatry, they diagnose themselves with at least one, and at times all ten, of the personality disorders. The DSM-IV-TR defines a personality disorder as follows: *An enduring pattern of inner experience and behavior that deviates markedly from the expectations of the individual's culture.*

This "marked deviation" is manifested in the following ways:
- Cognition — skewed or biased perception and interpretation of self, others, and the environment
- Emotional Responses (**affect**) — are either too flattened or too exaggerated
- Ability to Relate to Others — has difficulties in relationships
- Impulse Control — has a reduced ability to restrain impulses

For a personality disorder to be present the features listed above must be inflexible, present over a broad range of situations, and be evident at least by early adulthood. Some significant aspect of the person's life (usually work or a close relationship) must be interfered with because of his or her personality features, which justifies the use of the term "disorder." There is no such thing as a "normal" personality. Everyone has a unique set of quirks, eccentricities, and coping strategies. When these features are present but do not interfere with a person's ability to manage in society, they are referred to as **personality traits** instead of a personality disorder. Each personality disorder affects roughly one to three percent of the general population.

Points on Diagnosing Personality Disorders

The DSM-IV-TR convention for assigning different conditions to different axes (**multiaxial approach**) was outlined in *Chapter 2*. Recall that major psychiatric disorders are recorded on Axis I and personality disorders are listed on Axis II.

It is possible to have both a major psychiatric disorder and a personality disorder at the same time. It is also possible to suffer from two or more personality disorders simultaneously, though in practice there is usually one pattern that is more prominent than the others.

The DSM-IV-TR uses the concept of clusters to subdivide the ten personality disorders:
- **Cluster A** — personalities having a core of "odd or eccentric" characteristics
- **Cluster B** — "dramatic, emotional, or erratic" characteristics
- **Cluster C** — "anxious or fearful" characteristics

In many cases it is easier to assign someone's aberrant characteristics to a particular cluster than it is to a specific personality disorder. There is considerable overlap among the conditions within each cluster, and it can take a clinician weeks or months to make an accurate diagnosis.

Choosing movie depictions of personality disorders is also a challenging task. There are thousands of memorable and intriguing characters that unfortunately were not suitable for inclusion in this book because they didn't meet the descriptions contained in the DSM-IV-TR. Some of the personality disorders have scores of examples — an entire book could be written cataloging and discussing antisocial and borderline personalities. Some of the other personality disorders are difficult to find in film because their depictions aren't very interesting to watch, particularly schizoid personality disorder, which causes people to shun relationships, express little to no emotion, and take virtually no pleasure in activities.

215

Paranoid Personality

Understanding the Condition

Literally translated from Greek, paranoia means "a mind beside itself." Historically, paranoia has been applied to a diverse array of conditions and was often used to refer to the presence of any type of mental illness. The DSM-IV-TR contains three conditions in which paranoia is a dominant feature: paranoid schizophrenia; delusional disorder, persecutory (paranoid) type; and paranoid personality disorder (the mildest form).

In common parlance, paranoia is used to refer to any degree of suspiciousness or vigilance. The main feature of paranoid personality disorder (PPD) is a pervasive distrust of others such that the motives of other people are interpreted as being deliberately hurtful. Patients with PPD have difficulty maintaining friendships because of their continual accusations of malevolence, exploitation, deception, and humiliation.

PPD in the Movies

Paranoid people are often portrayed in movies as individuals who are pitted against grim, faceless organizations such as greedy corporations or secret government agencies. Frequently, the main character has skills or knowledge that would be of use to "the bad guys" and he or she must convince skeptical friends that something sinister is going on. However, if someone is really being pursued or persecuted, then it isn't paranoia.

Another common portrayal of paranoid patients involves their litigious nature. They are intolerant of even minor or unintentional slights, and often play the role of the friendless, cranky person who brings frivolous legal action against others. A more positive depiction involves someone who keeps track of a seemingly minor piece of information (such as the license plate of a double-parked car) that turns out to be important in solving a major crime.

216

Making the Diagnosis

PPD is diagnosed using the following criteria:

i. *Automatically suspects that others are exploitative or malevolent* — without any reasonable or rational basis

ii. *Doubts the loyalty of those around him or her* — again, such doubts are unjustified

iii. *Avoids confiding in others* — because of fears that information so disclosed would be used against him or her

iv. *Reads hidden, derogatory comments into everyday events*

v. *Bears Grudges for Long Periods of Time*

vi. *Perceives that his or her character is constantly under attack* — and reacts/counterattacks quickly and angrily

vii. *Doubts Fidelity of Spouse* — where such suspicions are not warranted

Associated Features

- People with PPD are often hostile and guarded
- Paranoid people readily blame others for their own disappointments, faults, or problems
- Autonomy is very important in PPD; they have huge trust issues and are uncomfortable if they have to depend on others; however, they often feel at ease around those who share their opinions, philosophy, views of the world, etc.
- Paranoia is often at the heart of bigotry and racism
- In some instances, the continued and unwarranted accusations by those with PPD actually induces others to treat them unfairly (let the crime fit the punishment), which only serves to justify their confrontational nature
- *"Paranoid personalities see themselves as righteous and mistreated by others. Other people are viewed as treacherous and covertly manipulative. They believe that other people want to interfere with them in a hidden or secret way, often under the guise of innocence. Paranoid patients spend much of their time looking for clues that will betray the hidden motives of their persecutors"* (adapted from Beck and Freeman, 1990)
- *"Paranoid personalities are driven, arrogant, unromantic, and may be successful in solitary professions"* (adapted from Akhtar, 1995)

217

Shine

The main character's father, Peter (played by Armin Mueller-Stahl), exhibits behavior consistent with the diagnosis of PPD. Early in the film we see him actively discouraging David from socializing with others. Peter is fanatically devoted to keeping his family together, believing that anything one might need should be available within the family. He tells David repeatedly that "*no one will love you like I do.*" Peter is very wary of others, having unwarranted suspicions of their motives, even though everyone involved is benevolent towards David (particularly his first music teacher). Despite this, Peter shows gratitude to no one. In the scene where Peter reluctantly parades David over to his music teacher's house, he coldly informs the teacher that he cannot pay for the lessons. Rather than thanking the man for his generosity, he believes he has won a victory by saving money.

Later, David receives an offer from a family in America to stay with them as part of a scholarship he receives. As David and his sisters excitedly read the letter, their father becomes enraged and burns it, presumably because the host family offers many luxuries that he has not been able to provide.

Peter sees David's eventual (and utterly necessary) departure as a personal rejection, telling him that he cannot return, and that he will lose his family and be punished for the rest of his life. Shortly after David's departure, his father burns a scrapbook of newspaper clippings documenting his successes. We see Peter following David's career, but many years pass before he will agree to have one last meeting, which is anything but a rekindling of their relationship.

Peter tries to provide his family with more amenities than he had as a child. Early in the film, Peter is (at times) depicted as a loving father who plays with his children, is desperately concerned with their success, and gives them advice that could serve as his motto, "*Life is cruel — only the fit survive, the rest get crushed.*"

218

The Caine Mutiny

The U.S.S. Caine, a fictitious W.W.II minesweeper, is described by her initial skipper Lt. Cmdr. DeVriess (Tom Tully) as a *"beaten up tub"* in the *"junkyard navy."* The ship and crew are noticeably in need of an overhaul when Lt. Cmdr. Philip Francis Queeg (played by Humphrey Bogart) takes command. Queeg makes it clear that he runs things by the book. He is focused on order and obedience and views every small transgression as a deliberate challenge to his authority. Shortly after taking command, Queeg berates a sailor for leaving his shirttail out and, while so occupied, steams over a tow line. He cannot accept that he has done something wrong and files a report insisting that the equipment was faulty. Many incidents follow where Queeg's paranoia loses him the affection and respect of the officers and crew, particularly a strip search as part of an investigation to discover the fate of a missing quart of strawberries. Eventually Queeg is relieved of his command when he is unable to safely guide the ship through a typhoon.

In the ensuing court martial, Queeg is correctly diagnosed as having PPD, described as: unreasonable suspiciousness of others, feelings of persecution, and always feeling as if he was in the right. The court martial scene involving Queeg's testimony is a superb example of this condition. An excerpt is as follows:

"They were all disloyal. I tried to run the ship properly by the book, but they fought me at every turn. If the crew wanted to walk around with their shirttails hanging out, that's all right, let them! Take the tow line — defective equipment, no more, no less. But they encouraged the crew to go around scoffing at me and spreading wild rumors about steaming in circles and then 'Old Yellowstain' (his nickname). I was to blame for Lieutenant Maryk's incompetence and poor seamanship. Lieutenant Maryk was the perfect officer, but not Captain Queeg. Ah, but the strawberries! That's where I had them. They laughed at me and made jokes, but I proved beyond the shadow of a doubt, and with geometric logic, that a duplicate key to the wardroom icebox did exist."

Schizoid Personality

Understanding the Condition

The schizoid personality disorder (SzdPD) is the fourth of five diagnoses that have the prefix "schiz." The first three were presented in the chapter on psychotic disorders: schizophrenia, schizophreniform disorder, and schizoaffective disorder. All of these conditions (as well as the fifth one, schizotypal personality disorder) may well have a common genetic basis and share some clusters of symptoms.

People with SzdPD are aloof, introverted, and demonstrate a very narrow range of emotions. Their aversion to interacting with others may commonly be referred to as being "antisocial," but is more properly termed **asocial**. Other than family members, schizoid personalities neither have nor desire relationships. Indeed they lack the ability to experience pleasure in the things that other people enjoy doing. They are often oblivious to the thoughts and feelings of others. What makes SzdPD unique in this regard is that patients do not intentionally ignore social cues, rather, they are incapable of sensing the emotions of others.

SzdPD in the Movies

Schizoid characters are socially detached, stolid, and prefer to fade into the woodwork rather than be noticed. Hence, they make for fairly uninteresting movie characters. Frequent portrayals involve loners, hermits, and outcasts. Perhaps the most common depiction is the hero of western movies. The stranger rides into town, reluctantly gets involved in some unfair situation, does his bit to further the common good, and then promptly leaves, declining the warm thanks of the townsfolk and the advances of an attractive woman. There is one feature of SzdPD that is sometimes capitalized on in movies — their rich fantasy lives. While being externally bland, many schizoid individuals find considerable gratification in abstract activities such as role-playing games, at times with a sadomasochistic orientation.

Making the Diagnosis

SzdPD involves the following diagnostic criteria:

i. *Absence of close relationships*
ii. *Prefers solitary activities*
iii. *Little Interest in Sexual Activities*
iv. *Anhedonia* — doesn't seem to enjoy anything
v. *Lacks close friends or confidants*
vi. *Indifferent to praise or criticism*
vii. *Emotionally flat* — rarely show feelings of any sort

Associated Features

- SzdPD is considered to have a significant overlap with the **negative symptoms of schizophrenia** (see page 23), particularly anhedonia, social withdrawal, and flattened affect
- Occasionally, people have SzdPD before developing schizophrenia
- *"They are for the most part silent, inaccessible, and hard to understand. They have no desire to make an impact on others. They are not interested in impressing, influencing, or revealing themselves."* (adapted from Jung, 1921)
- *"The common characteristic of schizoid characters is an inability to get along with others. They maintain a front for the world to look at if it cares to, but they do not care what others think. They make gestures and go through the motions, but never really make lasting contacts. Most of them are seclusive, quiet, reserved, serious, eccentric, and stubborn. Others may appear to be mentally dull but usually are not."* (adapted from Menninger, 1930)
- *"Individuals with SzdPD are observers, not participants. They see themselves as self-sufficient loners. Others view them as dull, uninteresting, and humorless. Their thoughts are often vague and seem to be sporadic. This cognitive style contributes to their lack of emotional expression, since they do not perceive the social cues happening around them."* (adapted from Beck & Freeman, 1990)
- *"There are no fears or wishes. They can sustain formal social roles. Schizoid patients may marry but not understand a spouse's wish for more intimacy."* (adapted from Benjamin, 1993)

221

The Net

Angela Bennett (Sandra Bullock) is an independent computer programmer who works out of her home. She displays many schizoid qualities in the first part of the film: rejecting a dinner offer in favor of ordering a pizza online, engaging in cyber-chat with an anonymous group, and avoiding even exchanging greetings with a neighbor. Angela has been in her house for four years and has yet to make a friend. She agrees to meet an employer only at his insistence. Angela hasn't had a vacation in six years, and when a computer malfunction at the airport delays her flight, she finds it difficult to be around people. Her vacation plans initially involve a beach, a book, and solitude. Ultimately, however, Angela is too animated, charismatic, and affectionate for this to be an accurate portrayal of SzdPD. She has interpersonal needs that a truly schizoid person wouldn't have and could not obtain as readily as Angela does in *The Net*.

Flesh and Bone

Arlis Sweeney (Dennis Quaid) lives a nomadic existence in rural Texas tending to his vending machines. Well into his thirties, he's never been married and until he meets Kay (Meg Ryan), hasn't been in love. Arlis is taciturn, wary of strangers, and quite content to spend most of his time in isolation driving on county roads between stops. He keeps his thoughts and feelings to himself, and appears to be emotionally flat during two very significant events in the movie (protecting Kay from his father, and then having to end his relationship with her).

The two major aspects of Arlis' character that are not consistent with SzdPD are his interest in sexual liaisons (with a number of women scattered throughout his territory), and his clear affection for Kay. Ultimately it is a gruesome event from Arlis' past that prevents them from staying together and not his lack of interest in pursuing a relationship with her.

For A Few Dollars More

Clint Eastwood portrays a mysterious, serape-clad, cigar-chewing bounty hunter in this western. He has no home, no friends, and no name — though he is referred to as "The Man With No Name/ Manco" in various write-ups about the movie. We are told nothing of his past or why he chooses this vocation. He interacts with people only in the context of getting information about the outlaw(s) he is seeking. His conversations with people are short, direct, and unadorned by social niceties.

We do not see Manco doing anything for enjoyment, such as taking a bath or eating a meal. When he is making a decision about staying in a hotel, Manco does ask about the availability of a woman. The hotel owner's wife fawns over him and is known to be indiscreet, but Manco does not pursue her.

Even when faced with trying to catch a gang of over a dozen murderous outlaws, Manco would prefer to work alone. He grudgingly accepts a limited partnership with another bounty hunter, Colonel Douglas Mortimer (Lee Van Cleef), whose marksmanship and tactics will clearly be helpful. Manco shares very little of himself even when he speaks with Mortimer — just that he may buy some land with the reward he receives from hunting the gang. Even after gathering up the bodies of the outlaws on a horse-cart and calculating his bounty at $27,000, Manco is stone-faced and simply rides back into town.

The cinematography in this movie assists with the "schizoid" feel of Manco. The long pauses, sparse dialogue, and one-dimensional aspects of the main characters give a good flavor of the aloof, detached, and joyless qualities that are central to SzdPD.

Schizoid

This is a slasher film starring Klaus Kinski as an immoral therapist. Contrary to the title, no schizoid characters appear in this movie.

Schizotypal Personality

Understanding the Condition

The word schizotypal is a contraction of the term **schizophrenic genotype**. This personality disorder is thought to be a milder expression of the genes that contribute to causing schizophrenia. This is the last of the terms that start with "schiz," though all are included in what is known as the **schizophrenic spectrum** of illnesses. It is thought that a greater percentage of people with schizotypal personality disorder (SztPD) eventually develop schizophrenia than those with SzdPD. However, the majority of patients with SztPD do not go on to have schizophrenia. From time to time, under stressful conditions, schizotypal patients can undergo transient periods of psychosis lasting minutes to hours, though they are not severe enough to warrant the diagnosis of a **brief psychotic disorder**.

SztPD is characterized by difficulties in relationships, marked anxiety in social situations, unusual thoughts and perceptions, and eccentric behavior. To put it plainly, schizotypal patients seem as if they are from a different planet. They have unusual beliefs based on superstitions or paranormal phenomena. They experience things that other people do not, and often draw sweeping, magical conclusions from these events. They often have many "fringe" interests such as: astrology; past-life regression; channeling; extra-sensory perception; shamanism, etc.

SztPD in the Movies

Schizotypal characters are tailor made for roles such as fortune tellers, clairvoyants, mystics, psychics, mediums, mind readers, and guides to other worlds. The presumptive ability of these characters to predict the future or to make revelations about others enhances plot development. The visions, predictions, and warnings offered by schizotypal characters often turn into self-fulfilling prophecies. In some movies, they are connected to supernatural elements that magically cause or fix problems.

Making the Diagnosis

Schizotypal personality disorder is diagnosed when the following features are present:

i.   *Misinterpreting events* — as if the radio or television had special messages just for the patient (these thoughts are called **ideas of reference)**

ii. *Odd beliefs/magical thinking* — believes that something can happen just by wishing it so; sees causal links between events that do not exist

iii. *Unusual perceptual experiences*

iv. *Odd thinking or speech*

v.   *Suspiciousness or paranoid thinking*

vi. *Emotional expression which is flat or unusual*

vii. *Odd, eccentric, or peculiar behavior*

viii. *Lacks close friends or confidants*

ix. *Excessive social anxiety*   that doesn't diminish with familiarity

Associated Features

- SztPD has an overlap with the **positive symptoms of schizophrenia**, particularly: perceptual disturbances, odd behavior and speech, and unusual ideas (that are not of delusional intensity)

- *"There is a tendency to follow idle and ineffectual lives, drifting and remaining on the periphery of society. Some appear only minimally connected to the external world. They appear lost in daydreams and occasionally blur fantasy and reality. They are often perceived as odd or peculiar in their behaviors."* (adapted from Millon, 1981)

- *"Schizotypal patients often lose sight of the overall situation. They believe that if they feel a negative emotion that it must be due to some negative external situation. Also, they believe that they have control over external situations when this is impossible."* (adapted from Beck & Freeman, 1993)

- *"Schizotypal patients elect to live separately, and reject the rest of the world. If their withdrawal from society is substantial and occurs over a long period of time, they lose touch with societal norms and develop their own rules for appearance, conduct, etc."* (adapted from Benjamin, 1993)

Grumpy Old Men

Ariel Truax (Ann-Margret) moves to Minnesota to teach American literature at a local university. At 1:30 a.m., she knocks on the door of her neighbor, John Gustafson (Jack Lemmon). Without introducing herself, she asks to use his bathroom even though hers is in perfect working order. She runs upstairs to his "personal" lavatory instead of taking his suggestion to use the guest washroom. Her plan is to learn something about Gustafson, and she believes that an inspection of someone's bathroom is even more revealing than a palm reading. When she emerges, she describes it as "fascinating" but offers nothing else.

Because they hadn't met prior to her late-night visit, Ariel took some of John's mail to find out his name and what ever else she could glean from the outside of an envelope. In order to explain her actions, Ariel quotes the dramatist Edward Albee and says, *"sometimes a person has to go a very long distance out of the way to come back a short distance correctly."* This remark can reasonably be considered a **non-sequitur** since John doesn't understand how her use of this quotation explains or justifies her commission of a *"federal offense"* (taking his mail).

Ariel places an order for herbal therapy oils at a local pharmacy. She is especially fond of the scent of *"fresh tea tree"* soaking into her pores. As her relationship with John develops, she tells him that she was immediately attracted to him because they share the same aura. This revelation is made after she enters his house to prepare dinner when he isn't home and wasn't expecting her.

Ariel is unconventional, free-spirited, and hedonistic. She has taught a variety of courses at the university level, enjoyed her marriage until her husband passed away, and is a source of inspiration to many of the other characters in the film. While she demonstrates some schizotypal traits and tendencies, her ideas and behaviors are adaptive and liberating, and are not disruptive enough to affect her life or the lives of those around her.

Hello Again

Shelley Long plays the role of Lucy Chadman, a woman who chokes to death on a Korean chicken ball. Lucy's sister Zelda (Judith Ivey) invokes a spell from a book she obtained from a *"white witch from Sandusky"* that brings Lucy back from the dead exactly one year later.

Zelda runs her own business called *Cosmic Light Books*, which is a haven for those with alternative or fringe beliefs. Zelda is outlandishly dressed and does unusual things during the film. When we first see Zelda, Lucy asks her for advice. Even before Lucy has finished explaining the situation, Zelda is trying to invoke a magician's spell to help with the problem. She lightly chastises a man for swatting a fly because it may have been a *"transmigrating soul."* Zelda detects emanations from other people's possessions, and in particular vibrations from brassieres. She makes potions, reads Tarot cards, conducts séances, and invokes incantations. In one scene, Zelda channels the spirit of a Jewish shoe store owner in front of a group of Lucy's husband's nonplussed medical colleagues. On the day that Lucy chokes to death, Zelda senses that her (Lucy's) aura has turned purple, which she believes to be strange. As Zelda looks up the significance of this in a book, Lucy chokes on a chicken ball in the bookstore.

Zelda demonstrates many of the characteristics of SztPD:
- Odd beliefs or magical thinking
- Unusual perceptual experiences
- Odd thinking and speech
- Inappropriate affect (expression of emotions)
- Peculiar behavior and appearance

There are some important features missing from Zelda's depiction of SztPD, in particular: suspiciousness, social anxiety, and a lack of close friends. Zelda describes herself as *"not dealing from a full deck."* While she may have been referring to Tarot cards, schizotypal individuals do not typically have intellectual deficits.

Antisocial Personality

Understanding the Condition

Patients with antisocial personality disorder (ASPD) are predators who exploit trust and goodwill. Antisocial personalities are persistently deceitful and show a marked lack of concern for the welfare of themselves and others. ASPD is characterized by guiltless, exploitative, and irresponsible behavior, with a lifelong pattern (present prior to the age of fifteen years) of disregard for the rights of others. People with ASPD are often referred to as **psychopaths**, **sociopaths**, or as having a **dyssocial personality disorder**. These terms are often used synonymously, although there are minor variations in their definitions. Criminal activity itself does not necessarily equate with ASPD. Those who run afoul of the law may do so for reasons other than having this personality disorder. Similarly, not all ASPDs have criminal records. Some carry on lengthy sprees of emotional or financial destruction without breaking laws (such as con men or business executives involved in immoral or unethical activities). Sigmund Freud hypothesized that humans are driven by powerful sexual and aggressive instincts, embodied in what he called the **id**. These primal urges are resisted by most people, but are acted upon by those with ASPD (which is nicely encapsulated by Dr. Robert Simon's book called *"Bad Men Do What Good Men Dream"*). Two other excellent references are Dr. Robert Hare's book *Without Conscience*, and *Bad Boys, Bad Men: Confronting Antisocial Personality Disorder* by Donald W. Black and C. Lindon Larson.

ASPD in the Movies

Popular media teems with antisocial characters. They fulfill the requirements of the "media id" — sex and violence — and are intriguing characters in dramas. Sociopaths are fascinating because they commit acts that strike at the core of moral society: murder, sexual assault, kidnapping, extortion, torture, etc. They carry out common fantasies of such behavior, satisfying many audience members' voyeuristic interests, and enhancing the action.

228

Making the Diagnosis

Previously, the diagnostic criteria for ASPD involved a checklist of specific criminal acts. The DSM-IV-TR considers both personality traits and socially deviant behaviors in defining this condition.

i.   *Criminal acts* — commits acts which are against societal norms and meet grounds for arrest
ii. *Deceitfulness* — which is persistent and for personal gain
iii. *Poor impulse control* — opportunistic and impatient
iv. *Aggressiveness/irritability* — often involved in assaults
v.   *Carelessness* — no regard for the safety of self or others
vi. *Irresponsibility* — failure to honor obligations in life's major areas (work, relationships, parenting, etc.)
vii. *Lack of conscience* — little or no remorse for the inconvenience or suffering of others

Conduct disorder, which precedes ASPD and is diagnosed prior to the age of 15 years, consists of four categories of behavior: aggression to people and animals; destruction of property; deceitfulness or theft; and serious violation of rules.

Associated Features

Dr. Hervey Cleckley in his book *The Mask of Sanity* enumerated the following core characteristics in describing ASPD:

* Superficial charm and good "intelligence"
* Absence of delusions and other signs of irrational thinking
* No clear reason for antisocial behavior
* Poor judgment and failure to learn from experience
* Pathologic egocentricity and incapacity for love
* Poverty of emotional reactions; absence of "nervousness"
* Unresponsiveness in general interpersonal relations
* Sex life is impersonal, trivial, and poorly integrated
* Failure to follow any life plan
* Unreliability, untruthfulness, and insincerity
* Lack of remorse or shame
* Specific loss of insight

Man Bites Dog

The English title of this Belgian film translated from French ("*It Happened in Your Neighborhood*") is a misnomer because no one actually sinks their canines into a canine. This movie is a "shockumentary" in which a film crew records the activities of a well-known criminal, Benoît (portrayed by Benoît Poelvoorde).

Benoît is a study in contradiction. One moment he passionately and poetically discusses his views on the intangibles of romance, and literally just minutes later, he shoots a stranger in the back. Benoît is an accomplished pianist, though he proudly proclaims that his new instrument is the blunderbuss.

Benoît has clearly made a commitment to a life of crime, and is both knowledgeable and versatile. At the beginning of the film he discusses the body weight to ballast ratios necessary to dispose of corpses so that they won't float. In the first week of the month he kills a mailman not only to "pinch pensions" but to locate elderly people with money. Benoît recognizes that a pill bottle contains heart medication and frightens an elderly woman to death because he thinks it is easier on her, as well as saving him a bullet. He seems to instinctively know where people hide money in their homes and has no hesitation in liberating it.

Benoît arguably meets all the DSM criteria for ASPD. At his core, he is a predator who senses and exploits the vulnerabilities of his prey for his own gain and pleasure.

Perhaps the most intriguing feature about Benoît is his domination of the film crew. With a mixture of charm and ruthlessness, he quickly becomes their leader and they assist him in several crimes. When the crew's budget gets low he offers to pay to keep the project running. He takes them out to restaurants and pubs to reward them for their endeavors. Even as the crew members are killed one by one, their loyalty to Benoît is unwavering.

Bad Influence

Rob Lowe portrays a charismatic, parasitic sociopath named Alex (although he uses many aliases throughout the film). Michael (James Spader) is a financial analyst grappling with the stresses of advancing his career and upcoming marriage to Ruth (Marcia Cross). Alex seems to have the answer to Michael's problems, which is to go on the offensive, seize opportunities, and ignore the consequences. Alex is initially a liberating and empowering force for Michael, giving him a lesson in Machiavellian strategy on how to stop being victimized by a co-worker. Alex seems to perform an altruistic act at the beginning of the film in rescuing Michael from being assaulted in a bar, but this was just an opportunity for him to steal Michael's wallet.

One evening Alex takes Michael to a party and orchestrates a sexual liaison for him with an attractive young woman named Claire (Lisa Zane). Later, Alex asks Michael about his biggest fear (marriage) and his greatest dream (getting promoted). Michael unwittingly enters into a Faustian pact with Alex, who "assists" him with both of these matters in a typically antisocial fashion. The engagement is abruptly broken off when Alex plays a video tape of Michael's sexual activities during an anniversary party at Ruth's parents' house. Michael gets the promotion after Alex viciously assaults the other candidate, causing him to withdraw his bid.

Michael soon realizes that he cannot operate on Alex's immoral level and asks him to take his leave. Alex thinks that he is still owed for the things he's done and unleashes the full force of his wrath on Michael. At the end of the film, after Michael has successfully avoided being framed for Claire's murder, a cornered Alex offers the following explanation for his actions: *"I didn't make you do anything that wasn't in you already. People are such hypocrites. They walk through their whole lives playing innocent until the day they die, but they're not innocent. I showed you that."*

Borderline Personality

Understanding the Condition

Unlike most of the other personality disorders, the name "borderline" doesn't bring about an immediate concept of what this condition involves. Terms such as "paranoid personality" or "dependent personality" clearly indicate the central feature of these conditions. In the ICD, borderline personality disorder is called the **emotionally unstable personality disorder**. When the term "borderline" was initially applied to this personality, it was chosen because patients' symptoms were deemed to be at the border between neurotic and psychotic disorders. The current criteria do not emphasize psychotic symptoms.

Borderline personality disorder (BPD) is a complex condition. At the heart of BPD are three characteristics: chaotic relationships; wide fluctuations in emotional state (**affect**); and an unstable sense of one's self or self image. People with BPD are "stably unstable" or "predictably unpredictable." The title of the book written by Dr. Jerold J. Kreisman and Hal Straus called *"I Hate You — Don't Leave Me"* captures the turmoil that patients with BPD experience in their close relationships.

BPD in the Movies

A common formula for cinematic portrayals of BPD is as follows: The borderline character, usually a woman, is attractive, talented, and alone. She makes herself available to a man who seems interested but is unavailable to her (because of a long-standing relationship). In spite of this, she magnifies the interest or affection shown to her, and uses increasingly dramatic means (often sexual) to win him over. To spice up the plot, he capitulates but tries to limit her expectations by reminding her that he's involved. She ignores this and becomes distraught at the idea of losing him, believing that he really does love her. Her actions become increasingly frantic until some violent intervention is necessary to stop the continual phone calls, visits, threats, etc.

232

Making the Diagnosis

BPD is diagnosed when the following features are present:

i. *Dramatic efforts to avoid being alone* — even if the "abandonment" is minor or imagined

ii. *A pattern of intense and unstable relationships*

iii. *Disturbances of self-image*

iv. *Self-damaging acts* — an inability to control impulsivity, such as: shoplifting; drug abuse; spending sprees; binge eating; etc.

v. *Suicidal threats or gestures* — such as overdoses which are not planned to be lethal; self-mutilation by cutting, slashing, or burning; suicide notes frequently written and left in areas where they are easily found

vi. *Marked affective instability* — frequent and dramatic changes in affect; such changes are frequently too short to be considered changes in mood, though such patients are often described as being "moody"

vii. *Persistent feelings of emptiness*

viii. *Difficulties with anger control* — frequently get inappropriately angry over matters which would not upset most people to the same degree

ix. *Thoughts of persecution or episodes of dissociation* — these occur transiently and are induced by stressful events

Associated Features

Syphilis used to be called "the great imitator" because it could cause manifestations in many parts of the body. BPD can be considered the great imitator of psychiatry because symptoms can be present from many different major diagnostic areas:

- Mood Disorders
- Eating Disorders
- Dissociative Disorders
- Psychotic Disorders
- Substance -Related Disorders
- Impulse-Control Disorders

In many instances, those with BPD may also have one or more disorders from the categories listed above. Some go on to develop significant medical problems from their continued substance abuse and repeated suicidal gestures.

Play Misty for Me

Misty is a song written and performed by Errol Garner. Evelyn (Jessica Walter) frequently calls a radio station to request that Misty be played by her favorite DJ, David (Clint Eastwood). While on the air, he puts in a plug for a restaurant, and then goes there when his show is finished. Evelyn waits all night for him to arrive, and they quickly develop an attraction for each other. David states early on that he doesn't want complications, and Evelyn seems to understand this. After they are intimate, she begins to pay him unexpected and unwanted visits. She completely idealizes David, but for him it is too much too soon. Evelyn demonstrates rapid changes in affect, particularly when someone is distracting her from focusing on David. In her rages, she yells and insults others, even when they are trying to be helpful.

Evelyn writes on David's mirror with lipstick, gives him presents, and calls him constantly. He reminds her that he doesn't want to begin a relationship, but she is not to be deterred and smothers him with attention. She calls him *"darling"* and is upset that he doesn't love her anymore (he never said that he did). When Tobie (Donna Mills), David's real love interest returns, Evelyn's efforts to avoid abandonment become frantic. She stalks him, copies the key to his home, trashes it, and assaults his housekeeper. While stalking David on another occasion, Evelyn completely misunderstands the purpose of his luncheon with another woman, and causes a scene that costs him a job offer. When David tries to end the affair, Evelyn ups the ante for leaving her. She will not believe that he doesn't want her. Evelyn begs for one last meeting, and forces David to care for her when she cuts her wrists. When he gets medical care for her, she misinterprets his actions as indicating that there is still something between them and manipulates him into spending the night holding her, which is the only way he can prevent her from doing something even more destructive. As David spends more time with Tobie, Evelyn's rage consumes her to the point where she tries to kill them both.

Single White Female

Allison (Bridget Fonda), hoping to find the perfect roommate, allows Hedra (Jennifer Jason Leigh) to move in with her. At first, Hedra appears to fit the bill — she is attentive, polite, and eager to develop a friendship. What isn't revealed until later in the film is that she is desperately searching for an unrealistic level of attachment to another woman. Hedra leads a transient, chaotic existence, but Allison doesn't conduct a background check.

Single White Female provides an excellent example of criteria three (identity disturbance) and seven (chronic feelings of emptiness). Hedra has no concept of being an individual; she idealizes Allison and defines herself as an identical twin. If it were possible, she would merge with Allison. Hedra wears her clothes, copies her hairstyle, and tries to keep her all to herself by interfering in Allison's relationship with boyfriend Sam (Steven Weber). The everyday things that she and Allison do together are of monumental importance to her, but she hides this under a self-effacing and bashful veneer.

Eventually, Allison wants to live with Sam and in doing so reneges on an agreement with Hedra that she would not have to move again. Hedra, who has coped in a functional way as long as she thought she was growing closer to Allison, feels utterly betrayed and sets about on a venomous course of revenge. The sense of rejection Hedra feels is overwhelming — she feels that she has no life without being close to Allison. Hedra engineers a clever scheme to bind Allison to her or face a murder charge for killing Sam. While Hedra commits murders and assaults, she does so in response to feeling abandoned. A person with ASPD generally does not require so personal an event to engage in similarly destructive behavior. *Play Misty for Me* and *Single White Female* have sensationalized violent endings which are not at all typical of BPD, but they do provide good examples of the extent of the rage patients feel when their relationships are threatened.

Histrionic Personality

Understanding the Condition

Some sources indicate that "histrionic" derives from the Greek word *hystera*, meaning uterus. Others indicate the origin is from the Latin word *histrio*, or actor. The key features of the histrionic personality disorder (HPD) are excessive expression of emotions and a strong desire to be the center of attention.

Histrionic people crave novelty, excitement, and stimulation. They are impulsive, easily bored, and seek immediate gratification. As a means of getting attention, histrionic people are frequently seductive, charming, and fanciful. They can become increasingly dramatic if their initial attempts at getting attention are not successful, such as causing a scene, fainting, or fabricating stories.

Histrionic people move from laughter to tears and back to laughter quite quickly, leaving the impression that their emotions are experienced on a superficial level. On occasion, they may embarrass friends with public displays of affection or emotion. Another feature of this condition that can be problematic is pervasive flirtatiousness and seductiveness. This is not usually directed at one person, but rather almost anyone, and can lead to difficulties in sustaining relationships.

HPD in the Movies

Histrionic characters are often cast in romantic roles and comedies. Their capricious style and vanity are qualities around which the plot can be built. They are good at attracting other characters and are naturals for "center of attention" situations. A classic pairing is that of a histrionic female with a male who has an obsessive-compulsive personality. Here, her unpredictability contrasts with his emotional constriction and pedantic nature. A variation on this theme sets the flair and *joie de vivre* of a histrionic character against the rigid, oppressive rules of society.

236

Making the Diagnosis

The DSM-IV-TR criteria for HPD are as follows:

i. *A strong desire to be the center of attention*
ii. *Seductive or provocative behavior with others*
iii. *Expression of emotions is shallow and changes rapidly*
iv. *Uses physical appearance to draw attention to self*
v. *Impressionistic style of speech* — lacks detail; only able to describe vague, global features
vi. *Theatrical and dramatic*
vii. *Easily influenced by others*
viii. *Exaggerates the closeness of relationships*

Associated Features

- Solicit compliments about their appearance
- Exaggerated responses to minor events
- Have an ongoing need for attention which is never satisfied
- Make up their minds hastily and arbitrarily
- Overly trusting of authority figures
- Quickly lose interest in tasks that involve repetition
- Flighty, gregarious, shallow, dramatic, disjointed, and fickle
- *"The emotional sympathies of patients are confined to the selfish furthering of their own wishes. They try ruthlessly to extort the most careful attention from those around them and are extremely sensitive to any perceived neglect. They try to make others give in to their complaints, accusations, and outbursts of temper. The sacrifices made by others only serve to pave the way for new demands. To secure the sympathy of those around them, they use exaggeration."* (adapted from Kraepelin, 1904)
- *"There is a marked dependence on external situations. They have a keen nose for anything new in the making. Because they are always seeking out new possibilities, stable situations seem suffocating. They seize on new objects or situations with great intensity, only to abandon them cold-bloodedly without any compunction as soon as the novelty wears off."* (adapted from Jung, 1921)
- *"They are. . . active, uncritical, and not very dependable. . . carefree, and witty people who play with life"* (adapted from Schneider, 1950)

Born Yesterday

This 1993 remake of the 1950 original stars Melanie Griffith as the "lovable ditz" Billie who is the girlfriend of a crooked business man. She sums up her philosophy of life aptly — *"I only know what I need to so I can get what I want."* She is a very attractive woman, but is principally in a relationship so that her boyfriend can show her off and impress others. However, after brief introductions, her boyfriend wants her to avoid conversations with prospective clients and foists her off on others so that she won't be an embarrassment. Billie is ultimately shown to be an intelligent woman, but for much of the film she prefers not to think about things and is content receiving expensive gifts and staying in posh hotels.

Gone With the Wind

Scarlett O'Hara (Vivien Leigh) displays many histrionic qualities as the quintessential southern belle. The scenes most consistent with HPD are at the beginning of the film prior to the outbreak of the Civil War. Scarlett is haughty, consumed with appearances, and displays shallow emotions. She is entirely in her element in the barbeque scene where she has several eligible young men admiring her and vying for the chance to bring dinner to her. She pouts in a very theatrical manner when she spots the man she yearns for in the company of another woman, and then throws a temper tantrum when he says he plans to marry this woman.

While the early scenes of Scarlett are excellent examples of histrionic attitudes and behaviors, two factors need to be considered here. First is the culture of the southern states prior to the Civil War. Scarlett's behavior is consistent with that of most of the other women shown in the film. Secondly, Scarlett is a young woman at the beginning of the film. While she never loses her histrionic qualities, they do not prevent her from developing into a strong, resourceful, and independent woman later in life.

A Streetcar Named Desire

Vivien Leigh won a second academy award in 1952 for her portrayal of another southern belle, Blanche DuBois, in this adaptation of the Tennessee Williams' play. Blanche flees the ruin she has brought to her life by moving in with her sister Stella (Kim Hunter) and brother-in-law Stanley (Marlon Brando). Blanche usually manages to become the center of attention and employs a repertoire of ways to accomplish this: animated gestures, a fast rate of speech, an air of superiority, fishing for compliments, distraction, and flirtatiousness.

Compared to Billie and Scarlett, it is easier to see how Blanche interacts with others in maladaptive ways, and how the concept of a "disorder" applies to her personality characteristics. She's a charming wastrel who has squandered the family fortune, something she attempts to disguise by dumping piles of paper in front of Stanley when he presses her to account for what has happened. This is a good demonstration of the vague and impressionistic style of thinking seen in HPD — Blanche just can't be bothered with the details. To her, all is seduction. She readily admits that she deceives others, and enjoys what she considers to be *"creating illusions"* about her and her activities. She flirts with every man she encounters, and though she'd like to be married again, she so mishandles the affections of Stanley's friend Mitch (Karl Malden) that he loses interest in her.

One scene in particular captures the essence of Blanche's suggestibility and dramatic need for attention. Blanche is waiting for Mitch to take her to dinner. He's running a few minutes late, and a knock on the door produces not him, but a teenage boy trying to collect money for his newspaper route. Blanche, who is in love with the idea of love, and possibly upset that Mitch is late, gives the boy an inappropriately passionate kiss that ends seconds before Mitch arrives. We later learn that Blanche was driven out of town for having an affair with one of her teenage students.

Narcissistic Personality

Understanding the Condition

Narcissus, a figure from Greek mythology, was said to be extraordinarily handsome. Once when Narcissus was fatigued from hunting, he came upon a pool of clear water. As he quenched his thirst, he was captivated by his own beauty and fell hopelessly in love with his reflection. He was so transfixed that he could not pull himself away from the pool and gradually wasted away and died there. The flowers that grew from the spot where his body lay also bear his name.

The core elements of narcissistic personality disorder (**NPD**) are: grandiosity, a perpetual need for admiration, and a lack of empathy. Many prominent authors have emphasized a distinction between a healthy or adaptive level of narcissism and pathological self-absorption. If people didn't put themselves first and at least take care of their basic needs, then further development wouldn't be possible. NPD can be a difficult diagnosis to apply to people in industrialized or developed societies because confidence, unshakeable optimism, and charm are characteristics which are usually rewarded. Many narcissistic people possess at least some degree of intelligence, ability, good looks, leadership potential, etc., but they have greatly inflated opinions of these qualities. The **ICD** has no analog for NPD in its list of personality disorders.

NPD in the Movies

In a number of movies, narcissism is a personality flaw that the plot sets out to correct. The main character is too self-centered to see the detrimental effects that his or her actions have on others. Narcissistic characters take all of the time, attention, and resources they can get, robbing others of opportunities and even recognition for their assistance. Usually an intervention of heroic, divine, or supernatural proportions is needed to teach the narcissistic character a lesson that reforms his or her greed, pride, envy, exploitative nature, selfishness, or deficient social conscience.

Making the Diagnosis

NPD is diagnosed on the presence of the following character traits:

i. *Exaggerated sense of self-importance*
ii. *Unrealistic fantasies* — of power, success, brilliance, beauty, love, etc.
iii. *Wants recognition for "specialness"* — can only be understood by, or insists on dealing with, highly regarded or accomplished people
iv. *Requires excessive amounts of admiration*
v. *Sense of entitlement* — expects automatic V.I.P. treatment and compliance with all of his or her expectations
vi. *Exploitative of Others*
vii. *Unempathic*
viii. *Persistent envy* — feels both envious of others and believes that he or she is the object of envy
ix. *Arrogant or Haughty Attitudes or Behaviors*

Associated Features

- Narcissistic personalities significantly exaggerate their own achievements and are disdainful of the accomplishments of others
- Whereas histrionic personalities appear to primarily seek attention, narcissists seek admiration, affirmation of their special status, and to exploit others for personal gain
- *"Narcissistic people are competitive, ambitious, and self-assured. They naturally assume positions of leadership, act in a decisive and unwavering manner, and expect others to recognize their special qualities and cater to them. Beyond being self-confident, they are audacious and persuasive, having sufficient charm to win others over to their own causes. Problematic in this regard is their lack of reciprocity and sense of entitlement — their assumption is that what they wish for is their due."* (adapted from Millon, 1994)
- *"Their main strategies consist of doing whatever they can to reinforce their superior status and expand their personal domain. They become angry with those who do not accord them the admiration they believe they are entitled to. . .* (adapted from Beck and Freeman, 1990)

Madame Bovary

Gustave Flaubert's novel has been made into many movies and television specials. The most recent release in English was made in 1949 and starred Jennifer Jones as Emma Bovary and Van Heflin as Charles Bovary. In the story, Emma is a beautiful young woman who spent several years in a convent prior to returning to her father's farm. She immersed herself in romance novels and spent her days fantasizing about. . ."*absurd dreams of fashion and luxury. . .ridiculous dreams of high romance and impossible love. . . Emma had a terrifying capacity for pursuing the impossible. . . she learned that the strange was beautiful and the familiar contemptible. . . that glamour and excitement was to be found in the far away and only boredom in the here and now.*"

Prior to getting married, Charles warns Emma that he must work hard to make up for a *"lack of talent"* and that he is not a very exciting person. Emma's sense of entitlement is apparent even during her wedding reception — the antics of the townspeople strike her as vulgar and she wishes to leave as soon as possible. During her first morning as a married woman she becomes frantic to remodel her house and contacts a linen draper, to whom she will eventually owe a huge (and unpayable) debt. When the house is decorated she has a soirée to impress her friends. A marquis in attendance invites her to a ball at his château. At that ball, Emma immediately abandons her husband and dances the evening away with a variety of wealthy, handsome men. Like Narcissus himself, she becomes entranced by the image of beauty that she sees in the mirror. In the company of other men, Emma is coy, seductive, and high-spirited. When her husband, who has been ignored all evening, interrupts to dance with her, she flees the ball in disgrace.

Emma goes on to shamelessly engage in a series of affairs. She is indifferent to her daughter, often ignoring her as she pursues other interests. Emma would like Charles to have more status in their community and berates him into planning a surgical procedure that, in the opinion of one member of the town, would

242

earn him the Legion of Honor. One of Emma's paramours summed up his experience with her as follows: *"I am a fairly courageous man, but I was afraid of you. . .You ask for something that consumes while it burns, that destroys everything it touches. I didn't want to be destroyed."* While Madame Bovary displays a number of histrionic traits, it is an excellent illustration of the exploitative and unempathic aspects of NPD.

Groundhog Day

Phil Connors (Bill Murray) is a weatherman sent to cover Groundhog Day in Puxsawtany, PA. Referring to himself as *"the talent,"* Phil is arrogant, condescending, and rude towards others. Through some supernatural intervention, he is forced to live the same day over and over again. Before he is let out of this conundrum, Phil must take a genuine interest in the people around him instead of exploiting them for personal gain.

Wall Street

Gordon Gekko (Michael Douglas) is a corporate raider who is particularly adept at finding companies that he can liquidate for a quick profit. Gekko thrives on insider trading and manipulates Bud Fox (Charlie Sheen), a young stock broker, into believing that he (Bud) must engage in illegal activities in order to be special or important enough to take up Gekko's time. Gekko displays many of the cardinal features of NPD, particularly: exploitation of others; a sense of entitlement; a lack of empathy for the lives he ruins; and a preoccupation with unlimited success. This is well demonstrated during his "Greed is Good" speech to the board of directors of a company that he is planning to take over. Ultimately, Gekko's narcissism leads to his undoing. After he has a falling out with Bud, he pummels him while spewing out a confession that is recorded by the police. Had he not returned to even the score in person, Gekko's lawyer had taken steps to ensure that he (Gekko) would not be linked to Bud's illegal trades.

Avoidant Personality

Understanding the Condition

In the ICD, this is called the **anxious personality disorder**, which is a better descriptive term. Patients with this condition are not principally seeking to avoid relationships, but rather to find an unusually high degree of acceptance in social situations. The essential features of the avoidant personality disorder (APD) are: social inhibition, feelings of being inadequate, and a hypersensitivity to negative evaluation even when it is constructive, mild, or imagined. Avoidant people have low self-esteem, are shy, and "avoid" situations where they feel they may be embarrassed.

At first glance, APD may seem similar to SzdPD because patients with both conditions end up being socially isolated. The major distinguishing characteristic between the two conditions is that in APD people long to have an active social life. Avoidant patients are so fearful of rejection or ridicule that they are inhibited around others. Another feature that distinguishes these disorders is that avoidant patients experience and display a full range of emotions, as opposed to the rather narrow affective range of SzdPD. APD has much in common with **social phobia** (found in the anxiety disorders chapter).

APD in the Movies

Passive, introverted, or isolated characters are not usually prime choices for lead roles in movies. Directors only have a limited number of scenes to help viewers familiarize themselves with the main characters. If something active or interesting isn't happening, this task is compounded. Possibly the most typical role for avoidant characters is that of the reluctant hero — someone with many fine personal qualities who just needs the right person or situation to help get started. Avoidant characters need a shot of courage, an enabling pep talk, an understanding romantic partner, or some crisis to get them off the sidelines.

Making the Diagnosis

APD is diagnosed on the basis of the following criteria:

i. *Occupation restricted to avoid others* — fears criticism, disapproval, or rejection

ii. *Needs a guarantee of acceptance* — before agreeing to participate in social situations

iii. *Intimate relationships restrained* — fears shame or ridicule

iv. *Preoccupied with thoughts of criticism or rejection* — will usually avoid situations where acceptance is not overtly clear

v. *Feels inadequate in interpersonal situations* — behaves in an inhibited fashion

vi. *Poor self-image* — sees self as inept, unappealing, or inferior, even when no one has expressed these sentiments

vii. *Reluctant to take personal risks* — for fear of embarrassment

Associated Features

- Avoidant people are hyper-alert to the thoughts and moods of those around them and constantly scan for disapproval
- Before accepting others as friends, avoidant people seem to construct stringent tests to ascertain that loyalty and safety await them in relationships
- *"They live life as a fragmentary experience. They do not assert themselves fully, but cannot submit to others either. Refusing to act and face the perils of the world, they prefer to live outside the struggle of life as if they live on a well-protected island."* (adapted from Kahn, 1931)
- *"Avoidant personalities, with little to no provocation, feel that others look down on them, do not take them seriously, and do not care for their company. Since they are unable to accept themselves, they cannot believe that others would befriend them when their shortcomings are (ostensibly) so apparent. On a deeper level, avoidant people appear to be convinced that others plainly despise them."* (adapted from Horney, 1945)
- *"The dominant features of APD are: confused and conflicted feelings; persistent intrusion of distracting and ambivalent thoughts; feelings of social isolation and worthlessness; and the anticipation/fear of humiliation and betrayal."* (adapted from Millon, 1969)

245

Zelig

Zelig is a fake documentary or "mockumentary" about a medical phenomenon occurring in the 1920's and 1930's. Leonard Zelig (Woody Allen) is a human chameleon. He changes his appearance, accent, demeanor, and opinions to seamlessly blend in with the people around him. At a speak-easy party, he "morphs" from a white gangster into a black trumpet player in a matter of minutes. On another occasion he swells up to 250 lbs. in the presence of two portly gentlemen. Two French visitors induce him to grow a pencil-thin moustache and speak their language in a passable manner.

Zelig is eventually brought to medical attention and becomes the principal focus of the psychiatrist Eudora Fletcher (Mia Farrow). In her company, Zelig assumes the appearance, bearing, and vocabulary of a colleague and identifies himself as a doctor. Under hypnosis, he explains to her that he changes himself around others because he wants to be safe and to be liked. The narrator nicely sums up Zelig's life. . . "*he wanted only to fit in, to belong, to go unseen by his enemies, and be loved. . .*"

While this comedy takes matters to a farcical extent, it captures the essence of APD, in showing Zelig's extreme desire to fit in with others. He is willing to compromise, sacrifice, and disavow any aspect of himself just to be liked and accepted. Avoidant patients, in order to obtain the unconditional guarantee of acceptance they seek, would do the same things that Zelig does if it were humanly possible. As is common for many people with APD, Zelig doesn't distinguish himself in any of his various occupations, doesn't pursue a relationship (at least in the first part of the film), or reveal any of his own thoughts or feelings.

Zelig's upbringing includes almost every unfortunate thing that could happen to a child. However, none of the events listed in his background should be seen as being clearly causative of APD.

Four Weddings and a Funeral

Charles (Hugh Grant) has two circles of friends; a larger one consisting of people who invite him to their weddings, and a smaller circle of unattached friends and family members. When Charles first sees Carrie (Andie MacDowell) he feels the "bolt of lightning" that tells him she's the one for him. Charles bumbles his way through an introduction and then puts his foot in his mouth when he insults another man's wife. Charles is seen shortly afterwards banging his head against a tree because of his shameful remark.

In spite of his awkwardness, Carrie gives Charles enough encouragement for him to feel secure around her, but he can't bring himself to make his feelings known before she returns home from the wedding. When he sees her three months later, she is already engaged. They shop for her wedding dress together and then go their separate ways. Charles turns and runs after Carrie to tell her how he feels, and does so in a manner that reveals his avoidant nature: *"Look. . . sorry. This is a really stupid question, particularly in view of our recent shopping excursion. But I just wondered, if by any chance. . . I just wondered. I really feel, in short, to recap in a slightly clearer version, the words of David Cassidy in fact, while he was still with the Partridge Family. I think I love you. And I just wondered whether by any chance if you wouldn't like to. . . no, of course not, um, I'm an idiot, he's not. Lovely to see you, sorry to disturb, got to get on."*

Charles seems to feel comfortable only in the company of his inner circle. He yearns for an intimate relationship and laments that he would like to be more than just a spectator at a wedding. In spite of the opportunities around him, Charles is reluctant to take risks and partake in new activities. He seems perpetually mired in self-reproach, particularly when he can't seem to get anywhere on time. While some of his friends express stronger negative views about themselves, Charles seems to lack the confidence to pursue Carrie, or someone else with whom he would feel the same lightning bolt of attraction.

Dependent Personality

Understanding the Condition

While almost everyone relies on others for important things such as love or nurturance, people with dependent personality disorder (DPD) do so to an excessive degree. They fear being alone, and often engage in clinging or submissive behaviors to try to elicit caregiving from those close to them. Dependent personalities are quite happy to delegate major life decisions to others.

People with DPD often work below their level of ability because they think that they are unable to function without the continual assistance of others. By appearing to be competent, they fear that abandonment will soon follow. Dependent people don't want to upset someone by taking a promotion, further, they are usually quite indecisive and do not gravitate towards leadership roles.

Dependent people will often go to considerable lengths to maintain bonds with others, including tolerating almost any form of abuse and engaging in masochistic behavior. They emphasize their weaknesses to make others feel more capable or important in their presence.

DPD in the Movies

Dependent personalities are often depicted in one of the following roles:

- A talented or worthy person who initially refuses to take a chance on growth or independence and requires some life event to propel him or her towards fulfillment
- The devoted spouse/parent/friend of an evil character; their need to stay attached to these stronger figures overrides an appreciation for the unethical or immoral things being done
- Sidekicks for the main character; dependent personalities selflessly devote their lives to supporting others, don't mind missing out on their share of the credit for heroic deeds, and often do tedious work for their more flamboyant partner

248

Making the Diagnosis

DPD is diagnosed when the following features are present:

i. *Indecisiveness* — requires an excessive amount of advice and reassurance before making even minor decisions

ii. *Delegates responsibility for major areas of life* — quite happily has someone else manage his or her life

iii. *Difficulty disagreeing with others* — for fear that it will lead to abandonment

iv. *Has difficulty initiating tasks* — because of a lack of self-confidence, not a lack of energy or ideas

v. *Goes to excessive lengths to obtain support and nurturance* — even to the point of doing something unpleasant or deprecating

vi. *Feels uncomfortable or helpless when alone*

vii. *When alone, urgently seeks another relationship* — may make poor choices because of the need to find attachment

viii. *Preoccupied with unrealistic fears of being left to care for self*

Associated Features

- The "center of gravity" for a dependent person lies in the person to whom he or she is attached, not with him or herself
- Dependent personalities are often pessimistic and full of self-reproach; their esteem comes from the support and encouragement they receive from others
- *"They show a marked need for affection and approval. They seek a special partner who will fulfill all expectations of life and take responsibility for good and evil. Dependent personalities have three characteristic attitudes: a pervasive feeling of weakness and helplessness; they readily subordinate themselves and feel that everyone is superior; thirdly, there is a tendency to view themselves by what others think of them, leading to a sense of self-esteem that rises and falls with the opinions of others."* (adapted from Horney, 1945)
- *"Dependent people feel 'the source of all good' to be outside of themselves, and the only way to get what they want is to receive it from someone else. They feel lost when alone because they feel that they cannot do anything without help."* (adapted from Fromm, 1947)

249

Death Becomes Her

The central theme in this movie is the perpetual competition between two old friends, actress Madeline Ashton (Meryl Streep) and writer Helen Sharp (Goldie Hawn). Dr. Ernest Menville (Bruce Willis) is a hapless pawn who is controlled by both women into being an accomplice in their underhanded schemes. At the beginning of the film, Ernest is a highly regarded plastic surgeon. Within seven years of marriage to Madeline, he loses his medical license, has become a raging alcoholic, and earns a living by cosmetically enhancing corpses at a funeral home. He avoids confrontations with Madeline to keep the peace, tolerates her affairs with younger men, and buffers her anguish at becoming older and losing her attractiveness.

Ernest's behaviors have many features consistent with DPD, but his attitudes do not. He longs to return to medical practice, regrets that he hasn't left Madeline, and eventually finds a way to live a fulfilling life without either woman. Someone with DPD would most likely have remained with Madeline or Helen (or both) and accepted their manipulative and disrespectful ways.

 # Rocky

At the beginning of the film, Adrian (Talia Shire) is a meek, subservient employee in a pet store. She can barely interact with Rocky (Sylvester Stallone) when he frequents the shop. Adrian is thirty years old, has never been in a man's home, and lives with her brother, Paulie. Paulie has to throw the Thanksgiving turkey out the door for Adrian to give up on serving him dinner and go out on a date with Rocky. Adrian has to weather Paulie's temper tantrums and cater to him, often getting up to replace his can of beer. Eventually, her bond with Rocky is strong enough that she confronts Paulie on his abusive nature and then leaves to live with Rocky. Adrian requires considerable encouragement from Rocky to enter into a relationship and in this way demonstrates some avoidant personality features (making this a less pure example of DPD).

250

What About Bob?

After driving his last therapist into an early retirement, Bob (Bill Murray) is referred to Dr. Leo Marvin (Richard Dreyfuss) who squeezes him in for an appointment just before taking a month's vacation. While Bob describes over a dozen symptoms in the initial appointment, Dr. Marvin quickly and astutely determines that Bob suffers from *"separation anxiety"* and *"an extreme need for family connections."* Later in the film, Dr. Marvin describes Bob to a colleague as *"human crazy glue."*

Bob feels a renewed sense of hope after this brief meeting but then spirals into despair when he realizes he won't be able to see Dr. Marvin for a month. Going to excessive lengths for nurturance, Bob makes repeated phone calls to Dr. Marvin's cottage and then cooks up a scheme to find out the actual address.

Once he arrives at the cottage, he simply cannot seem to manage on his own after experiencing the hospitality of Dr. Marvin's family. Even walking down a road winding through the woods is overwhelming for Bob because there are no people around him and he feels helpless. Bob finds ways to ingratiate himself with everyone around him as a means of prolonging his visit. In Bob's mind, every interaction turns into an invitation for further visits and deepening the attachment he feels towards his psychiatrist's family.

Bob has no life waiting for him back in the city and seems to exist only to receive treatment, attention, and advice from his doctor. Bob's need to feel connected to others is so strong that he is oblivious to the disruption he causes. As he begins to overstay his welcome, Bob is quite willing to endure increasingly dramatic behaviors on Dr. Marvin's part because he believes them to be new forms of therapy. Bob places complete trust in Dr. Marvin and would seemingly follow any advice that was offered, which is one of the cardinal characteristics of DPD.

Obsessive-Compulsive Personality

Understanding the Condition

Obsessive-Compulsive Personality Disorder (OCPD) bears a very similar name to **obsessive-compulsive disorder** (OCD), which is presented in the anxiety disorders chapter. In spite of this, these two conditions have less in common than their names would suggest. In the ICD, OCPD is called the **anancastic** (or **anankastic**) **personality disorder**, from the Greek word for "forced." Possibly the easiest metaphor to use for OCPD is that of a "living machine." Patients seek to control themselves and others to achieve a state of order and perfection. A classic description of OCPD includes orderliness, obstinacy, and parsimony. In common parlance, such people are called "anal" or "anal-compulsive," based on a stage in Freud's development theory. In industrialized nations, two sets of personality features appear to be particularly helpful. Narcissistic features have been discussed on page 240. Obsessive-compulsive traits are very helpful in getting through huge workloads, situations where attention to detail is critical, and where leisure activities can be easily pushed aside in favor of more work. However, in OCPD, these behaviors are a way of life.

OCPD in the Movies

Obsessive-compulsive characters, like narcissists, are often prime targets for having to learn that there is more to life. Frequent depictions are as harsh, mean-spirited control freaks such as domineering bosses or workaholic spouses. Often, some disaster or event occurs that causes the main character to have to adapt to a less absorbed lifestyle. There is usually an attractive member of the opposite sex supporting the change as well. In other portrayals, an obsessive character is the "know it all" who saves the day with some important piece of information (that apparently takes a lifetime of studying to have at one's command).

Making the Diagnosis

OCPD is diagnosed on the basis of the following diagnostic criteria:

i.   *Preoccupied with rules, details, lists, and organization* — to the extent where the point of the activity is lost; this can also be considered "missing the forest for the trees"

ii. *Perfectionism that interferes with task completion* — initial efforts and subsequent revisions never seem to be up to the person's internal standards of perfection

iii. *Excessively devoted to work* — so much so that there is no time spent in enjoying leisure activities

iv. *Overconscientious and inflexible about values, morals, ethics, etc.*

v.   *Hoards items* — is unable to discard items when they have little to no value

vi. *Reluctant to delegate tasks* — needs to ensure that others do things exactly as he or she would do them

vii. *Miserly spending habits*

viii. *Rigidity and stubbornness*

Associated Features

- Obsessive personalities like rules — both making them for others and following them themselves; when there are no rules to follow, they either take an inordinate amount of time to make decisions, or they become angry but cannot express this directly

- OCPD shares many features of the Type A personality: time urgency; competitiveness; and excessive devotion to work

- Strong emotions or emotionally expressive people make those with OCPD uneasy; similarly, they are not usually very affectionate and come across as being formal and stiff

- *"Obsessive-compulsive personalities have little faith in anything that they might get from the outside world. They feel secure when they hoard and save — spending is seen as a threat. Literally and metaphorically they surround themselves with a protective wall, with the main aim being to acquire as much as possible. Matters beyond their own frontiers are seen as dangerous and unclean — things which cannot be mastered or controlled."* (adapted from Fromm, 1947)

Unstrung Heroes

The main character's father, Sid Lidz (John Turturro), is a good example of an obsessive-compulsive personality. Sid is an inventor, and spends much of his time filming the experiments he conducts with his family because he believes that *"documentation is important."* We see Sid giving his son Steven (Nathan Watt) a birthday present. Though Steven wanted a camera, Sid built an apparatus that rises and lowers over Steven's bed like a canopy (largely for Sid's own satisfaction). Instead of trying to get Steven interested in this contraption, Sid reminds Steven that safety comes first and immediately demonstrates how to make a timely exit from his invention. Sid quickly loses his focus on the birthday celebration when another of his inventions doesn't work, and he becomes short-tempered with Steven. As he is being tucked into bed, Steven asks his mother if Sid is from another planet.

Sid quotes philosophers at dinner, which is out of context to the discussion occurring beforehand. His daughter Sandy asks how many stars there are, and Sid offers a very convoluted, complex answer that quickly bores her. Later, he asks her what the highest number is, and despairs when she says *"eleven"* (after he told her it was infinity). When Steven shows an interest in running for class president, Sid makes his son's bid a problem-solving exercise, diagramming their strategy on a chalkboard. Sid dreams of a *"Technotopia."* He tells Steven that:
"Everything can always be broken down into numbers."
"Science, pure science, will be earth's ultimate salvation."

This portrayal falls short in some aspects. Sid does have a warm side. He is very romantic and complimentary towards his wife. He obviously wants the best for his children, and in fact his logical thinking and problem-solving approaches help Steven later in the film. Sid allows some rules to be broken for the sake of fun, and is flexible about other matters when Steven shows a particular interest in them.

The Remains of the Day

Anthony Hopkins portrays butler James Stevens, though viewers would be hard pressed to know him by anything but 'Mr. Stevens.' Stevens is the prototype of the English butler: prim, meticulous, and utterly controlled. He is perpetually at work, saying that he can only feel contented when he has done all he can to be of service to his employer. Stevens reads not for enjoyment, but to further his knowledge and command of the English language.

Miss Kenton (Emma Thompson) is hired on as the housekeeper at the beginning of the film and develops an affection for Stevens that he also feels, but cannot bring himself to disclose. Most of his obsessive-compulsive traits become highlighted against her humanistic and compassionate ways. In one scene, Stevens' father, who is employed as the under-butler, is dying and the younger Stevens refuses to leave his post at dinner. When Stevens finally takes a break, his father has passed away. Unable to demonstrate any emotion upon seeing his father's body, Stevens sends the doctor away to attend to a visiting dignitary's blisters.

Miss Kenton delivers some flowers to Stevens' room and catches him napping with a book in his hands. She teases him about whether he is reading a 'racy' book and then pries it out of his hands. In a moment where he could have easily shown his feelings for her, Stevens instead cowers and asks her to leave because she is intruding on his private time. Miss Kenton finally turns her affections elsewhere and tells Stevens that she has accepted a marriage proposal. Later, she weeps audibly in her room and Stevens, upon hearing her, enters to investigate. Again, he has a chance to show some warmth and decency, but ultimately informs her of an area in the house that hasn't been dusted. Many years later after Miss Kenton separates from her husband, she and Stevens arrange a meeting. She's interested to see if he is receptive to a relationship with her. His purpose in meeting her is solely to ask if she will return to service as a housekeeper.

Diagnosis Illustrated

Movies

Paranoid Personality Disorder

Shine
The Caine Mutiny

Schizoid Personality Disorder

Flesh and Bone
For A Few Dollars More
The Net

Schizotypal Personality Disorder

Grumpy Old Men
Hello Again

Antisocial Personality Disorder

Bad Influence
Man Bites Dog

Borderline Personality Disorder

Play Misty for Me
Single White Female

Histrionic Personality Disorder

A Streetcar Named Desire
Born Yesterday
Gone With the Wind

Narcissistic Personality Disorder

Groundhog Day
Madame Bovary
Wall Street

Avoidant Personality Disorder

Four Weddings and a Funeral
Zelig

Dependent Personality Disorder

Death Becomes Her
Rocky
What About Bob?

Obsessive-Compulsive Personality Disorder

The Remains of the Day
Unstrung Heroes

Chapter 16

Mental
Retardation

Mental Retardation

Understanding the Condition

The term "mental retardation" (**MR**) strikes some people as cruel, antiquated, or at least politically incorrect. The word "retard" itself means slowness or hindrance. The subnormal mental functioning that is the hallmark of MR may most accurately be described as a mental deficiency or disability. In recent years, terms such as "special" or "challenged" have been used and certainly sound less pejorative. Because the DSM-IV-TR still uses MR, it will also be used here.

Intelligence quotient (IQ) is measured by the following formula:

IQ = Mental Age/Chronological Age x 100

Mental age is determined by use of a standardized assessment such as the Wechsler Intelligence Scale, which has age-appropriate versions for children, adolescents, and adults. By definition, the IQ of someone with precisely average intelligence is 100. The population overall is becoming more intelligent and in the last several decades the average IQ would have increased to about 115 if adjustments weren't made to the scoring system. IQ testing is accurate to within approximately 5 points. IQ rarely varies after the age of 18 years and test scores are considered to be reliable indicators of enduring general intellectual ability.

MR is diagnosed when a person's IQ is 70 or below, which on a bell curve is two standard deviations below average and affects just over 2% of the population.

The classification of MR according to IQ in the DSM-IV-TR is as follows:
- Dull normal 80 to 90
- Mild MR 50/55 to 70
- Severe MR 20/25 to 35/40
- Borderline 70 to 79
- Moderate MR 35/40 to 50/55
- Profound MR below 20/25

Making the Diagnosis

MR is diagnosed based on the following criteria:

i. *IQ of 70 or below*
ii. *Onset is before the age of 18 years*
iii. *Impairment in adaptive functioning is present in the following areas:*

- *Communication*
- *Self-care*
- *Home Living*
- *Social and Interpersonal Skills*
- *Use of Community Resources*

- *Work*
- *Leisure*
- *Health*
- *Self-Direction*
- *Academic Skills*

Associated Features

- A person with an IQ of less than 70 who did not have significant deficits in adaptive behavior would not be diagnosed with MR
- There are a variety of assessment scales that measure adaptive functioning or behavior
- Culture, education, language skills, native tongue, socioeconomic status, and a variety of other factors can affect scores on IQ tests
- People with dementia have mental functioning in a normal IQ range at age 18 years, which is a distinguishing feature between this illness and MR
- MR is more common in boys, with a gender ratio of 1.5:1
- The cutoff age of 18 years was selected because some people with intellectual impairments can develop their adaptive functioning to the point where the diagnosis of MR no longer applies
- The DSM-IV-TR specifies the following causes of MR:
  - Heredity
  - Early alterations of embryonic development
  - Environment influences
  - Mental disorders
  - Pregnancy and problems around the time of birth
  - Medical conditions acquired in infancy or childhood
- Some patients with MR have an array of language, movement, and behavior abnormalities

Charly

This movie is based on the novel *Flowers for Algernon* by Daniel Keyes. Algernon is the name of a laboratory mouse who undergoes a (completely fictitious) surgical procedure to increase his intelligence. The scientists who pioneer this operation are looking for a person who is willing to undergo the same procedure.

Charly Gordon (Cliff Robertson) suffers from **mild mental retardation**. He lives in a rooming house, attends night school to improve his knowledge, and is employed at a bakery. His IQ is measured by a group of scientists and some of the scenes depicted in the film are part of intelligence testing. Charly scores a performance IQ of 59, a verbal IQ of 69, and a full scale IQ of 70. The principal difficulties that are depicted relating to MR are Charly's academic and communication skills. He has a limited vocabulary and often doesn't understand what other people are saying. His spelling is phonetic and contains many reversed letters. Charly has a chalk board in his room to remind him of the next day's events and in one scene writes, "Wensday, wirk, shcool" on it. Other features of MR that are accurately depicted in this film are Charly's interest in activities below his chronological age, disinhibited behavior, and limited problem solving skills.

I Am Sam

Sam Dawson (Sean Penn) is a man with **mild mental retardation** who functions at about the level of a seven-year old. He is gainfully employed, lives independently, and manages his life successfully until he becomes a single parent. The stresses and strains of raising a child highlight Sam's limitations and he eventually is brought to the attention of children's protective services and the courts.

In the audio commentary on the DVD, the director indicates how much research went into this film. Parts of the story were pieced together from actual experiences of people with psychiatric disorders. Two of Sam's close friends, Brad (Brad Silverman) and Joe (Joseph Rosenberg) are actually actors with disabilities.

What's Eating Gilbert Grape

Arnie Grape (Leonardo DiCaprio) lives with his family in rural Iowa. He appears to have suffered from some serious illness when he was born and as a result was not expected to live past the age of ten. At the beginning of the film Arnie is just days shy of his eighteenth birthday. He's managed to develop physically but suffers from **moderate mental retardation**. Arnie is a handful and requires constant attention from his siblings to keep out of trouble. Left unsupervised Arnie likes to climb things, his favorite structure being the town water tower. He has no awareness of the potential danger in doing this. Arnie has the following deficits in adaptive functioning:

- Communication — repeats the phrases of others (**echolalia**); Arnie raises his voice often and inappropriately; he often leaves articles and prepositions out of his speech
- Work — accompanies his brother to a grocery store but can't be trusted with any responsibilities or tasks
- Self-care — cannot bathe himself and spends an entire night shivering in cold bath water because he can't figure how to get out of the tub
- Leisure — disinhibited; activities are of low complexity
- Home Living — entirely dependent on his family
- Health — places himself in jeopardy by his fascination with climbing trees and the water tower
- Social and Interpersonal Skills — inappropriately blunt or silly when speaking with others
- Self-Direction — needs constant attention and supervision

When Arnie gets overwhelmed or feels that he is responsible for doing something wrong, he smacks himself repeatedly with both hands. Repetitive, self-injurious behaviors like this are a common finding among people with moderate-to-severe MR.

Movie	Features/Diagnosis
Charly	Mild Mental Retardation
I Am Sam	Mild Mental Retardation
What's Eating Gilbert Grape	Moderate Mental Retardation; Impairment in Adaptive Functioning

Chapter 17

Substance-
Related
Disorders

Substance-Related Disorders

Understanding the Condition

Substance-related disorders comprise a vast and fascinating area of psychiatry, but also a tragic one. The DSM-IV-TR considers a **substance** to be a drug of abuse, a medication (both over-the-counter (OTC) and prescribed), or a toxin. The range of psychological symptoms that can be caused by substances is staggering. Substance use and abuse can produce symptoms that are indistinguishable from psychiatric conditions that have no known cause. It may take a period of abstinence ranging from days to months to ascertain what effects a substance was actually causing. For this reason, psychiatrists are keenly interested as to whether a person has been taking substances or has a medical illness, as these factors must be considered before an accurate diagnosis can be made.

The DSM-IV-TR devotes its largest chapter to substance-related disorders, and breaks them down into two groups. The first group, **substance use disorders**, describes the pattern of use as well as the related effects on lifestyle. The second group, **substance-induced disorders**, details the symptoms and complications related to the use of specific substances.

Any substance, even water, taken in sufficient amounts will poison the brain to the point where it can't work properly. As a result of this malfunction, psychiatric symptoms develop (such as hallucinations, delusions, or mood changes). Any of the changes in cognition, emotion, perception, or behavior seen in other psychiatric conditions can also be caused by substance use. When this occurs, a person is diagnosed with a **substance-induced condition** instead of the **primary psychiatric disorder**.

The range of substances that affect the human brain is astronomical. A fascinating and well-referenced resource is *The Encyclopedia of Psychoactive Substances* by Richard Rudgley.

264

Substance Use Disorders

Substance Abuse

This condition is diagnosed when a pattern of substance use causes significant impairment in some major aspect of a person's life, and the following criteria are met:

i.   *Failure to fulfill major role obligations at work, home, or school*
ii. *Use continues in physically hazardous situations (e.g. driving a motor vehicle)*
iii. *Legal problems*
iv. *Interpersonal problems*

These symptoms must occur in the same twelve-month period. If the criteria are met for substance dependence (see below), then it takes priority and substance abuse would not be diagnosed.

Substance Dependence

Two features are central to the concept of dependence:

i.   **Tolerance** — *the same amount of a substance no longer produces the desired effect, or larger amounts are required to achieve the usual level of intoxication*
ii. **Withdrawal** — *in the absence of taking a substance, characteristic abstinence symptoms occur, or the substance is taken to specifically avoid the onset of withdrawal symptoms*

The other features of dependence are:

iii. *The substance is taken in larger amounts than was originally intended*
iv. *There is a persistent desire to quit and efforts to cut down on the substance use are unsuccessful*
v.   *Considerable time is involved in substance-related activities*
vi. *Important social, occupational, or recreational activities are given up to engage in substance use*
vii. *Substance use continues despite being aware that physical or psychological problems have developed*

Substance-Induced Disorders

Substance Intoxication

i.   *A predictable and reversible syndrome occurs after the substance enters the body*

ii. *Maladaptive changes occur in cognition, emotion, perception, or behavior that are related to the effects of the substance*

Substance Withdrawal

i.   *After tolerance occurs, reduction or discontinuation of the substance causes a predictable syndrome*

ii. *The withdrawal syndrome causes maladaptive changes in cognition, emotion, perception, or behavior*

Because substance use can mimic primary psychiatric disorders, the DSM-IV-TR provides a distinct set of diagnoses that are also coded on Axis I. These diagnoses indicate both the major type of symptoms experienced, and that a substance caused the symptoms:

- Substance-Induced Delirium
- Substance-Induced Persisting Dementia
- Substance-Induced Persisting Amnesia
- Substance-Induced Psychotic Disorder
- Substance-Induced Mood Disorder
- Substance-Induced Anxiety Disorder
- Substance-Induced Sexual Dysfunction
- Substance-Induced Sleep Disorder

Most substances of abuse can cause psychotic, mood, anxiety, or sleep problems. Sexual disorders are somewhat less common. Alcohol and some sedative medication can cause amnesia (blackouts). Alcohol and inhalants (such as gasoline) can cause permanent brain damage (dementia). Almost every substance has a recognizable intoxication syndrome, and most have withdrawal symptoms. Both physical and psychological components of intoxication and withdrawal can be present.

Substances of Abuse

While the range of abusable substances varies from lettuce seeds to puffer fish, the DSM-IV-TR narrows them down into the following categories:

- Alcohol
- Amphetamines — stimulants that have some medical uses; they have a similar action to cocaine but have a longer duration; common street names are: uppers, speed, meth, crank, bennies, dexies, crystal, ice, glass
- Caffeine
- Cannabis — officially known as tetrahydrocannabinol (THC)
- Cocaine — a powerful stimulant that also provides a rush of euphoria for a short duration; some common street names are: coke, blow, toot, nose candy, big C, and white lady
- Hallucinogens — the prototype of this class of substance is lysergic acid diethylamide (LSD), which causes perceptual distortions, depersonalization, and other effects; common street names are: acid, illusion, blotter, yellow sunshine, sugar cube; hallucinogens are also sometimes called psychedelics
- Inhalants — these volatile substances are used for their stupefying effects; examples include glue, gasoline, and aerosols; common terms for their use are huffing and bagging
- Nicotine
- Opioids — also called **opiates**, these substances cause euphoria and decrease pain; they range from illicit substances like heroin to prescription medication like morphine
- Phencyclidine — also known as PCP; this was initially developed as an anesthetic and shares some of the effects of LSD; commonly called angel dust, peace pill, and hog
- Sedative-hypnotics and anxiolytics — this class of substances induces a calming effect (sedatives and anxiolytics) or induces sleep (hypnotics); the class of benzodiazepines is best known by Valium® and Librium®; barbiturates are called blue heaven, reds, yellows, rainbows, and many other names

Depictions of intoxication and/or withdrawal states for the groups of substances listed above constitute the remainder of this chapter.

Alcohol Intoxication

The principal physical signs include:

i.   *Slurred speech*
ii. *Incoordination*
iii. *Unsteady gait*
iv. *Nystagmus*
v.   *Decreased ability to concentrate or pay attention*
vi. *Stupor or Coma*
vii. *Labile Mood*
viii. *Impaired Judgment*
ix. *Inappropriate Sexual or Aggressive Behavior*

Alcohol Withdrawal

The main signs and symptoms of alcohol withdrawal are:

i.   *Sweating*
ii. *Rapid heart rate*
iii. *Insomnia*
iv. *Nausea or vomiting*
v.   *Transient hallucinations or illusions (auditory, tactile, visual)*
vi. *Agitation*
vii. *Anxiety*
viii. *Tremors*
ix. *Seizures*

- Withdrawal symptoms can begin as soon as 6 hours after alcohol intake has been reduced or stopped

Alcohol Withdrawal Delirium

This condition is also known as **delirium tremens**, or the **DTs**. This is a withdrawal that is complicated by a disturbance in level of consciousness, disorientation, language disturbance, inability to focus one's attention, and perceptual disturbances. It tends to occur after prolonged and heavy alcohol consumption.

Affliction

The "affliction" referred to in this movie is the double curse of alcohol dependence and physical abuse. Glen Whitehouse (James Coburn) is a menacing bear of a man who is inebriated during the whole film, as well as in various flashbacks. When we first see Whitehouse, he is sitting in his living room in a **stuporous state** with his door open in the middle of a New Hampshire winter. His wife has frozen to death upstairs, but when he tries to rouse her, he doesn't even notice that she has passed away. Later at her funeral he has again been drinking and demonstrates many signs of alcohol intoxication, including:

- Slurred speech
- Unsteady gait
- Incoordination
- Labile mood

His **impaired judgment** and **inappropriate aggressive behavior** in the funeral scene are particularly well portrayed as Whitehouse tries to become violent when giving a tribute to his wife and has to be restrained by one of his sons.

Hoosiers

"Shooter" Flatch (Dennis Hopper) is the town drunk in this story about a rural 1950's Indiana basketball team that wins the state championships. Flatch is both a keen observer of the game and the proud father of one of the players. He is offered the position of assistant coach if he can remain sober. Flatch agrees, but shows up inebriated at one game and walks with an **unsteady gait** directly onto the court when he arrives. Other signs of intoxication portrayed in this scene are **slurred speech**, **incoordination**, and **impaired judgment**. Flatch finally agrees to give up drinking and is admitted to the local hospital. Here, he goes into alcohol withdrawal and is shown to be **anxious**, **agitated**, **sweating**, and **tremulous**. Later, he describes transient hallucinations ("bad visions") but does not go on to experience an alcohol withdrawal delirium.

The Lost Weekend

This movie provides a superb depiction of many aspects of **alcohol dependence**, and a reasonably accurate view of **alcohol withdrawal**. Don Birnam (Ray Milland) is a besotted writer manqué who is fully supported by his brother. Birnam showed promise many years earlier, but scarcely gets an idea before he has to reach for a bottle to conjure up the muse.

Birnam explains to a bartender why he continues to drink even though he recognizes that it is ruining his life: *"It shrinks my liver, doesn't it? It pickles my kidneys, yes. But what does it do to my mind? It tosses the sandbags overboard so the balloon can soar. Suddenly, I'm above the ordinary. I'm confident, supremely confident. I'm walking a tightrope over Niagara Falls. I'm one of the great ones. I'm Michelangelo molding the beard of Moses. I'm Van Gogh painting pure sunlight. I'm Horowitz playing the Emperor Concerto. I'm John Barrymore before the movies got him by the throat. I'm Jessie James and his two brothers — all three of them. I'm W. Shakespeare. And out there, it's not 3rd Avenue any longer, it's the Nile, man. And down it goes the barge of Cleopatra."*

Later, he gives the same bartender a description of what it is like to be alcohol dependent: *"Are you ever scared when you wake up? So scared that the sweat starts out of you? You ever lie in your bed looking at the window, the daylight coming through, and you start to wonder — is it getting lighter or is it getting darker? Is it dawn or is it dusk? It's a terrifying problem, because if it's dawn you're dead. The bars are closed. The liquor stores aren't open until 9:00 a.m. And you can't last until 9:00 a.m. Or it may be Sunday. That's the worst. No liquor stores at all and you guys wouldn't open a bar until 1:00 p.m. Why? Why?"*

Birnam sinks to the lowest point of his life during the weekend depicted in the film. He resorts to pawning items that aren't his, theft, and robbery in order to obtain more whiskey.

Eventually, Birnam's thirst outstrips his means and he lapses into a mild withdrawal state, and is visibly **sweating** and **agitated** only a few hours after his last drink. He falls down a set of stairs and finds himself being held involuntarily in a detoxification center.

Bim (Frank Faylen), the male nurse working at the detox, brusquely informs Birnam of the terrors that await those who descend into **delirium tremens** (**DTs**). When another patient in the unit abruptly develops hallucinations, Birnam slips out and browbeats a shop owner into giving him a bottle of whiskey. Having consumed this amount of alcohol would have staved off withdrawal symptoms for many more hours, but later that night he again develops problems.

Birnam initially develops **sweating**, **insomnia**, **tremors**, **anxiety**, and **agitation**. As his withdrawal worsens, he begins to hallucinate. At first he imagines seeing a mouse poking its head out of a crack in the wall. Then, a bat starts to circle the room and Birnam becomes upset by his **visual hallucinations**. Finally, the bat descends on the mouse and bites it, leaving a trail of blood oozing down the wall.

In the scene, Birnam is suffering from **alcohol withdrawal with perceptual disturbances**, not the DTs. Someone with Birnam's pattern of consumption would certainly be expected to have a complicated withdrawal, but progression to DTs isn't automatic.

The usual time course of withdrawal symptoms is as follows:
• Tremulousness in 6 to 8 hours
• Perceptual/psychotic disturbances in 8 to 12 hours
• Seizures in 12 to 24 hours
• DTs in 72 hours

However, some patients go directly into DTs and do not follow this progression. DTs are a medical emergency and require urgent attention. They are more likely to develop in older patients who are malnourished and have active medical problems.

Days of Wine and Roses

Joe Clay (Jack Lemmon) works in public relations and spends much of his time socializing after hours on behalf of his clients. At the beginning of the film, he appears to be what is commonly called a "functional alcoholic" who drinks everyday but still manages in social and occupational roles.

Joe meets Kirsten Arnesen (Lee Remick), a teetotaler, but soon convinces her to try a Brandy Alexander. Soon, Kirsten has replaced her fondness for chocolate with an addiction to alcohol. The extent of her problem with alcohol first becomes obvious when, while intoxicated, she burns down their apartment by being careless with a cigarette.

After losing a series of jobs, Joe realizes that his drinking is beyond his control. He manages to avoid alcohol for several weeks but then goes on a bender and ends up in the violent ward of a psychiatric hospital going through the DTs. Here, Joe can be seen **sweating** and writhing on the floor in a **highly agitated state**. He experiences **perceptual abnormalities** that cause him to be absolutely terrified of the hospital staff when they come to check on him. He is so **disoriented** and **confused** that he requires a straitjacket so that he doesn't hurt himself or anyone else. The major inconsistencies in this portrayal are that the DTs are more likely to develop after prolonged drinking (not after a once-in-a-month binge), and they would have taken a longer period of time to start.

Joe is visited by Jim Hungerford (Jack Klugman) who tells him about Alcoholics Anonymous (AA). Joe is able to achieve sobriety, but Kirsten is not, and Hungerford paints a very accurate picture of what to expect in this situation when he says that to an alcohol-dependent person, *the bottle is God.*

As a sad irony, the title of the movie is from a poem by Ernest Dowson, who was alcohol dependent and died at age 32.

Amphetamine Intoxication

The principal signs and symptoms are:
i.   *Changes in heart rate (increased or decreased)*
ii.   *Dilated pupils*
iii. *Blood pressure changes (increased or decreased)*
iv.   *Sweating or cold chills*
v.   *Nausea or vomiting*
vi.   *Weight loss with prolonged use*
vii. *Movements are either speeded up or slowed down*

With higher amounts and prolonged use, the following can occur:
viii. *Muscle weakness*
ix.   *Slowed rate of breathing*
x.   *Chest pain*
xi.   *Irregular heart rate*
xii. *Movement disorders*
xiii. *Confusion, seizures, and coma*

Amphetamine Withdrawal

i.   *Mood changes (tending toward depression)*
ii.   *Fatigue*
iii. *Dreams that are vivid and unpleasant*
iv.   *Sleep changes*
v.   *Appetite increases*
iv.   *Movements are either speeded up or slowed down*

Associated Features of Amphetamine Use

- The above signs and symptoms can occur within hours to days of stopping stimulants
- Amphetamines affect the brain much like cocaine does
- Perceptual disturbances, particularly tactile hallucinations, can occur with amphetamine use
- A syndrome similar to **schizophrenia, paranoid type** can develop with amphetamine use

273

Requiem for a Dream

Like the string quartet that plays much of the soundtrack of this film, *Requiem for a Dream* involves four people. Harry Goldfarb (Jared Leto) wants to become a big-time drug dealer. In the process, he becomes a polysubstance abuser and is shown in this film taking heroin, cocaine, and marijuana. Harry's mother Sara is a lonely widow whose main connections to the outside world are her television and the other women in her apartment building. Sara receives a general invitation to be part of the audience for a television show. This opportunity rallies her, and in a short time becomes the focus of her life. Her expectations soar, and she actually envisions herself being a featured guest, and decides that she would like to lose some weight before her appearance.

Sara tries dieting, but is tormented by a continual craving for food. Then, on the recommendation of one of the ladies from the apartment building, she attends a diet clinic and receives a prescription for amphetamines. Sara is soon full of vitality. Her appetite is suppressed and she loses weight seemingly effortlessly. She has energy and radiates confidence. In the scene where Harry returns to tell her he is buying her a television set, Sara is **euphoric**, **talkative**, and **restless**. She exhibits the **stereotyped behavior** of grinding her teeth. Because the medications are prescribed for her, Sara ignores Harry's warning and continues to take the amphetamines in increased amounts because they eventually stop having the same effect on her appetite.

When she increases her dose, Sara develops **amphetamine intoxication with perceptual disturbances**. She has a vivid hallucinatory experience of her apartment being turned into a set for the television appearance that she longs for. Her refrigerator comes to life and demands to be fed. Sara becomes highly agitated and confused, and ends up admitted to a hospital. At the time of her decompensation, Sara has signs and symptoms that would appear to be consistent with a psychotic disorder.

Caffeine Intoxication

The principal signs and symptoms are:
i. *Restlessness*
ii. *Nervousness*
iii. *Excitement*
iv. *Insomnia*
v. *Flushed face*
vi. *Increased urination*
vii. *Stomach or bowel disturbances*
viii. *Muscle twitching*
ix. *Rapid heart rate*
x. *Periods of inexhaustibility*
xi. *Agitation*

In higher doses, the following can occur:
xii. *Cardiac arrythmia*
xiii. *Rambling thought and speech*

Caffeine Withdrawal

The withdrawal from caffeine is quite variable and as such does not have a consistent set of symptoms.

No Movie Example Available

Cannabis Intoxication

The principal signs and symptoms are:

i. *Impaired coordination*
ii. *Elevated mood* (**euphoria**)
iii. *Anxiety*
iv. *Slowed sense of time*
v. *Impaired judgment*
vi. *Red eyes* (**conjunctival injection**)
vii. *Increased appetite* ("**the munchies**")
viii. *Dry mouth*
ix. *Accelerated heart rate*

Cannabis Withdrawal

There is no recognized physical withdrawal from cannabis.

Associated Features of Cannabis Use

- Cannabis can cause perceptual disturbances
- **Depersonalization** and **derealization** can occur
- Acute anxiety states and paranoia have been reported with cannabis use
- Marijuana smoke contains more carcinogens than tobacco

Reefer Madness/Tell Your Children

This 1938 film has been released under a variety of names and has become a cult classic. *Reefer Madness* has been called a propaganda film that sets out to inform the viewer of the evils of marijuana by way of a high school principal lecturing to concerned parents at a PTA meeting.

The prologue to the film indicates that marijuana is a "violent narcotic" and its use causes the following effects: *"The first effect is sudden, violent, uncontrollable laughter, then comes dangerous hallucinations — space expands, time slows down, almost standing still. Fixed ideas come next, conjuring up monstrous extravagances, followed by emotional disturbances — the total inability to direct thoughts, the loss of all power to resist physical emotions, leading finally to acts of shocking violence, ending often in incurable insanity."*

Much of the movie centers on the activities of the high school students who are patrons of a drug dealer named Jack (Carleton Young). They go to an apartment rented by a woman named Mae (Thelma White) in order to purchase "reefers" (marijuana cigarettes). The initial effects of marijuana are laughter, vigorous dancing, and an accelerated tempo of piano playing. This progresses to activities such as physical intimacy (pre-marital) and poor scholastic performance. However, by the end of the film, there has been: a hit-and-run motor vehicle accident, an attempted sexual assault, two murders, one suicide, and a verdict that one student has become incurably insane due to marijuana.

While some of the signs and symptoms of marijuana use are depicted accurately, there are a number of exaggerations, particularly the "shocking acts of violence" and "incurable insanity."

The movie makes the clear assertion that marijuana use leads to a direct increase in violent crime. One fictitious report is used to illustrate this where an axe-wielding boy kills his entire family.

The film states that marijuana is a more dangerous drug than either morphine or heroin, which is medically inaccurate.

True Romance

Floyd (Brad Pitt) is a minor character in this action picture. He is only present in a couple of scenes, but appears to be under the influence of marijuana in all of them. Floyd has a pipe known as a "bong" or a "hookah" often used to smoke hashish, which is a concentrated resin derived from marijuana plants. Floyd exhibits some of the typical signs of marijuana intoxication: **euphoria**, **slowed sense of time**, and **impaired judgment**.

Cocaine Intoxication

The principal signs and symptoms are:
i.   Mood changes (**euphoria** to **affective blunting**)
ii.   Hypervigilance
iii. Interpersonal sensitivity
iv.   Anxiety or tension
v.   Volatility
vi.   Impaired judgment
vii. Heart rate changes (increased or decreased)
viii. Dilated pupils
ix.   Blood pressure changes (increased or decreased)
x.   Sweating or cold chills
xi.   Nausea or vomiting
xii. Weight loss with prolonged use
xiii. Movement changes (increased or decreased)

With higher amounts and prolonged use, the following can occur:
xiv.   Muscle weakness
xv.   Slowed respiration
xvi.   Chest pain
xvii. Irregular heart rhythm
xviii. Confusion
xix.   Seizures
xx.   Involuntary movements
xxi.   Coma

Cocaine Withdrawal

Cocaine withdrawal is often called a "crash" and occurs after prolonged use, called a "run" or a "binge." Symptoms include:
i.   Fatigue
ii. Vivid and unpleasant dreams
iii. Sleep changes (increased or decreased)
iv. Increased appetite
v.   Movement changes (increased or decreased)

Blow

Blow is based on the life of drug dealer "Boston" George Jung (Johnny Depp), and was a novel written by Bruce Porter. As a child, Jung saw his parents constantly fight about money, and he vowed to live a life where this wouldn't be a problem for him. As a young man, he moved to California and became a marijuana dealer. He eventually got caught and convicted, stating that he entered prison with a *"bachelor's degree in pot and left with a doctorate in cocaine."*

As Jung's success as a cocaine dealer grows, he begins to use it regularly. He mentions that he was once told the lethal amount of cocaine was approximately 1 to 1.5 grams. On one occasion, he snorted 10 grams in ten minutes. While Jung uses cocaine for most of the film, the psychological and physical effects take a back seat to the lifestyle and business aspects of the drug trade. Jung is at times **tense**, **hypervigilant**, and has a **labile mood**, but there are developments in the plot that contribute to these features (such as his mother phoning the police and having him arrested). When Jung watches the birth of his daughter, he **collapses** in the delivery room because of the **cardiac complications** of cocaine. Prior to his collapse, we see him making **involuntary movements** (particularly his right arm and hand). He is also standing away from the table, doesn't have his surgical mask on, and appears to be **confused**. When Jung is in prison and away from cocaine, his **weight increases** significantly.

Some of the more flagrant psychological effects of cocaine are portrayed by his wife Mirtha (Penélope Cruz). Though she is a dramatic and impulsive person to begin with, she becomes **reckless**, **destructive**, and **unable to control herself**. The scene where she nearly causes a car crash in front of a police cruiser is a particularly good example of the **mood lability**, **impaired judgment**, and instantaneous **anger** that is seen with cocaine intoxication. She also **loses weight** to the point where one party guest estimates her weight at about 80 lbs.

Clean and Sober

Daryl Poynter (Michael Keaton) is a real estate agent whose life falls apart within days. A woman he barely knows overdoses on cocaine in his home, lapses into a **coma**, and dies a few days later. Poynter embezzles money from an escrow account to support his habit, but loses most of it on the stock market.

In the first scene of the film, Poynter wakes up and immediately begins to snort cocaine. Though he has an abrasive and self-centered personality, Poynter is noticeably **tense**, **easily moved to anger**, and demonstrates **interpersonal sensitivity** during a phone call just after he uses cocaine. The embezzlement has already taken place prior to the start of the movie, which is an example of the **impaired judgment** that accompanies cocaine use. Poynter is also alcohol dependent, making this portrayal less accurate because it is impossible to ascribe certain behaviors, signs, or symptoms exclusively to one substance.

Scarface

Tony Montana (Al Pacino) is a Cuban refugee who, through a blend of ruthlessness and cunning, establishes himself as a top-level cocaine dealer. As the movie progresses, both Montana and his wife Elvira (Michelle Pfeiffer) use increasing amounts of cocaine. Elvira seems to use cocaine to control her appetite, but does not display many of the signs of acute intoxication. Montana becomes increasingly erratic as he consumes larger and larger amounts. He becomes **hypervigilant** and **suspicious** of everyone. Montana kills his long time associate Manny (Steven Bauer), double crosses his Bolivian supplier, and becomes increasingly confused and disorganized due to cocaine use.

In the action-packed final sequence of the film, Montana snorts a considerable amount of cocaine, which causes him to **sweat profusely** and become irritable and very tense.

Hallucinogen Intoxication

The principal signs and symptoms are:

i. *Marked mood changes*
ii. *Ideas of reference*
iii. *Fear of losing one's mind*
iv. *Thoughts of persecution*
v. *Impaired judgment*
vi. *Dilated pupils*
vii. *Accelerated heart rate*
viii. *Sweating*
ix. *Palpitations*
x. *Blurred vision*
xi. *Tremors*
xii. *Incoordination*

Hallucinogen Withdrawal

There is no recognized physical withdrawal from hallucinogens.

Hallucinogen Persisting Perception Disorder (Flashbacks)

A **flashback** is a transient re-experience from a period of hallucinogen intoxication. Usually a disturbance in perception occurs, with people recognizing that it is related to previous drug use (as opposed to the hallucinations that occur during psychotic disorders). The perceptual disturbances tend to be visual and include: geometric shapes, flashes of color, afterimages, halos around objects, or persistence of images after looking away. Various triggers can cause flashbacks: entry into a dark room, anxiety, fatigue, or use of other recreational drugs. Flashbacks usually stop after a few months, but may persist longer.

Blue Sunshine

This movie doesn't purport to portray the effects of hallucinogens, it is more of a thriller with a medical twist. During college a group of students took a version of LSD called "blue sunshine." Ten years later, these people are becoming physically ill, manifested by hair loss and splitting headaches. Then with little provocation, they become homicidal maniacs before taking their own lives. These victims haven't used drugs in years, and in the context of the story, have sustained chromosomal damage leading to their erratic behavior.

The portrayals in this movie are somewhat consistent with acute intoxication with PCP. The assailants become agitated and assaultive. They exhibit a decreased sensitivity to pain and keep on fighting even after they have been injured, which can be seen with PCP use.

In the Name of the Father

Gerry Conlon (Daniel Day-Lewis) was falsely imprisoned for fifteen years for the bombing of an English pub. While incarcerated, he befriends a man who has a large supply of LSD that was smuggled in by coating it on a puzzle of the British Empire, which he is allowed to keep in his cell.

After his first use of LSD (he chooses Nepal), Conlon is euphoric (marked mood changes) and has visual disturbances. One of the other prisoners is moving his forearm in front of Conlon's face, which often causes the perception of seeing rings or lines shoot out of the ends of fingers. Eventually Conlon finds this unsettling and pushes the man's arm away.

Conlon goes on to use the LSD on a regular basis. Conlon's father Guiseppe, imprisoned with him, states that the younger Conlon *"hasn't said a sensible word"* in the two weeks that he's been using LSD on a regular basis.

Easy Rider

This movie follows the adventures of two counterculture bikers as they head out *"in search of America."* Their initial journey takes them from Los Angeles to New Orleans. The two main characters are Wyatt "Captain America" Earp (Peter Fonda) and Billy (Dennis Hopper). They partake of a number of substances on their journey, including cocaine, marijuana, and alcohol.

When the duo arrives in New Orleans, they enter a brothel and ask for two women. Mary (Toni Basil) and Karen (Karen Black) are persuaded to go to a cemetery to "get high." All four of them drink alcohol and take hits of LSD while they are there.

It is rumored that the female actors actually took acid during the filming of Easy Rider, making their depiction quite real. All four people become disinhibited, disorganized, and distraught. The psychedelic effects of LSD are enhanced for the viewer by use of a fisheye lens, rapid alteration of images, and the apparent inclusion of a roll of film that was only partially exposed.

Karen has a dramatic response to the acid. She skips merrily through the cemetery, then pounds up against a wall, and later weeps thinking that she is already dead. Her mood ranges from ecstatic to dysphoric. She repeats certain phrases during the scene, such as *"I just wanted to be pretty,"* and *"I know you."* Karen also demonstrates the repetitive behavior of picking at her hair.

Wyatt takes an interest in the small things around him. He ends up weeping in the arms of an enclosed statue muttering things that he would probably say to a mother who abandoned him. In some scenes he appears to be watching someone read a book. Wyatt also adopts some unusual postures, such as standing with his fist to the sky. Billy becomes sexually focused and has intercourse with Karen. Later, he is depicted as trying to comfort her from the emotional storm that she is experiencing.

Fear and Loathing In Las Vegas

Raoul Duke (Johnny Depp) and Dr. Gonzo (Benicio Del Toro) drive from Los Angeles to Las Vegas in search of the *"American Dream."* Duke has the trunk in his convertible loaded with most types of abusable substances, but appears to be under the influence of LSD ("blotter acid") at the beginning of the film and then takes another hit as he is driving. In every scene in this movie the two main characters are under the influence of mind-altering substances.

The first effect of LSD that Duke experiences is the **visual hallucination** of bats swarming around him. He becomes quite agitated and stops the car to let Gonzo drive. They pick up a hitchhiker (Tobey Maguire), and it is here that Duke's aberrant thought processes are clearly portrayed. Duke is quite paranoid that the hitchhiker will seek out the police as soon as possible, illustrating **thoughts of persecution**. Duke displays **impaired judgment** repeatedly by driving recklessly, brandishing firearms, leaving restaurants without paying, etc. While he doesn't explicitly convey that he is afraid of losing his mind, Duke is uncertain on a few occasions whether he's actually said something or only thought it. During the drive in the desert, Gonzo develops **palpitations** for which he takes amyl nitrite (an inhalant).

When Duke reaches the hotel in Las Vegas, he displays many of the physical signs of hallucinogen intoxication. He is **sweating** profusely, has **blurred vision**, is **tremulous**, and demonstrates **incoordination** by falling backwards at the counter. Then, Duke begins to have profound visual disturbances. The woman's face at the hotel check-in counter undergoes a number of distortions before she turns into a lizard. In the bar, blood flows around the stools, making Duke think that he needs golf shoes in order to be able to walk out safely. The patrons in the bar all turn into reptiles that are engaged in some sort of feeding frenzy that leaves them covered in blood.

Inhalant Intoxication

The principal signs and symptoms are:

i. *Belligerence*
ii. *Assaultiveness*
iii. *Apathy*
iv. *Euphoria*
v. *Impaired judgment*
vi. *Dizziness*
vii. *Involuntary eye movement* (**nystagmus**)
viii. *Incoordination*
ix. *Slurred speech*
x. *Unsteady gait*
xi. *Lethargy*
xii. *Slowed reflexes*
xiii. *Slowed Movements*
xiv. *Tremor*
xv. *Muscle weakness*
xvi. *Blurred vision or double vision* (**diploplia**)
xvii. *Coma*

Inhalant Withdrawal

There is no recognized physical withdrawal from inhalants.

Associated Features of Inhalant Use

- As a group, the inhalants encompass a wide range of chemical compounds; it is not usually possible to distinguish which substance someone has used by clinical effects alone
- Inhalant intoxication usually involves a mixture of substances obtained from a legal commercial source
- Inhaled substances consist of: gasoline, glue, paint and paint thinner, cleaners, correction fluid, and spray-can propellants
- Hydrocarbons and volatile substances are very toxic and cause damage in a wide a variety of areas including: the brain, liver, kidneys, heart, and bone marrow

285

Blue Velvet

Frank Booth (Dennis Hopper) carries with him a container of amyl nitrite, which he inhales through an oxygen mask before engaging in sexual or violent acts. Nitrites do have legitimate medical uses, but are abused because they give a "head rush" and mild sense of euphoria. Booth's use of amyl nitrite in a sexual situation is an accurate portrayal because it has the action of both prolonging and intensifying orgasm. It is sometimes taken in the form of a glass capsule that makes a popping sound when broken, hence the street name "poppers."

The Basketball Diaries

Jim Carroll (Leonardo DiCaprio) is a high school student in New York City. Though he is a talented basketball player and writer, he squanders much of his talent by engaging in recreational drug use and a number of crimes (vandalism, theft, etc.). Carroll is a **polysubstance abuser** in that he tries a wide variety of drugs during the course of the film.

In the first couple of minutes of the film, Carroll and his friends board the Staten Island Ferry and use an inhalant. They pour a yellowish liquid onto a rag and in turn hold it over their mouths and noses. Unfortunately for the sake of this portrayal, Pedro (James Madio) is overcome by the fumes and vomits on another passenger named Vinnie (Vincent Pastore). Vinnie gives chase and the full effects of the inhalant aren't depicted in this scene.

Mickey (Mark Wahlberg) later reads from Carroll's diary about one of their sniffing episodes. They were inhaling carbolic cleaning fluid. After 4 deep inhalations, Carroll felt as if he was *"sailing someplace else with little bells ringing in his ears."* He also describes a vision in which he was paddling a *"canoe on black water that was flowing backwards,"* and that he saw in the clouds *"spooky fun house faces that were laughing at him."*

286

Nicotine Intoxication

There is no recognized intoxication syndrome from nicotine.

Nicotine Withdrawal

The principal signs and symptoms are:

i.   *Mood changes (toward depression)*
ii. *Insomnia*
iii. *Irritability, frustration, or anger*
iv. *Anxiety*
v.   *Poor concentration*
vi. *Restlessness*
vii. *Slowed heart rate*
viii.*Increased appetite leading to weight gain*

Associated Features of Nicotine Use

*   Nicotine withdrawal begins within 24 hours of quitting
*   Cigarette smoking is significantly more common among patients with chronic psychiatric illnesses — up to 90% compared to 30% of the general population
*   95% of those who smoke at age 20 become regular smokers

No Movie Example Available

Opioid Intoxication

The principal signs and symptoms are:
i. *Initial euphoria*
ii. *Mood changes (ranging toward apathy and dysphoria)*
iii. *Changes in movement (increased or decreased)*
iv. *Impaired judgment*
v. *Slurred speech*
vi. *Drowsiness*
vii. *Decreased attention span and poor memory*

In higher doses the following can occur:
viii. *Coma*
ix. *Death (from respiratory depression)*

Opioid Withdrawal

The principal signs and symptoms are:
i. *Dysphoric mood*
ii. *Nausea or Vomiting*
iii. *Muscle and joint pain*
iv. *Tearing (**lacrimation**) and runny nose (**rhinorrhea**)*
v. *Dilated pupils*
vi. *Sweating*
vii. *Body hair standing up (**piloerection**)*
viii. *Diarrhea*
ix. *Yawning*
x. *Fever*
xi. *Insomnia*

Associated Features of Opioid Use

- Opioids include natural opioids (morphine), semi-synthetic (heroin) and synthetic (codeine, methadone, fentanyl, etc.)
- In addition to pain reduction, opioids are prescribed for anesthesia, control of diarrhea, and to reduce coughing
- Withdrawal symptoms can begin in as soon as 6 hours

Drugstore Cowboy

This movie is based on the novel by James Fogel, who at the time of the film's release in 1989 had spent thirty-five of his fifty-three years in jail on drug-related charges. *Drugstore Cowboy* is about a group of four "dope" addicts who rob pharmacies in the Pacific Northwest.

The leader of the group Bob (Matt Dillon), gives a detailed description of the high he gets from **opioid intoxication**: *"Upon entering my vein, the drug would start a warm edge that would surge along until the brain consumed it in a gentle explosion that began in the back of the neck and rose rapidly until I felt such pleasure that the whole world sympathized and took on a soft, lofty appeal. Everything is grand then. Your worst enemy wasn't so bad. The ants in the grass, they were just doing their thing. Everything took on the rosy hue of unlimited success. You could do no wrong, and as long as it lasted, life was beautiful."*

Later, he is explaining to an intake coordinator at a methadone clinic why he feels harassed by her questions: *"I'm a junkie. I like drugs. I like the whole lifestyle, but it just didn't pay off. You know, you don't see my kind of people, because my kind of people don't come down here and beg dope. They go out and get it. And if they miss, they go to jail and they kick along with nothing in some holding tank."*

When asked if he would be interested in becoming an addiction counselor, Bob scoffs at the idea and offers the following explanation: *"To begin with, nobody, and I mean nobody can talk a junkie out of using. You can talk to them for years, but sooner or later they're going to get a hold of something. Maybe it's not dope, maybe it's booze, maybe it's glue, maybe its gasoline. Maybe it's a gunshot in the head. But something, something to relieve the pressure of everyday life, like having to tie their shoes."*

This movie also depicts a death from overdose. Nadine (Heather Graham) is not a regular user of opioids, and being unaware of how much to take, makes a fatal miscalculation.

289

 **Basquiat**

Jean Michel Basquiat (Jeffrey Wright) was a New York City artist who gained initial recognition for his graffiti (commonly referred to as being a "tagger"). In a bold move, he shows some of his postcard-sized productions to Andy Warhol, who likes them and very soon afterwards becomes a friend and collaborator. Prior to attaining celebrity status, Basquiat is depicted as being a recreational drug user. As his fame and income grew, so did his use of illicit substances. He died of a heroin overdose at the age of twenty-seven in 1988.

There is one scene that contains an accurate portrayal of **opioid intoxication**. Morpheus was the Greek God of dreams, and it is his name from which the word morphine is derived. Heroin is a semi-synthetic compound made from the opium poppy plant. After using heroin, Basquiat is seen to be in a hypnotic state staring at a sheet of canvas that covers his floor. He starts imagining that he sees a growing stack of car tires on the canvas. When it gets to a certain height, he smears part of the tread with white paint. Basquiat seems both pleased and amused by his drug-induced vision, which is an example of the **initial euphoria** that accompanies opioid use. He seems rather **drowsy** after using the heroin, and has difficulty sustaining his **attention**. His head keeps nodding up and down, which is called "being on the nod." Basquiat is revived from this trip by his girlfriend Gina (Claire Forlani), who pounds on his chest until he is conscious. Opioids depress the respiratory center in the brain, which is why they are lethal in overdose.

 **The Basketball Diaries**

The first time that Jim Carroll (Leonardo DiCaprio) uses heroin he says that it was like, *"a long heat wave shot through his body."* Almost immediately, he felt that every ache and pain was flushed out of his body, along with any feeling of sadness or guilt. Carrol abuses

290

several different types of recreational drugs in this movie, but clearly has more difficulty with heroin than any of the others.

In a short span of time, Carroll becomes a regular user. He meets all the criteria for **substance dependence** listed on page 265. After clearly being intoxicated during a game, he quits the basketball team in a fit of anger even though he was one of their star players. Carroll also drops out of high school, and in a heart-wrenching scene, derides his mother to the point where she has no choice but to kick him out of their apartment.

Soon after leaving, Carroll turns to a life of crime to support his heroin addiction. Virtually all of his time is involved in either obtaining money to buy heroin or being under its influence. He shares needles with others and has no concern about the health risks in doing so. He sleeps on the street and in derelict housing with other addicts. In addition to becoming a car thief and burglar, he becomes a sex trade worker to support his habit. Carroll becomes aware of how much he's lost to heroin when he watches a former friend talk about the basketball team's success on television. Yet nothing seems to pull him out of his addiction.

One heroin trip leaves Carroll unconscious in the snow, and it is by mere chance that he is found by his friend Reggie (Ernie Hudson). Carroll soon goes into opioid withdrawal and accurately portrays many signs and symptoms, including:
- Dysphoric mood
- Tearing and runny nose
- Muscle and joint pain
- Insomnia

The portrayal of opioid use in this film is particularly good because it isn't glamorized. Carroll loses everything after becoming a heroin addict — his education, his friends, his mother, his dignity, his health, and very nearly his life (on several occasions). He is utterly unable to stop on his own, and it is only after a period of incarceration that gives him the opportunity and perspective to muster the strength to give up his addiction.

Phencyclidine Intoxication

The principal signs and symptoms are:
i.   *Belligerence*
ii. *Assaultiveness*
iii. *Impulsiveness*
iv. *Unpredictability*
v.   *Movement changes*
vi. *Impaired judgment*
vii. *Involuntary eye movements* (**nystagmus**)
viii.*High blood pressure*
ix. *Increased heart rate*
x.   *Reduced pain sensation (can be profound)*
xi. *Incoordination*
xii. *Trouble enunciating words* (**dysarthria**)
xiii.*Muscle rigidity*
xiv. *Enhanced sense of hearing* (**hyperacusis**)

In higher doses, the following complications can result:
xv. *Seizures*
xvi. *Coma*

Phencyclidine Withdrawal

There is no recognized physical withdrawal from PCP.

Associated Features of Phencyclidine Use
- Aggressive behavior is an especially worrisome feature of PCP use, particularly when it is coupled with a decreased response to pain
- Disorganized thinking, perceptual changes, and **depersonalization** occur with PCP use
- PCP was originally created as a "dissociative anesthetic" for use in humans, but was quickly recognized as unsuitable; it was used for some period of time after this by veterinarians, but has since stopped being manufactured

- Common street names for PCP are: angel dust, peep, ozone, and PeaCe Pill (the capitalized letters indicating PCP)
- When PCP is mixed with marijuana and smoked, the combination is referred to as: KJ (killer joints), crystal supergrass, and Shermans
- The principal effects of ingesting PCP are: decreased inhibitions, deadening of pain, dissociative episodes, hallucinations, and sensory deprivation
- PCP induces amnesia to the point that users sometimes forget that they even took the drug
- In higher doses, PCP can cause a number of physical complications, including: seizures, slowed respiration, heart problems, kidney failure, and extremely high blood pressure
- Large doses of PCP can last as long as 2 days, which is much longer than the effects of LSD
- Flashbacks also occur after PCP use
- PCP use can cause a full range of psychiatric symptoms; what occurs most often is a syndrome resembling acute psychosis with paranoid thinking, catatonic or disorganized behavior, and incoherent speech
- A reference for more information is: *PCP: The Dangerous Angel (Encyclopedia of Psychoactive Drugs Series 1)* by Solomon H. Snyder and Marilyn Carroll

No Movie Example Available

Sedative-Hypnotic or Anxiolytic Intoxication

The principal signs and symptoms are:

i. *Inappropriate behavior (particularly sexual or aggressive)*
ii. *Labile mood*
iii. *Impaired judgment*
iv. *Slurred speech*
v. *Incoordination*
vi. *Unsteady gait*
vii. *Involuntary eye movements (**nystagmus**)*
viii. *Decreased attention span and poor memory*

In higher amounts, the following can occur:
ix. *Stupor*
x. *Coma*

Sedative-Hypnotic, or Anxiolytic Withdrawal

The principal signs and symptoms are:

i. *Sweating*
ii. *Accelerated heart rate*
iii. *Tremors*
iv. *Insomnia*
v. *Nausea or vomiting*
vi. *Transient hallucinations or illusions (auditory, tactile, or visual)*
vii. *Agitation*
viii. *Anxiety*
ix. *Seizures*

Associated Features of Sedative-Hypnotics

- The intoxication and withdrawal states are very similar to those seen with alcohol

Valley of the Dolls

The title of this movie, based on the Jacqueline Susann novel, has a double meaning. "Dolls" refers to both the women in this story, and the capsules that they take to weather the stress and strain of their careers in show business.

The introduction and stylized graphics indicate that there are four types of dolls: red, blue, green, and yellow. Each color is ostensibly taken by one of the female leads. However, the colors of the capsules aren't emphasized in the movie.

"Reds" and "dolls" were nicknames for the barbiturate secobarbital, although this isn't identified in the movie. The character whose use of dolls is most visible is Neely O'Hara (Patty Duke). Neely is a talented dynamo, but the demands on her time cause her to look for both a stimulant for the days and a sedative at night. She notes that the dolls give her energy and have caused a decrease in her weight. Because of the drug use, Nelly does display **inappropriately aggressive behavior**, **impaired judgment**, and **labile mood** in several scenes.

The effects that a sedative-hypnotic medication has often depends on the mood of the user. Someone like Neely who is energetic and high-strung may become disinhibited and boisterous. Other users would report that the drug made them tired and mellow.

A disturbing portrayal is given by Jennifer North (Sharon Tate). Upon finding that she has a malignant tumor, Jennifer overdoses on dolls. Though there are no physiological effects of her overdose depicted, Jennifer would most likely have become **stuporous** and lapsed into a **coma** before passing away.

The depiction of the use of sedative-hypnotics in this movie is modest at best. The effects of the "dolls" are not clearly portrayed, and the few effects that are mentioned are not specific to this class of medications.

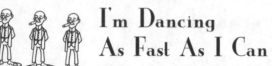

I'm Dancing
As Fast As I Can

This movie is based on the book by the same title. Barbara Gordon (Jill Clayburgh) is a highly successful New York TV producer who specializes in making documentaries about people in unfortunate circumstances. She runs on nerves and nicotine, and at the beginning of the film is taking up to 90mg of Valium® per day. Barbara is **benzodiazepine dependent** and pops pills whenever she encounters a stressful situation. She has a pill bottle on her table at work and two tablets secreted in her cigarette package. Just like someone with an addiction to alcohol, Barbara has bags of pills stashed in many hiding places in her apartment. Prior to going to a ceremony where she is nominated for (and wins) an award, she sews a small sac onto her dress that contains two Valium® pills.

She demonstrates some of the signs of benzodiazepine intoxication during her acceptance speech. Her **memory is impaired** and her thoughts are not fluent. After leaving the stage, she struggles momentarily with one of the assistants who reaches for the award because Barbara forgets that they are just props and the real item will be sent to her when it is engraved.

Barbara then decides to abruptly quit taking Valium® and hangs up on her psychiatrist before he can explain the risks. For the first several hours she feels fine because Valium® has a long duration of action. Later she clearly develops **benzodiazepine withdrawal**, shown by the following symptoms:
- Tremors
- Agitation
- Insomnia
- Anxiety

In the scene on the beach, Barbara has a generalized **seizure**, which is a serious complication of benzodiazepine withdrawal. She develops a serious craving for more Valium® and tries to surreptitiously order more from a pharmacy.

Movie	Features/Diagnosis
Affliction	Alcohol Dependence
	Alcohol Intoxication
Hoosiers	Alcohol Dependence
	Alcohol Intoxication
	Alcohol Withdrawal
The Lost Weekend	Alcohol Dependence
	Alcohol Intoxication
	Alcohol Withdrawal
Days of Wine and Roses	Alcohol Dependence
	Alcohol Intoxication
	Alcohol Withdrawal Delirium
Requiem for a Dream	Amphetamine Intoxication
	Amphetamine Withdrawal
Reefer Madness/ Tell Your Children	Cannabis Intoxication
True Romance	Cannabis Intoxication
Blow	Cocaine Intoxication
	Cocaine Withdrawal
Clean and Sober	Cocaine Intoxication
Scarface	Cocaine Intoxication
Blue Sunshine	Hallucinogen Intoxication
Easy Rider	Hallucinogen Intoxication
In the Name of the Father	Hallucinogen Intoxication

Fear and Loathing In Las Vegas	Hallucinogen Intoxication
Blue Velvet	Inhalant Intoxication
The Basketball Diaries	Inhalant Intoxication Opioid Intoxication Opioid Withdrawal
Drugstore Cowboy	Opioid Intoxication Opioid Dependence
Basquiat	Opioid Intoxication
Valley of the Dolls	Sedative-Hypnotic/Anxioltyic Dependence
I'm Dancing As Fast As I Can	Sedative-Hypnotic/Anxiolytic Dependence Sedative-Hypnotic/Anxioltyic Withdrawal

Chapter 18

Mental Disorders
Due to
Medical
Conditions

Just as substance use can cause a condition indistinguishable from a primary psychiatric disorder, many physical illnesses can be the cause of a mental disorder. Disease processes can poison the brain, deprive it of oxygen and glucose, attack nerve cells, take up space inside the skull which compresses brain tissue, affect the pituitary gland which controls much of the body's hormone regulation, etc. The DSM-IV subdivides mental disorders due to a **general medical condition** (**GMC**) into the following subtypes:

- Psychotic Disorder Due to a GMC
- Dementia Due to a GMC
- Amnestic Disorder Due to a GMC
- Personality Change Due to a GMC
- Mood Disorder Due to a GMC
- Anxiety Disorder Due to a GMC
- Sexual Dysfunction Due to a GMC
- Sleep Disorder Due to a GMC

These conditions are listed as the Axis I diagnosis and the GMC itself is recorded on Axis III. Rather than a full presentation of these conditions, selected examples showing how general medical conditions cause psychiatric symptoms will be listed.

Psychotic Disorder
Due to a Head Injury

Jesus of Montreal

This is a Canadian movie done in French with English subtitles. Daniel Coulombe (Lothaire Bluteau) is hired by a church to revamp the Passion play, the crucifixion of Christ, for a summer theater. The production becomes an instant hit but the new content displeases the religious authorities and they shut down the play. Without permission the actors begin one last performance and a scuffle ensues, knocking Coulombe, who had been playing Jesus, to the ground from his cross. He sustains a head injury and loses consciousness. He awakens in a busy hospital ER and decides to leave. A blood vessel has ruptured in his brain causing him to have both psychological and physical symptoms. For the last half hour of his life, Daniel seems to believe that he is Jesus and offers guidance to people in a subway station. Many of the statements he makes are similar to the lines he had in the play. While no one actually asks him to identify himself, his demeanor after the head injury is quite different from his usual personality. It seems reasonable to assume that if he had been asked who he was, he well may have said Jesus. This would be a delusion, qualifying him for the diagnosis of psychotic disorder due to a head injury.

Dementia Due to a Metabolic Abnormality

Lorenzo's Oil

This is a heart-wrenching movie which is based on a true story. Lorenzo Odone (played by a variety of actors) is a bright, healthy five year-old boy who among other things speaks three languages. His father works for the World Bank and after spending three years in Africa, Lorenzo and his family return home. Within a short period of time Lorenzo develops an increasing number of behavior problems. He has angry outbursts, becomes hyperactive and inattentive, and is moody. Lorenzo's teachers cannot handle these disruptions and want him placed in a special education class.

Lorenzo has a thorough medical investigation and is found to have a rare inherited metabolic abnormality called adrenoleukodystrophy (ALD). This progressive condition kills brain cells, leading to dementia and a wide range of physical complications. As his ALD progresses Lorenzo becomes withdrawn, forgetful, emotionally labile, and develops a number of neurological deficits, all of which are due to loss of brain function secondary to his metabolic abnormality.

Amnestic Disorder and Personality Change Due to Anoxia

Regarding Henry

Henry Turner (Harrison Ford) is a hard-charging, successful lawyer. He is the picture of compassion during a big case but is arrogant, dictatorial, and selfish socially. Proving that smoking can indeed be hazardous to one's health, Turner tries to buy cigarettes from a convenience store that is being robbed. The nervous gunman shoots Turner twice — once in the right side of the head and the other in the left side of his chest. Surprisingly it is the chest wound that causes the most damage. The bullet hits a major vessel and Turner's blood loss is so severe that his brain is deprived of oxygen (**anoxia**) and is permanently damaged.

Turner undergoes a lengthy physical and mental rehabilitation. At first he is mute and then recovers his vocabulary very slowly. He has significant memory gaps, forgetting even his own daughter. He needs to be reminded how to tie shoelaces, read, and which types of food he enjoyed. He has the ability to learn new things and does not deteriorate in mental function after his recovery, making this a good portrayal of an **amnestic disorder due to a GMC**.

Turner's personality also changes after his assault. He is shy, indecisive, whimsical, and more emotionally expressive. The DSM-IV-TR specifies a number of subtypes for **personality changes due to a GMC**, none of which accurately describes the new Henry. The subtypes are:

- Labile Type
- Aggressive Type
- Paranoid Type
- Disinhibited Type
- Apathetic Type
- Combined Type

Mood Disorder
Due to Porphyria

The Madness of King George

King George III lived from 1738 to 1820. He was the British monarch in power when America declared its independence. This movie is based on the play *The Madness of George III* and incorporates many historical facts about his life and health.

King George (Nigel Hawthorne) has psychiatric difficulties that are apparent from the beginning of the film. He is boisterous, disinhibited, and distractible. When he encounters a pig farm and a game of cricket he cannot help but to energetically throw himself into the action. King George is perpetually rushing and speaks rapidly to those around him. He ravishes an attractive noblewoman in front of the queen and other members of his entourage. His mood, while generally jovial, is labile. He has several angry outbursts. In one scene the king speaks in rhymes. He has difficulty restraining his impulses and at times his behavior becomes outlandish and is an embarrassment to the country. In the portrayal shown in this movie, King George has signs and symptoms that are consistent with the **hypomanic phase**, and later the **manic phase of bipolar disorder**.

King George's physical ailment is a matter of speculation but is noted at the end of the film to be porphyria. This word comes from the Greek "porphyra," meaning purple. Porphyria is a defect in hemoglobin synthesis that can be either congenital or acquired. The reference to the color purple stems from the urine of affected patients, which ranges from dark red to brown. King George is depicted as suffering from severe intermittent abdominal pain and constipation, both of which are consistent with porphyria. Other common psychiatric complications of porphyria include depression and psychosis.

Movie	Features/Diagnosis
Jesus of Montreal	Psychotic Disorder Due to a Head Injury
Lorenzo's Oil	Dementia Due to a Metabolic Abnormality
Regarding Henry	Amnestic Disorder Due to Anoxia; Personality Change Due to Anoxia
The Madness of King George	Mood Disorder Due to Porphyria

Chapter 19

Resources

Reel Psychiatry was intended to be a resource for both the general public and healthcare professionals. In order to enhance the usefulness of this book, key organizations in the U.S. and Canada are provided in this chapter. Listing an organization in this chapter is not meant to imply an endorsement. This collection aims to include organizations that provide resources for both education and support. The author also recognizes that there are many helpful resources that could not be included due to space limitations. Readers who feel particularly strongly about the presence or absence of an organization are encouraged to contact the publisher to pass along their opinions. The absence of a psychiatric condition from this chapter indicates that resources could not be found. The author is particularly indebted to Martha Wilke, BSc.OT for her kind efforts in collecting the information in this chapter.

U.S. Resources
General Mental Health Organizations
American Psychiatric Association
1000 Wilson Boulevard, Suite 1825
Arlington, VA 22209-3901
Telephone: 703-907-7300, Toll Free: 888-35-PSYCH
Web Address: www.psych.org

American Psychological Association
750 First Street NE
Washington, DC 20002-4242
Telephone: 202-336-5500, Toll Free: 800-374-2721
Web Address: www.apa.org

At Health Mental Health
14241 NE Woodinville-Duvall Road, #104
Woodinville, WA 98072-8564
Phone: 360-668-3808, Toll Free: 888-284-3258, Fax: 360-668-2216
Web Address: www.athealth.com/

Health-Center
Web Address: www2.health-center.com/mentalhealth/

Mental Health Matters
c/o Get Mental Help, Inc.
19206 65th Place NE
Kenmore, WA 98028
Web Address: www.mental-health-matters.com

Mental Help Net
Web Address: www.mentalhelp.net/

National Alliance for the Mentally Ill (NAMI)
Colonial Place Three
2107 Wilson Blvd, Suite 300
Arlington, VA 22201
Telephone: 703-524-7600, Toll-Free: 800-950-NAMI
Web Address: www.nami.org

National Institute of Mental Health (NIMH)
6001 Executive Boulevard,
Room 8184, MSC 9663
Bethesda, MD 20892-9663
Telephone: 301-443-4513, Fax: 301-443-4279
Web Address: www.nimh.nih.gov

National Mental Health Association
2001 N. Beauregard St., 12th Floor
Alexandria VA 22311
Telephone : 703-684-7722, Toll Free: 800-969-6642, Fax: 703-684-5968
Web Address: www.nmha.org

National Mental Health Consumer Self-Help Clearinghouse
1211 Chestnut Street
Philadelphia PA 19107-6312
Telephone: 215-751-1810, Toll Free: 800-553-4539, Fax: 215-636-6312
Web Address: www.mhselfhelp.org

The Substance Abuse and Mental Health Services Administration's (SAMHSA)
National Mental Health Information Center
P.O. Box 42490, Washington, DC 20015
Telephone: 301-443-1805, Toll Free: 800-789-2647, Fax: 301-984-8796
Web Address: www.mentalhealth.samhsa.gov/

Psychotic Disorders
Schizophrenia
National Alliance for Research on Schizophrenia and Depression (NARSAD)
60 Cutter Mill Road, Suite 404
Great Neck, NY 11021
Telephone: 516-829-0091, Toll Free: 800-829-8289, Fax: 516-487-6930
Web Address: www.narsad.org/

The National Schizophrenia Foundation (NSF)
403 Seymour Ave., Suite 202
Lansing, MI 48933
Telephone: 517-485-7168, Toll Free: 800-482-9534, Fax: 517-485-7180
Web Address: www.nsfoundation.org

Schizophrenia-Help Resource Center
Web Address: www.schizophrenia-help.com

Schizophrenics Anonymous
15920 W. Twelve Mile
Southfield MI 48076
Telephone: 313-477-1983
Web Address: www.sanonymous.org

The Online Resource for Schizophrenia
Web Address: www.mentalwellness.com

Schizoaffective Disorder
The Schizoaffective Disorder Information Center
Web Address: www.schizoaffective.org

Mood Disorders
General
Depression and Related Affective Disorders Association (DRADA)
Meyer 3 — 181, 600 North Wolfe Street
Baltimore, MD 21287-7381
Telephone: 410-955-4647
Web Address: www.drada.org

Depression
All About Depression
Web Address: www.allaboutdepression.com

Depressed Anonymous
DSS Inc., P.O. Box 17414
Louisville, KY 40217
Telephone: 502-569-1989
Web Address: www.depressedanon.com

Depression and Bipolar Support Alliance (formerly National Depressive and Manic-Depressive Association)
730 N. Franklin, Suite 501
Chicago, IL 60610-7204
Telephone: 312-642-0049, Toll Free: 800-826-3632, Fax: 312-642-7243
Web Address: www.dbsalliance.org

Freedom From Fear
308 Seaview Ave.
Staten Island, NY 10305
Telephone: 718-351-1717, Fax: 718-667-8893
Web Address: www.freedomfromfear.com

National Alliance for Research on Schizophrenia and Depression (NARSAD)
60 Cutter Mill Road, Suite 404
Great Neck, NY 11021
Telephone: 516-829-0091, Toll Free: 800-829-8289, Fax: 516-487-6930
Web Address: www.narsad.org/

National Foundation for Depressive Illness, Inc. (NAFDI)
P.O. Box 2257
New York, NY 10116
Telephone: 800-239-1265
Web Address: www.depression.org

Mania/Bipolar Disorder
Bipolar Disorders Information Center
Web Address: www.mhsource.com/bipolar/

Bipolar Resource
Web Address: www.bipolarresource.com

Bipolar World
Web Address: www.bipolarworld.net

Manic Depressives Anonymous (MDA)
P.O. Box 212
Collingswood, NJ 08107
Web Address: www.manicdepressivesanon.org

Pendulum Resources
Web Address: www.pendulum.org

The Depression and Bipolar Support Alliance
(formerly National Depressive and Manic-Depressive Association)
730 N. Franklin, Suite 501
Chicago, IL 60610
Telephone: 312-642-0049, Toll Free: 800-826-3632, Fax: 312-642-7243
Web Address: www.dbsalliance.org

The Society for Manic Depression
48 Random Road
Rye, NH 03870
Web Address: www.societymd.org

Anxiety Disorders
General
Anxieties.com
Web Address: www.anxieties.com

Anxiety Coach
1340 Remington Road, Suite D
Schaumburg, IL 60173
Telephone: 847-605-0453, Fax: 708-570-6823
Web Address: www.anxietycoach.com

Anxiety Self-Help
Web address: www.anxietyselfhelp.com

Anxiety Disorders Association of America
8730 Georgia Avenue, Suite 600
Silver Spring, MD 20910
Telephone: 240-485-1001, Fax: 240-485-1035
Web Address: www.adaa.org

Anxiety/Panic
549 Knights Circle
Nampa, ID 83687
Telephone: 208-442-0160, Fax: 208-442-5424
Web Address: www.anxietypanic.com

Association for Advancement of Behavior Therapy
305 Seventh Avenue, Suite 1601
New York, NY 10001-6008
Telephone: 212-647-1890, Fax: 212-647-1865
Web Address: www.aabt.org

Center for Anxiety and Stress Treatment
4225 Executive Square, Suite 1110
La Jolla, CA 92037
Telephone: 619-542-0536, Fax: 619-542-0730
Web Address: www.stressrelease.com

Freedom from Fear
308 Seaview Avenue
Staten Island, NY 10305
Telephone: 718-351-1717, Fax: 718-667-8839
Web Address: www.freedomfromfear.com

National Anxiety Foundation
3135 Custer Drive
Lexington, KY 40517
Telephone: 859-272-7166
Web Address: www.lexington-on-line.com/naf.html

The Anxiety Network International Home Page
Web Address: www.anxietynetwork.com

The Anxiety Panic Internet Resource (tAPir)
Web Address: www.algy.com/anxiety

Agoraphobia
Agoraphobia and Panic Disorder Recovery
Web Address: www.paniccure.com

Agoraphobics Building Independent Lives, Inc. (ABIL)
400 West 32nd St.
Richmond, VA 23225
Telephone: 804-353-3964, Fax: 804-353-3687
Web Address: www.anxietysupport.org

AIM (Agoraphobics in Motion)
1719 Crooks St.
Royal Oak, MI 48067-1306
Telephone: 248-547-0400
Web Address: www.aim-hq.org

Open Door Outreach, Inc.
608 Russell Ave. S.
Minneapolis, MN 55405
Telephone: 612-377-2467, Fax: 612-928-6716

Obsessive-Compulsive Disorder (OCD)
Awareness Foundation for OCD and Related Disorders
435 Alberto Way, Suite #3
Los Gatos, CA 95032
Telephone: 408-395-8509
Web Address: www.ocdawareness.com

National Institute of Mental Health
c/o OCD Outpatient Research
Building 10, Room 3D41
10 Center Drive, MSC 1264
Bethesda, MD 20892
Telephone: 301-496-3421

Obsessive-Compulsive Anonymous
P.O. Box 215
New Hyde Park, NY 11040
Telephone: 516-739-0662
Web Address: www.hometown.aol.com/west24th

Obsessive-Compulsive Foundation, Inc.
337 Notch Hill Road
North Branford, CT 06471
Telephone: 203-315-2190, Fax: 203-315-2196
Web Address: www.ocfoundation.org

Obsessive-Compulsive Information Center
Madison Institute of Medicine
7617 Mineral Point Road, Suite 300
Madison, WI 53717
Telephone: 608-827-2470, Fax: 608-827-2479

Our Courage Defines Us (OCDU)
P.O. Box 9123
Niskayuna, NY 12309-0123
Web Address: www.ocdpeer.com

Panic Disorder
Agoraphobia and Panic Disorder Recovery
Web Address: www.paniccure.com

The Panic Center
Web Address: www.paniccenter.net

The Panic Disorders Institute
97 W. Bellevue Dr.
Pasadena, CA 91105
Telephone: 626-577-8290, Fax: 626-795-3527
Web Address: www.algy.com/pdi

Phobic Disorders
Phobics Anonymous
P.O. Box 1180
Palm Springs, CA 92263
Telephone: 619-322-2673

Social Anxiety Institute
2058 East Topeka Drive
Phoenix, AZ 85024
Telephone: 602-230-7316
Web Address: www.socialanxietyinstitute.org

Social Phobia/Social Anxiety Association
Web Address: www.socialphobia.org

Posttraumatic Stress Disorder (PTSD)
Gift from Within
16 Cobb Hill Road
Camden, ME 04843
Telephone: 207-236-8858, Fax: 207-236-2818
Web Address: www.giftfromwithin.org

National Center for PTSD
Web Address: www.ncptsd.org

PTSD Alliance
Toll Free: 877-507-PTSD
Web Address: www.ptsdalliance.org/home2.html

PTSD Support Services
Web Address: www.ptsdsupport.net

The Sidran Institute — Traumatic Stress Education and Advocacy
200 E. Joppa Road, Suite 207
Towson, MD 21286
Telephone: 410-825-8888, Fax: 410-337-0747
Web Address: www.sidran.org

Trauma Anonymous
Web Address: www.bein.com/trauma/index.html

Somatoform Disorders
Conversion Disorder
National Organization of Rare Disorders (NORD)
55 Kenosia Avenue, P.O. Box 1968
Danbury, CT 06813-1968
Telephone: 203-744-0100, Toll Free: 800-999-6673, Fax: 203-798-2291
Web Address: www.rarediseases.org

Factitious Disorders and Malingering
Factitious Disorder by Proxy/Munchausen by Proxy
Factitious Disorder by Proxy/Munchausen by Proxy
Web Address: www.mbpexpert.com

Munchausen by Proxy Survivors Network
Web Address: www.mbpsnetwork.com

Dissociative Disorders
General
The Sidran Institute
200 E. Joppa Road, Suite 207
Towson, MD 21286
Telephone: 410-825-8888, Fax: 410-337-0747
Web Address: www.sidran.org

Dissociative Identity Disorder (DID)
Healing Hopes — Together in Healing
Web Address: www.healinghopes.org

MPD/DID Anonymous
Web Address: www.geocities.com/Athens/Rhodes/9354/index.html

NEEDID Support Network
(Network to Explore and Express Dissociative Identity Disorder)
Web Address: www.needid.bizland.com/needid1.htm

Sexual and Gender Identity Disorders
General
Sexual Addiction Recovery Resources (SARR)
C/O Steve Goodrich
P.O. Box 18972
Boulder, CO 80308-1972
Web Address: www.sarr.org

Pedophilia
Molesters Anonymous
c/o Dr. Jerry Goffman, Ph.D.
1850 N. Riverside Ave., Suite 220
Rialto, CA 92376
Telephone: 909-355-1100, Fax: 909-370-0438

National Institute for the Study, Prevention, and Treatment of Sexual Trauma
104 E. Biddle Street
Baltimore, MD 21202
Telephone: 410-539-1661
Web Address: www.fredberlin.com

Sexual Dysfunctions
Consortium for Improvement in Erectile Function (CIEF)
c/o CogniMed Inc., P.O. Box 1028
Madison, NJ 07940
Toll Free: 800-720-7779, Fax: 877-403-5765
Web Address: www.erectilefunction.org/default.htm

Network for Excellence in Women's Sexual Health (NEWSHE)
Web Address: www.newshe.com/

Transvestic Fetishism
Tri-Ess: The Society for the Second Self, Inc.
Web Address: www.tri-ess.org/

Gender Identity Disorder
International Foundation for Gender Education (IFGE)
P.O. Box 540229
Waltham, MA 02454-0229
Telephone: 781-899-2212, Fax: 781-899-5703
Web Address: www.ifge.org/

The American Boyz, Inc.
Web Address: http://home.iximd.com/~amboyz/

The Gender Identity Disorder Sanctuary
Web Address: www.mhsanctuary.com/gender/

The Harry Benjamin International Gender Dysphoria Association, Inc. (HBIGDA)
1300 South Second Street, Suite 180
Minneapolis, MN 55454
Telephone: 612-625-1500, Fax: 612-626-8311
Web Address: www.hbigda.org/

Eating Disorders
General
Body Positive
Web Address: www.bodypositive.com

Academy for Eating Disorders (AED)
6728 Old McLean Village Drive
McLean, VA 22101
Telephone: 703-556-9222, Fax: 703-556-8729
Web Address: www.aedweb.org/

American Anorexia/Bulimia Association, Inc. (AB/AA)
165 W. 46th Street, Suite 1108
New York, NY 10036
Telephone: 212-575-6200

Anorexia Nervosa and Related Eating Disorders, Inc. (ANRED)
P.O. Box 5102
Eugene, OR 97401
Telephone: 503-344-1144
Web Address: www.anred.com

Bulimia Anorexia Self Help, Inc. (BASH)
6125 Clayton Avenue, Suite 215
St. Louis, MO 63139
Telephone: 314-567-4080

Center for Eating Disorders
St. Joseph Medical Center
7601 Osler Dr.
Towson, MD 21204-7582
Telephone: 410-427-2100
Web Address: www.eating-disorders.com/

Center for the Study of Anorexia and Bulimia
1 West 91st Street
New York, NY 10024
Telephone: 212-595-3449

Eating Disorders Anonymous (EDA)
18233 N. 16th Way
Phoenix, AZ 85022
Web Address: www.eatingdisordersanonymous.org

Eating Disorder Recovery Online
Telephone: 520-323-3734, Toll Free: 888-520-1700
Web Address: www.edrecovery.com/

Eating Disorder Referral and Information Center
Web Address: www.edreferral.com

EDEN — Eating Disorders Education Network
P.O. Box 131247   8465 Faussett Rd.
Ann Arbor, MI 48119-1247   Fenton, MI 48430
Telephone: 810-750-2106 or 734-476-0278, Fax: 810-750-4541
Web Address: www.comnet.org/eden/

Food Addicts Anonymous (FDA)
World Service Office
4623 Forest Hill Blvd., Suite #109-4
West Palm Beach, FL 33415-9120
Telephone: 561-967-3871, Fax: 561-967-9815
Web Address: www.foodaddictsanonymous.org/

National Association of Anorexia Nervosa and Associated Disorders (ANAD)
P.O. Box 7
Highland Park, IL 60035
Telephone: 847-831-3438, Fax: 847-433-4632
Web Address: www.anad.org

National Eating Disorders Association (NEDA)
603 Stewart St., Suite 803
Seattle, WA 98101
Telephone: 206-382-3587
Web Address: www.nationaleatingdisorders.org/p.asp?WebPage_ID=337

National Eating Disorder Organization (NEDO)
6655 South Yale Ave.
Tulsa, OK 74136
Telephone: 918-481-4044
Web Address: www.laureate.com

Support, Concern, and Resources for Eating Disorders (SCaRED)
Web Address: www.eating-disorder.org/scared.html

The Alliance for Eating Disorders Awareness
P.O. Box 13155
North Palm Beach , FL 33408-3155
Telephone: 561-841-0900, Fax: 561-881-0380
Web Address: www.eatingdisorderinfo.org

The Something Fishy Website on Eating Disorders
Web Address: www.something-fishy.org/

Anorexia Nervosa
National Anorexia Aid Society (NAAS)
5796 Karl Road
Columbus, OH 43229
Telephone: 614-436-1112

Sleep Disorders
General
American Sleep Disorders Association
Web Address: www.asda.org

Sleepnet.com
Web address: www.sleepnet.com

American Academy of Sleep Medicine
One Westbrook Corporate Center
Suite 920
Westchester, IL 60154
Telephone: 708-492-0930, Fax: 708-492-0943
Web Address: www. aasmnet.org/

International Sleep Medicine Association
614 South 8th St., Suite 282
Philadelphia, PA 19147
Telephone: 443-593-2285, Fax: 443-593-2285
Web Address: www.1sleep.com/

National Center on Sleep Disorder Research
Two Rockledge Center Suite 10038
6701 Rockledge Drive MSC 7920
Bethesda, MD 20892-7920
Telephone: 301-435-0199, Fax: 301-480-3451
Web Address: www.nhlbi.nih.gov/about/ncsdr/

National Sleep Foundation (NSF)
1522 K Street, NW, #500
Washington, DC 20005
Telephone: 202-347-3471, Fax: 202-347-3472
Web Address: www.sleepfoundation.org/about.html

Breathing-Related Sleep Disorder (Sleep Apnea)
American Sleep Apnea Association
1424 K Street NW, Suite 302
Washington, DC 20005
Telephone: 202-293-3650, Fax: 202-293-3656
Web Address: www.sleepapnea.org

Circadian Rhythm Sleep Disorder
Circadian Sleep Disorders Association
Web Address: www.circadiandisorders.org/

Narcolepsy
Narcolepsy Network, Inc.
10921 Reed Hartman Highway
Cincinnati, OH 45242
Telephone: 513-891-3522, Fax: 513-891-3836
Web Address: www.narcolepsynetwork.org/

Stanford School of Medicine, Center for Narcolepsy
Sleep Disorders Clinic, Department of Psychiatry and Behavioral Sciences
Psychiatry and Behavioral Sciences Building
401 Quarry Road
Stanford, CA 94305-5730
Web Address: www-med.stanford.edu/school/Psychiatry/narcolepsy/

317

Sleep Terror Disorder
Night Terror Resource Center
Web Address: www.nightterrors.org/

Impulse-Control Disorders
Pathological Gambling
Gamblers Anonymous International Service Office
P.O. Box 17173
Los Angeles, CA 90017
Telephone: 213-386-8789, Fax: 213-386-0030
Web Address: www.gamblersanonymous.org

The Compulsive Gambling Center, Inc.
924 East Baltimore Street
Baltimore, MD 21202
Telephone: 410-332-1111, Toll Free: 800-567-8238, Fax: 410-685-2307
Web Address: www.lostbet.com

The National Council on Problem Gambling, Inc.
208 G Street, NE
Washington, D.C. 20002
Telephone: 202-547-9204, Fax: 202-547-9206
Web Address: www.ncpgambling.org

Trimeridian, Inc. — Resources for Problem Gambling
12220 N. Meridian St., Suite 180
Carmel, IN 46032
Telephone: 317-848-9920, Toll Free: 877-NO-GAMBLE (877-664-2625)
Web Address: www.trimeridian.com

Trichotillomania
Trichotillomania Learning Center
303 Potrero #51
Santa Cruz, CA 95060
Telephone: 831-457-1004, Fax: 831-426-4383
Web Address: www.trich.org

Personality Disorders
General
The Personality Disorders Foundation
Web Address: http://pdf.uchc.edu/

Borderline
Borderline Personality Disorder — H.O.P.E.
Web Address: www.soulselfhelp.on.ca/borderpd.html

BPD Sanctuary
P.O. Box 886
Selah, WA 98942
Web Address: www.mhsanctuary.com/borderline/

Borderline Personality Disorder Central (BPD Central)
P.O. Box 070106
Milwaukee, WI 53207-0106
Toll Free: 888-357-4355 or 800-431-1579
Web Address: www.bpdcentral.com/

Borderline Personality Disorder Research Foundation (BPDRF)
New York State Psychiatric Institute
Box 121, 1051 Riverside Drive
New York, NY 10032
Telephone: 212-543-6247, Fax: 212-543-6800
Web Address: www.borderlineresearch.org/

National Education Alliance for Borderline Personality Disorder (NEA—BPD)
P.O. Box 974
Rye, NY 10580
Telephone: 914-835-9011
Web Address: www.borderlinepersonalitydisorder.com/

Treatment and Research Advancements National Association for Personality Disorder
(TARA APD)
23 Greene St.
New York, NY 10013
Telephone: 888-4-TARA-APD
Web Address: www.tara4bpd.org/

Narcissistic
N-Courage — A Narcissism Resource and Information Site
Web Address: www.n-courage.net/

Narcissistic Personality Disorder Sanctuary
P.O. Box 886
Selah, WA 98942
Web Address: www.mhsanctuary.com/narcissistic/index.html

Narcissistic Personality Disorder Today
Web Address: www.mental-health-today.com/narcissistic/

Avoidant
Avoidant Personality Disorder (AvPD)
Web Address: http://open-mind.org/SP/Articles/1c.htm

Mental Retardation
American Association on Mental Retardation (AAMR)
444 North Capitol Street, NW, Suite 846
Washington, D.C. 20001-1512
Telephone: 202-387-1968, Toll Free: 800-424-3688, Fax: 202-387-2193
Web Address: www.aamr.org

American Association of People with Disabilities (AAPD)
1819 H Street, NW, #330
Washington, DC 20006
Telephone: 202-457-0046, Fax: 202-457-0473
Web Address: www.aapd.org/

Best Buddies International Headquarters
100 SE Second St., Suite 1990
Miami, FL 33131
Telephone: 305-374-2233, Toll Free: 800-89-BUDDY, Fax: 305-374-5305
Web Address: http://www.bestbuddies.org

Consortium for Citizens with Disabilities (CCD)
11331 H Street, NW, Suite 301
Washington, DC 20005
Telephone: 202-783-2229, Fax: 202-783-8250
Web Address: www.c-c-d.org

Division on Mental Retardation & Developmental Disabilities (MRDD)
The Council for Exceptional Children
1110 North Glebe Road, Suite 300
Arlington, VA 22201-5704
Telephone: 703-620-3660, Toll Free: 888-232-7733
Web Address: www.mrddcec.org

The Arc of the United States
1010 Wayne Avenue, Suite 650
Silver Spring, MD 20910
Telephone: 301-565-3842, Fax: 301-565-3843, Fax: 301- 565-5342
Web Address: www.thearc.org/

The Quality Mall
150 Pillsbury Drive SE, Room 204
Minneapolis, MN 55455
Telephone: 612-624-6328, Fax: 612-625-6619
Web Address: www.qualitymall.org/main/

Waisman Center
University of Wisconsin-Madison
1500 Highland Avenue
Madison, WI 53705-2280
Telephone: 608-263-5776 or 608-263-5910, Fax: 608-263-0529
Web Address: www.waisman.wisc.edu/index.htmlx

Substance-Related Disorders
General
Addiction Intervention Resources, Corporate Headquarters
1043 Grand Ave. Suite 379
St. Paul, MN 55105
Telephone: 651-222-6740, National Call Center: 800-561-8158
Web Address: www.addictionintervention.com

Chemically Dependent Anonymous (CDA)
General Services Office
P.O. Box 423
Severna Park, MD 21146-0423
Web Address: www.cdaweb.org

National Clearinghouse for Alcohol and Drug Information (NCADI)
Web Address: www.health.org

National Council on Alcoholism and Drug Dependence, Inc.
20 Exchange Place, Suite 2902
New York, NY 10005
Telephone: 212-269-7797, Fax: 212-269-7510
Web Address: www.ncadd.org

National Institute on Drug Abuse
National Institutes of Health
6001 Executive Boulevard, Room 5213
Bethesda, MD 20892-9561
Web Address: www.drugabuse.gov/NIDAHome.html

Substance Abuse and Mental Health Services Administration
5600 Fishers Lane
Rockville, MD 20857
Web Address: www.samhsa.gov/

The National Center on Addiction and Substance Abuse at Columbia University
633 Third Avenue, 19th Floor
New York City, NY 10017-6706
Telephone: 212-841-5200, Fax: 212-956-8020
Web Address: www.casacolumbia.org/

Alcohol
Al-Anon/Alateen World Service Office
1600 Corporate Landing Parkway
Virginia Beach, VA 23454-5617
Web Address: www.al-anon.org

Alcohol Abuse and Alcoholism Prevention, Treatment and Recovery
25954 Eden Landing Road
2nd Floor
Hayward, CA 94545-3816
Web Address: www.alcoholmd.com

Alcoholics Anonymous (AA) World Services, Inc.
Box 459, Grand Central Station
New York, NY 10163
Telephone: 212-870-3400
Web Address: www.aa.org

Lowe Family Foundation
3339 Stuyvesant Place NW
Washington, DC 20015
Telephone: 202-362-4883, Fax: 202-362-9419
Web Address: www.lowefamily.org/home.html

National Institute of Alcohol Abuse and Alcoholism
6000 Executive Boulevard — Willco Building
Bethesda, MD 20892-7003
Web Address: www.niaaa.nih.gov/index.htm

Amphetamines
Crystal Meth Anonymous
8205 Santa Monica Blvd. PMB 1-114
West Hollywood, CA 90046-5977
Telephone: 213-488-4455
Web Address: www.crystalmeth.org/

EscapeMeth
Web Address: www.escapemeth.com

Life or Meth?
Web Address: www.lifeormeth.org

Cannabis
Marijuana Anonymous World Services
P.O. Box 2912
Van Nuys, CA 91404
Toll Free: 800-766-6779
Web Address: www.marijuana-anonymous.org/

Cocaine
Cocaine Anonymous World Service Office (CAWSO)
3740 Overland Ave., Suite. C
Los Angeles, CA 90034
Telephone: 310-559-5833
Web Address: www.ca.org

Inhalants
National Inhalant Prevention Coalition
2904 Kerbey Lane
Austin, TX 78703
Telephone: 512-480-8953, Toll Free: 800-269-4237, Fax: 512-477-3932
Web Address: www.inhalants.org/

Nicotine
Action on Smoking and Health (ASH)
2013 H Street NW
Washington, DC 20006
Web Address: www.ash.org

Nicotine Anonymous World Services
419 Main Street, PMB# 370
Huntington Beach, CA 92648
Telephone: 415-750-0328
Web Address: www.nicotine-anonymous.org

QuitNet — Quit Smoking All Together
Web Address: www.quitnet.org

Opioids
Narcotics Anonymous World Service Office
P.O. Box 9999
Van Nuys, California 91409
Telephone: 818-773-9999, Fax 818-700-0700
Web Address: www.na.org

Sedative-Hypnotics/Anxiolytics
Benzodiazepine Anonymous
11633 San Vicente Blvd., Suite 314
Los Angeles, CA 90049
Telephone: 310-652-4100

Prescription Anonymous, Inc.
P.O. Box 10534
Gaithersburg, MD 20898-0534
Web Address: www.prescriptionanonymous.org

Canadian Resources
General Mental Health Organizations
Canadian Mental Health Association, National Office
2160 Yonge Street
Toronto, ON M4S 2Z3
Telephone: 416-484-7750, Fax: 416-484-4617
Web Address: www.cmha.ca

Canadian Psychiatric Association
260-441 MacLaren Street
Ottawa, ON K2P 2H3
Telephone: 613-234-2815 ext. 227, Fax: 613-234-9857
Web Address: www.cpa-apc.org

Canadian Psychological Association
151 Slater Street, Suite 205
Ottawa, ON   K1P 5H3
Tel: 613-237-2144, Toll Free: 800-472-0657, Fax: 613-237-1674
Web Address: www.cpa.ca

Internet Mental Health
Web Address: www.mentalhealth.com/

Health Canada — Headquarters
A.L. 0900C2
Ottawa, ON K1A 0K9
Telephone: 613-957-2991, Fax: 613-941-5366
Web Address: www.hc-sc.gc.ca/hppb/mentalhealth/

Mental Health Resources Canada
Web Address: www.mentalhealthresources.ca/

Psychotic Disorders
Schizophrenia
Canadian Schizophrenic Foundation
16 Florence Ave.
Toronto, ON M2N 1E9
Telephone: 416-733-2117, Fax: 416-733-2352

Schizophrenia Society of Canada
(formerly Canadian Friends of Schizophrenics)
50 Adacia Ave., Suite 205
Markham, ON L3R 0B3
Telephone: 905-415-2007, Fax: 905-415-2337
Web Address: www.schizophrenia.ca

Schizoaffective Disorder
Organization for Bipolar Affective Disorders (OBAD)
1019 — 7th Ave. SW
Calgary, AB T2P 1A8
Telephone: 403-263-7408
Web Address: www.obad.ca

World Fellowship for Schizophrenia and Allied Disorders
124 Merton Street, Suite 507
Toronto, ON M4S 2Z2
Telephone: 416-961-2855, Fax: 416-961-1948
Web Address: www.world-schizophrenia.org/

Mood Disorders
General
Canadian Network for Mood and Anxiety Treatments (CANMAT)
Web Address: www.canmat.org

Feeling Blue
www.feelingblue.com
www.psychcanada.com

Depression
The Depression Information Line (Canada)
Toll-free: 888-557-5051, code 8000

Bipolar Disorder
Organization for Bipolar Affective Disorders (OBAD)
1019 — 7th Ave SW
Calgary, AB T2P 1A8
Telephone: 403-263-7408
Web Address: www.obad.ca

Anxiety Disorders
General
Canadian Network for Mood and Anxiety Treatments (CANMAT)
Web Address: www.canmat.org

Obsessive-Compulsive Disorder (OCD)
Obsessive Compulsive Information & Support Centre Inc.
204 — 825 Sherbrook St.
Winnipeg, MB R3A 1M5
Telephone: 204-942-3331, Fax: 204-975-3027
Web Address: www.members.shaw.ca/occmanitoba

Sexual and Gender Identity Disorders
The Centre for Addiction and Mental Health (CAMH)
Gender Identity Clinic
33 Russell Street
Toronto, ON M5S 2S1
Telephone: 416-535-8501
Web Address: www.camh.net/mental_health/gender_identity_clinic.html

Eating Disorders
Anorexia Nervosa and Bulimia Association
767 Bayridge Drive, P.O. Box 20058
Kingston, ON K7P 1C0
Telephone: 613-547-3684
Web Address: www.phe.queensu.ca/anab/

Bulimia/Anorexia Nervosa Association
300 Cabana Road East,
Windsor, ON N9G 1A3
Telephone: 519-969-2112, Fax: 519-969-0227
Web Address: www.bana.ca

Eating Disorder Education Organization (EDEO)
6R20 Edmonton General Hospital
11111 Jasper Avenue
Edmonton, AB T5K 0L6
Telephone: 780-944-2864, Toll free in Alberta: 888-404-3336, Fax: 780-413-1536
Web Address: www.edeo.org

National Eating Disorders Information Center (NEDIC)
CW 1-211, 200 Elizabeth Street
Toronto, ON M5G 2C4
Telephone 416-340-4156, Toll Free:866-633-4220, Fax 416-340-4736
Web Address: www.nedic.ca/

Substance-Related Disorders
General
Canadian Centre on Substance Abuse
300 — 75 Albert Street
Ottawa, ON K1P 5E7
Telephone: 613-235-4048, Toll Free: 800-559-4515, Fax: 613-235-8101
Web Address: www.ccsa.ca

The Centre for Addiction and Mental Health (CAMH)
33 Russell Street
Toronto, ON M5S 2S1
Telephone: 416-535-8501
Web Address: www.camh.net

Opioids
Canadian Assembly of Narcotics Anonymous
P.O. Box 25073, RPO West Kildonan
Winnipeg, MB R2V 4C7
Web Address: www.cana-acna.org

Sleep Disorders
Canadian Sleep Society
c/o The School of Psychology
Laval University
Ste. Foy, QC G1K 7P4
Web Address: www.css.to/

Mental Retardation
The Canadian Health Network
Web Address: www.canadian-health-network.ca/customtools/homee.html

References

Quest for Answers: A Primer of Understanding and Treating Severe Personality Disorders
S. Akhtar
Jason Aaronson Publishers, Northvale, NJ, 1995

Diagnostic and Statistical Manual of Mental Disorders, 4th Ed., Text Revision
American Psychiatric Association; Arlington, VA, 2000

Introductory Textbook of Psychiatry, 2nd Ed.
N.C. Andreason & D.W. Black
American Psychiatric Press, Inc.; Washington D.C., 1995

Cognitive Therapy of Personality Disorders
A.T. Beck & A. Freeman
Guilford Press, New York, 1990

Interpersonal Diagnosis and Treatment of Personality Disorders
L.S. Benjamin
Guilford Press, New York, 1993

Bad Boys, Bad Men: Confronting Antisocial Personality Disorder
D.W. Black with C. Lindon Larson
Oxford University Press, New York, 1999

Psychiatric Dictionary, 7th Ed.
R. J. Campbell
Oxford University Press; New York, 1996

The Mask of Sanity
H. Cleckley
Mosby, St. Louis, 1941

The Encyclopedia of Phobias, Fears, and Anxieties
R. Doctor and A. Khan
Facts on File, Inc., New York, 1989

DSM-IV Handbook of Differential Diagnosis
M.B. First, H.A. Pincus & A. Frances
American Psychiatric Press, Inc., Arlington, VA, 1995

Man For Himself
E. Fromm
Holt, Rinehart & Winston, New York, 1947

Psychiatry and the Cinema, 2ⁿᵈ Ed.
G.O. Gabbard and K. Gabbard
American Psychiatric Press, Inc.; Washington D.C., 1999

Psychodynamic Psychiatry in Clinical Practice, 3ʳᵈ Ed.
G.O. Gabbard
American Psychiatric Press, Inc., Arlington, VA, 2000

Manic-Depressive Illness
F.K. Goodwin and K.R. Jamison
Oxford University Press, New York, 1990

Legal Neurology and Malingering: Cases and Techniques
W.F. Gorman
Warren H. Green Publishers, St. Louis, 1993

Without Conscience
R. Hare
The Guilford Press, New York, 1993

Our Inner Conflicts
K. Horney
Norton, New York, 1945

Uppers, Downers, All Arounders, 4th Edition
D.S. Inaba and W.E. Cohen
CNS Publications, Inc., Ashland, OR, 2000

Psychological Types
C. Jung
Rasher Verlag, Zurich, Switzerland, 1921

Psychopathic Personalities
E. Kahn
Yale University Press, New Haven, 1931

Synopsis of Psychiatry, 8ᵗʰ Ed.
H. Kaplan & B. Sadock (Editors)
Williams & Wilkins; Baltimore, 1998

Comprehensive Textbook of Psychiatry, 7ᵗʰ Ed.
B.J. Sadock & V.A. Sadock, Editors
Lippincott, Williams & Wilkions, Baltimore, 2000

Lectures on Clinical Psychiatry
E. Kraepelin
Wood Publishers, New York, 1904

Psychiatry: A Textbook, 8ᵗʰ Ed.
E. Kraepelin
Barty, Leipzig, Germany, 1913

I Hate You Don't Leave Me
J.J. Kreisman and H. Strauss
Avon Books, New York, 1991

Malingering and Deception in Adolescents: Assessing Credibility in Clinical and Forensic Settings
J.T. McCann
American Psychological Association, Washington, D.C., 1998

Psychoanalytic Diagnosis: Understanding Personality Structure in the Clinical Process
N. McWilliams
Guilford Press; New York, 1994

The Human Mind
K. Menninger
Alfred Knopf Publishers, New York, 1930

Modern Psychopathology: A Biosocial Approach to Maladaptive Learning and Functioning
T. Millon
Saunders, Philadelphia, 1969

Disorders of Personality. DSM-III, Axis II
T. Millon
Wiley, New York, 1981

MIPS: Millon Index of Personality Styles Manual
T. Millon, L. Weiss, C. Millon, and R. Davis
The Psychological Corporation, San Antonio, 1994

Disorders of Personality: DSM-IV and Beyond, 2nd Ed.
T. Millon & R. D. Davis
John Wiley & Sons; New York, 1995

DSM-IV Made Easy: The Clinician's Guide to Diagnosis
J. Morrison
Guilford Press; New York, 1995

I Know You Really Love Me: A Psychiatrist's Journal of Erotomania, Stalking, and Obsessive Love
D.R. Orion
Wiley Publishing, Hoboken, NJ, 1997

Clinical Manual of Psychiatric Diagnosis and Treatment
R.W. Pies
American Psychiatric Press, Inc., Arlington, VA, 1994

Disordered Personalities, 2nd Ed.
D.J. Robinson
Rapid Psychler Press; Port Huron, MI, 1999

Mnemonics & More for Psychiatry
D.J. Robinson
Rapid Psychler Press, Port Huron, MI, 2001

Clinical Assessment of Malingering and Deception, 2ⁿᵈ Ed.
R. Rogers, Editor
The Guilford Press, New York, 1997

The Encyclopaedia of Psychoactive Substances
R. Rudgley
St. Martin's Press, New York, 1999

Psychopathic Personalities, 9ᵗʰ Ed.
K. Schneider
Cassell Publishers, London, England, 1950

Bad Men Do What Good Men Dream: A Forensic Psychiatrist Illuminates the Darker Side of Human Behavior
R.I. Simon
American Psychiatric Press, Inc., Arlington, VA, 1996

I'm Eve
Chris Costner Sizemore
Doubleday & Co., Inc., Garden City, NY, 1977

PCP: The Dangerous Angel (Encyclopedia of Psychoactive Drugs Series 1)
S.H. Snyder, Series Editor
Chelsea House Publishers, New York, 1985

DSM-IV Casebook: A Learning Companion to the Diagnostic and Statistical Manual of Mental Disorders
R.L. Spitzer, M. Gibbon, A.E. Skodol & M.B. First
American Psychiatric Press, Inc., Arlington, VA, 1994

Psychiatry for Medical Students, 3ʳᵈ Ed.
R. Waldinger
American Psychiatric Press, Inc., Arlington, VA, 1997

Subject Index

Movie Index

The Author

Dave Robinson is a psychiatrist practicing in London, Ontario, Canada. His particular interests are general adult psychiatry, undergraduate and postgraduate education. A graduate of the University of Toronto Medical School, he completed a Residency in Family Practice before entering the Psychiatry Residency Program. He is a faculty member in the Department of Psychiatry at the University of Western Ontario in London, Canada.

The Artist

Brian Chapman is a resident of Oakville and Manitoulin Island, Ontario, Canada. He was born in Sussex, England and moved to Canada in 1957. His first commercial work took place during W.W. II when he traded drawings for cigarettes while serving in the British Navy. Now retired, Brian was formerly a Creative Director at Mediacom. He continues to freelance and is versatile in a wide range of media. He is a master of the caricature, and his talents are constantly in demand. He doesn't smoke anymore. Brian is an avid trumpeter, and performs regularly with a variety of bands.

Rapid Psychler Press was founded in 1994 with the aim of producing textbooks and resource materials that further the use of humor in psychiatric education. In addition to textbooks, Rapid Psychler specializes in producing 35mm slides, overhead transparencies, and digital graphics for presentations.

Rapid
Psychler
Press

340